# CESMM2
## IN PRACTICE

# CESMM2
## IN PRACTICE

**R. G. McCAFFREY** FRICS
**RICHARD G. McCAFFREY** BTech, CEng, MICE, MIWEM
**MICHAEL J. McCAFFREY** DipBE, MSc, FRICS

BSP PROFESSIONAL BOOKS

OXFORD LONDON EDINBURGH

BOSTON PALO ALTO MELBOURNE

First edition published by Granada
    Publishing 1983
Second edition published by BSP
    Professional Books 1988

British Library
Cataloguing in Publication Data
McCaffrey, R. G.
    CESMM2 in practice—2nd. ed.
    1. Civil engineering. Measurement,
    Standards: Institution of Civil
    Engineers. Civil engineering
    standard method of measurement.
    User-Manuals.
    I. Title   II. McCaffrey, Richard
    G.   III. McCaffrey, Michael
    J.   IV. McCaffrey, R. G. Civil
    engineering standard method of
    measurement.
    624'.028'7

ISBN 0–632–01826–7

BSP Professional Books
A division of Blackwell Scientific
    Publications Ltd
Editorial Offices:
Osney Mead, Oxford OX2 0EL
    (Orders: Tel. 0865 240201)
8 John Street, London WC1N 2ES
23 Ainslie Place, Edinburgh EH3 6AJ
Three Cambridge Center, Suite 208,
    Cambridge MA 02142, USA
667 Lytton Avenue, Palo Alto,
    California 94301, USA
107 Barry Street, Carlton, Victoria 3053,
    Australia

Printed and bound in Great Britain by
Butler & Tanner Ltd, Frome and London

# Contents

# Preface to the Second Edition

The need for a second edition of our book arises as a natural consequence of the publication of the second edition of the *Civil Engineering Standard Method of Measurement (CESMM2)**. Essentially CESMM2 is just an up-date and general overhaul of its predecessor. But the changes to the format and layout of the Work Classification and the various alterations to the provisions have meant that we have had to substantially re-write the text. In so doing we have added information and made improvements including:

- An extra chapter dealing with the new Class Y – Sewer Renovation.
- Two new measured examples with three new drawings and two new specimen Bills of Quantities with one new drawing. There are also twenty additional figures with specimen descriptions and diagrams.
- Tables re-configured to match the four types of CESMM2 Rules which replace the former Notes. Many of the Rules are the old Notes renumbered and categorised. But some are new and others introduce fresh conventions. The Tables have been revised to include these changes.
- Commentary re-written and examples revised in line with the changes and additions made in CESMM2.

Our aim is unchanged – An easy-to-use reference for those interested in the practical aspects of measurement and bill compilation. The books is comprehensive. Every CESMM item and Rule is referenced and because of this the book must be read in conjunction with the CESMM.

Throughout we advise and give illustrations of how we think the CESMM should be applied in any given situation:

- Tables collect together all information such as descriptive features, CESMM references, Rules and units of measurement for associated groups of bill items. Commentary explains the Rules and indicates where additional description or amending Preamble is appropriate. And typical additional description and/or amending Preamble is suggested.
- Measured examples illustrate what to measure and how to measure it, how to describe work, the detail to be given in item descriptions and the systematic approach to the taking and recording of dimensions. Commentary guides the reader through the measurements.
- Specimen item descriptions linked to diagrams show how an item of work relates to its bill description.
- Specimen Bills of Quantities give typical item descriptions and illustrate Bill layout and the use of CESMM codes. Commentary highlights features.

The two or so years that have elapsed since the publication of CESMM2 have been needed to gain experience in applying the new rules and changes – an essential prerequisite to the publication of a practice manual. We believe that CESMM2 consolidates the radical new approach of CESMM1 and that the civil engineering sector of the construction industry now has an established method of measurement which is logical and well structured. We hope that this book will continue to provide helpful guidance on its application in practice.

We thank Janet Zalega, the Partnership Secretary, for the care she has taken word processing the script.

*January 1988*

**R.G. McCaffrey, Richard G. McCaffrey & Michael J. McCaffrey**
**R.G. McCAFFREY & PARTNERS, ASHFIELD HOUSE, ASHFIELD ROAD, IDLE, BRADFORD BD10 9AF**

* *The Civil Engineering Standard Method of Measurement*, second edition, available from Telford International Bookshop, Institution of Civil Engineers, Great George Street, Westminster SW1P 3AA.

# Preface to the First Edition

The aim of this book is to provide an easy-to-use reference for those interested in the practical aspects of measurement and bill compilation in accordance with the *Civil Engineering Standard Method of Measurement (CESMM)**. The book should be read in conjunction with the CESMM to which frequent reference is made.

Initially matters of general application are covered by a commentary on CESMM Sections 1 to 7. Subsequently, in chapters on the 24 classes of the Work Classification, the descriptive features and notes in each class are combined into Tables which summarise the CESMM rules. Commentaries on these Tables, specimen bills of quantities and measured examples are used to describe and illustrate how we apply the CESMM rules in practice. A statement of the measurement procedures and conventions adopted in the Examples is given in Chapter 1.

Our descriptions and illustrations of how we apply the rules reflect our understanding of those interpretations of the CESMM offered in *Measurement in Contract Control* by Martin Barnes (Institution of Civil Engineers – London 1977). Our experience is that these interpretations, although not official, are widely accepted in practice and we recommend *Measurement in Contract Control* to those readers who wish to study the reasoning and intentions involved in the CESMM.

As the results of the current review of the CESMM are not yet known we have not been able to include them in the book. However, we understand that there will not be any major revisions, the main aim being to clarify and amend the CESMM in order to correct any errors and remove misunderstandings.

The radical new approach of the CESMM has aroused considerable comment since its publication in 1976 and we hope, therefore, that this book will provide readers with helpful guidance on its practical application.

We thank the Institution of Civil Engineers for granting us permission to adapt the tables in the CESMM and use them in this book.

We would also like to thank Paul Rhodes for assisting with the preparation of the drawings and are most grateful to Janet Zalega, secretary to R.G. McCaffrey, for the care she has taken in typing the script.

*September 1982*

R.G. McCaffrey
Richard G. McCaffrey
Michael J. McCaffrey

Bradford, West Yorkshire

* *The Civil Engineering Standard Method of Measurement*, available from Telford International Bookshop, Institution of Civil Engineers, Great George Street, Westminster SW1P 3AA.

# 1 Measurement – Procedure and Conventions

Before proceeding with reference to the Civil Engineering Standard Method of Measurement (CESMM) it is thought appropriate to outline certain conventions and define some terms which apply to bill preparation and measurement processes generally and which are used in subsequent chapters. The present Chapter is devoted to this. Particular reference to the CESMM starts in Chapter 2.

## Preparation of Bills of Quantities

Bills of Quantities are usually prepared using one of three methods, namely the traditional method, a method known as "cut and shuffle" or with the aid of a computer.

The worked Examples in this book follow the traditional method which comprises:-

1. "Taking off" - taking dimensions from drawings and entering them, with appropriate descriptions, on dimension sheets.

2. "Squaring the dimensions" - working out the areas, volumes, etc., from the dimensions and totalling the results for each item on the dimension sheets.

3. "Abstracting" - transferring the totals and items from the dimension sheets to abstract sheets in bill order and collecting together quantities for like items so that they may be cast to totals in readiness for billing.

4. "Billing" - writing the draft bill from the abstract.

Stages (2), (3) and (4) above are collectively known as "working up". Every calculation and every transferred entry performed during any stage is checked by a second person to ensure there has been no arithmetical or copying errors.

## Dimension Sheets

Traditional dimension sheets are ruled as shown on Plate 1. Each sheet is ruled with an identical set of four columns each side of a vertical centre line.

The individual columns in each set of four are termed:-

| Timesing Column | Dimension Column | Squaring Column | Description Column |
|---|---|---|---|

## Dimensions Sheets (cont.

The dimension column is used for entering the dimensions and the timesing column is used for entering any multiplication factor which applies to the dimensions. The squaring column is used for entering resultants calculated from the dimensions and their multiplication factors. The description column is used for entering the descriptions of the work to which the dimensions relate. Additionally, the right hand side of the description column is used to build up dimensions; these preliminary calculations are known as "wastes". Location references of the work are sometimes entered on the right hand side of the description column.

Dimension sheets are used working from top to bottom of the left hand set of columns and then continuing down from top to bottom of the right hand set of columns. In most of the worked Examples in this book, only the left hand set of columns are used for dimensions. The right hand set being reserved for commentary.

## Identification and Numbering of Dimension Sheets

Each dimension sheet should be headed with its job name, number or other code.

Completed dimension sheets should be numbered. On small jobs where one person is taking the whole of the dimensions they can be numbered consecutively as the measuring proceeds. On larger jobs where a number of people are engaged on taking dimensions, it is prudent to number sheets consecutively as batches are issued for taking off and to keep a running total of the sheets issued. When the completed sheets are collected a check can then be made to ensure that all sheets are accounted for. Spoiled and unused sheets should be retained until this check is complete. If necessary the collected dimension sheets should be re-arranged into a convenient order for future reference during admeasurement and re-numbered consecutively before abstracting starts. On jobs with a large number of sheets an index to the dimensions is useful.

## Entering Dimensions on the Dimension Sheets

The dimensions for lengths, areas and volumes are entered in the dimension column to two places of decimals.

Drawings will usually be dimensioned in millimetres or in metres to three decimal places. Waste collections should be made using the dimensions given on the drawings. Rounding off to two places of decimals for transfer to the dimension column should be left until the waste is collected to a total.

Dimensions are set down under each other in the dimension column with a line drawn beneath, as shown on Plate 1. A single dimension with a line beneath indicates that it is a linear dimension. Two dimensions with a line beneath indicates a set of two dimensions from which the area of a surface is to be calculated. Three dimensions with a line beneath indicates a set of dimensions from which the volume of a solid is to be calculated. Numbers for numbered items are entered in the centre of the dimension column with a line beneath.

Within each set of dimensions, the dimensions are set down in the order of (1) length, (2) width and (3) depth or height. This order should always be used.

## Entering Dimensions on the Dimension Sheets

| | | |
|---|---|---|
| | 3.00 | linear dimension. |
| | 4.00<br>3.00 | dimensions to calculate area. |
| | 6.00<br>5.00<br>3.00 | dimensions to calculate volume. |

### "Timesing"

| | | |
|---|---|---|
| 3/ | 4 | indicates multiply by 3. |
| 3/2/ | 7.00<br>3.00 | indicates multiply by 6. |
| 2/3/2/ | 5.00<br>3.00<br>2.00 | indicates multiply by 12. |

### "Dotting On"

| | | |
|---|---|---|
| 4/<br>2/ | 5.00 | indicates multiply by (4+2) = 6. |
| 2/3/<br>/2/ | 4.00<br>3.00 | indicates multiply by 10. |
| 3/2/6/ | 3.00<br>3.00<br>2.00 | indicates multiply by 30. |

### Irregular Figures

| | | |
|---|---|---|
| ½/ | 6.00<br>3.00 | area of a triangle base 6.00m height 3.00m. |
| 22/<br>7/ | 5.00<br>5.00 | area of a circle 5.00m. radius. |
| 22/<br>7/ | 10.00 | circumference of a circle 5.00 m radius (10.00m diam) |

PLATE 1

## Setting Out Items On Dimension Sheets

| | Timesing | Dimension | Squaring | Description |
|---|---|---|---|---|
| 1) | BRICK RETAINING WALL - DRAWING 32/1A | | | |
| 2) | | | | Wall above d.p.c. |
| 3) | | | | Engin bkw. Class B. engin bks. as B.S. 3921 in ct mor unless o/w described |
| 4) | | | | 6790<br>2/440 = 880<br>5910 |
| | | 5.91 | | Thickn. 440 mm., vert. stra. walls; English bond |
| | | 2.20 | 13.00 | |
| | 2/ | 2.25 | | |
| 5) | | 1.95 | 8.78 | U331 (returns. |
| | | | 21.78 | |
| 6) | | 1.30 | | Ddt |
| | | 1.25 | 1.63 | (want. |
| | | | 20.15 | |
| 7) | | 0.95 | | Ddt. Ditto, do |
| | | 1.50 | 1.43 | U331 (panel. |
| 8) | | | | & |
| 9) | | | | Add Thickn. 215 mm vert stra. walls; Flemish bond<br>U321 |
| 10) | | 5.19 | NIL | Surf. features B.o. edge copgs. |
| | | 5.91 | 5.91 | |
| | 2/ | 2.25 | 4.50 | U371 |
| | | | 10.41 | |

NOTES FOR GUIDANCE IN SETTING OUT ITEMS AND DIMENSIONS

1) Title of job or title of part of job should be entered at the head of each sheet. Alternatively a mnemonic code may be entered.

2) Side headings should be entered to indicate which particular part of the piece of work is being measured.

3) Where a particular specification type is predominant a note or heading as indicated will avoid the need to keep repeating the type in the item descriptions.

4) Note that waste calculations are entered preceding the item to which they relate.

5) Location notes as shown in the waste column are of great help in following the dimensions later. Such notes should be used extensively to identify dimensions.

6) Ddt = Abbreviation for Deduct. Deductions which relate to immediately preceding items may be entered as shown; the deduction being made on the dimensions sheet as shown. This type of deduction will usually occur where a figure or solid with indents or voids has been measured overall and the indents or voids (known as "wants") need to be deducted.

7) Indicates a deduction which will be carried to the abstract.

8) The sign "&" is used to denote that the same dimensions apply to each item description.

9) Items should be coded as CESMM.

10) Incorrect dimensions are cancelled by writing "NIL" against them in the squaring column

PLATE 2

## "Timesing"

Timesing is effected by entering the required number followed by an oblique stroke. The convention 2/ means multiply by 2. The convention 2/2 means 2 x 2 and so on. The conventions are illustrated on Plate 1.

Decimal fractions are not used in the timesing column because the decimal point may be mistaken for the "dotting on" symbol (See next paragraph). They are expressed as equivalent vulgar fractions. The line between the numerator and denominator of the vulgar fraction should be horizontal, to prevent it being mistaken for the oblique timesing stroke.

## "Dotting on"

When repeating dimensions which have been timesed previously it may be found that they cannot be multiplied and it is required to add. In these circumstances resort is made to what is called "dotting on". A dot in the timesing column is used in place of the conventional plus sign to indicate an addition to the multiplying factor previously entered. The convention is illustrated on Plate 1.

## Setting out Dimensions and Other Conventions

Dimensions and related descriptions should be set down on the dimension sheets in a manner which can be easily followed and related to the drawings at a later date. Locational references given at the right hand side of the description column should be used wherever possible.

## Deductions

When surfaces or solids are perforated by openings or their outline is indented, it is convenient to first over measure by assuming either that they are unperforated or that they are of regular outline, as the case may be, and to follow with deductions to adjust for the openings or indents. In such cases the symbol "Ddt" is added as a prefix to the item description attached to the dimensions which are to be deducted. See worked Examples.

## Bracketing Dimensions

When more than one set of dimensions relate to the same item description, the dimensions are bracketed. See worked Examples.

## Use of Ampersand

When the same dimensions apply to more than one item description, ampersand inserted centrally in the description column before each succeeding description after the first, signifies that the same dimensions apply to each of the items. See worked Examples.

## Abbreviations

Abbreviations are used when writing item descriptions during taking off and abstracting.

There is no standard dictionary of abbreviations for civil engineering work. It is simply a matter of adopting those which are in general use in the organisation in which one works.

In this book the abbreviations have not been reduced to the shortest

Abbreviations (cont.

practical level. To avoid having to look up the meaning of abbreviations when examining the Examples, the aim has been to restrict them to a level readily understandable to anyone familiar with civil engineering work.

Abstracting

The sequence of items in the taking off is not necessarily the same as that of the finished bill. An abstract provides the facility to arrange items in bill order and to collect together the quantities of like items, in readiness for drafting the bill of quantities. It will be found convenient in some instances to transfer items direct from the dimension sheets to the appropriate place in the bill. This operation is termed "billing direct". When an abstract is used, it will note items which are not abstracted and which are to be billed direct. The dimension sheets will also be marked to indicate the items or series of items noted in the abstract for billing direct.

EXAMPLE 1.1 - Specimen Abstract

The Example which follows on the next page is the Abstract prepared from the Measured Example EE.1 in Chapter 7.

When an item with its quantities is transferred from the dimension sheets to an abstract, it is lined through on the dimension sheets, with a vertical line, by the person preparing the abstract, to indicate it has been abstracted. The convention is illustrated in Column (6) of the Measured Example EE.1., Chapter 7. Items in other Columns of Example EE.1 have been abstracted but in the interest of clarity in the Measured Example they have not been lined through. The lining through of the person checking is indicated in the Example by a line of dashes.

When casting the quantities of like items to totals in an abstract, the totals for billing are the resultants after quantities noted as deducts have been subtracted from the positive quantities. Deductions are lined through on the abstract with a curled line to indicate they have been deducted from the positive quantities. The convention is illustrated in the centre pair of columns in the Abstract, Example 1.1.

Billing

Billing consists of drafting the bill of quantities in the form it will be reproduced and issued. For bills of quantities prepared in accordance with the CESMM, it is convenient to use the CESMM code numbers as item numbers in the Bill. Within each Part of the bill, or within each sectionalised group of items within a Part, the items are arranged in order of ascending code number. The abstract should arrange the items in the proposed bill order making billing a simple exercise of copying but substituting the words of the descriptions in full in place of the abbreviations previously used.

EXAMPLE 1.2 - Specimen Part of a Bill of Quantities

The Example on the last page of this Chapter is the Earthworks Part of the Bill of Quantities prepared from the Abstract (Example 1.1).

The person drafting the Bill lines through with a diagonal line, each item in the abstract as it is transferred to the Bill. The convention is illustrated on the first item of the Abstract (Example 1.1). Lining through by the person checking is indicated by a line of dashes. To maintain clarity for the purpose of the Example, other items in the Abstract have not been lined through.

EXAMPLE 1.1

7

## EARTHWORKS - CUTTING and EMBANKMENT - DRG E/D/1

C/Excavn. for cutts., topsoil, Excavd Surf 150 mm
below Orig Surf.
E210

230.35 (1

C/Excavn. for cutts.,
Comm. Surf. u/s topsoil,
Excavd. Surf. 450 mm
above Final Surf
E220.1

1119.60 (2

C/Excavn. for cutts.,
Comm. Surf 450mm
above Final Surf
E220.2

187.52 (2

S/Excavn. ancills.,
prepn. of excavd. surfs.
E522.1

440.10 (4

S/Ditto
vert.
E522.2

44.01 (4

---

C/Excavn. ancills.,
disposal of excavd. matl.,
topsoil
E531

Ddt
230.35 (1   60.53 /(5
131.87   37.80 (5
98.48   33.54 (6
    131.87

C/Excavn. ancills.,
disposal of excavd. matl.
E532

Ddt
1119.60 (2   986.23 (3
187.52 (2
136.49 (3
1443.61
986.23
457.38

C/Fillg., embanks., sel.
excavd. matl other than
topsoil or rock
E624

Ddt
986.23 (3   136.49 (3
136.49
849.74

---

S/Fillg. thickn. 150 mm
excavd. topsoil
E641.1

403.50 (5

S/Ditto upon
surfs 10 - 45°
to hor.
E641.2

251.97 (5
223.57 (6
475.54

S/Fillg., ancills., prepn.
of filld. surfs.
E722.1

279.90 (4

S/Ditto., vert
E722.2

27.99 (4

S/Landscaping, grass
seedg.
E830.1

403.50 (5

S/Ditto. upon
surfs e. 10°
to hor.
E830.2

251.97 (5
223.57 (6
475.54

| Number | Item description | Unit | Quantity | Rate | Amount £ | p |
|---|---|---|---|---|---|---|
| | EARTHWORKS. | | | | | |
| | Excavation. | | | | | |
| E210 | For cuttings, topsoil; Excavated Surface 150 mm below Original Surface. | m3 | 230 | | | |
| E220.1 | For cuttings; Commencing Surface underside of topsoil, Excavated Surface 450 mm above Final Surface. | m3 | 1120 | | | |
| E220.2 | For cuttings; Commencing Surface, 450 mm above Final Surface. | m3 | 188 | | | |
| | Excavation ancillaries. | | | | | |
| E522.1 | Preparation of excavated surfaces. | m2 | 440 | | | |
| E522.2 | Preparation of excavated surfaces; vertical. | m2 | 44 | | | |
| E531 | Disposal of excavated material, topsoil. | m3 | 98 | | | |
| E532 | Disposal of excavated material. | m3 | 458 | | | |
| | Filling. | | | | | |
| E624 | Embankments, selected excavated material other than topsoil or rock. | m3 | 850 | | | |
| E641.1 | Thickness 150 mm, excavated topsoil. | m2 | 404 | | | |
| E641.2 | Thickness 150 mm, excavated topsoil; upon surfaces 10 - 45 degrees to the horizontal. | m2 | 476 | | | |
| | Filling ancillaries. | | | | | |
| E722.1 | Preparation of filled surfaces. | m2 | 280 | | | |
| E722.2 | Preparation of filled surfaces; vertical. | m2 | 28 | | | |
| | Landscaping. | | | | | |
| E830.1 | Grass seeding. | m2 | 404 | | | |
| E830.2 | Grass seeding; upon surfaces exceeding 10 degrees to the horizontal. | m2 | 476 | | | |

(1)       To Part 3 Summary     Page total

COMMENTARY

Headings, sub-headings and descriptions in the "Item description" column have all been ended with a full stop. Within descriptions a semicolon is used to separate basic from additional description. This convention is suggested in "The CESMM2 Handbook" published by Thomas Telford London and is adopted in all Bill Examples in this book.

The abstract total is here rounded upwards for item Code E532 so that the rounded bill quantities for filling plus disposal balance with those for excavation

In this Example, and in all examples in this book, CESMM code numbers are used as Item numbers (See Section 4 and Class E of CESMM. See also pages 16 and 17 and Chapter 7 of this book).

See paragraph 5.9 on page 21 and Fig. 6 on page 22 of this book for explanation of lines drawn across the "Item description" column.

# 2 The Sections of the CESMM

The rules and provisions of the Civil Engineering Standard Method of Measurement (CESMM), are applicable to the preparation of bills of quantities for and the measurement of civil engineering work. They are not intended to apply to the preparation of bills of quantities for or the measurement of mechanical engineering, electrical engineering or building work.

The CESMM is intended for use in conjunction with "the I.C.E. Conditions of Contract"* and makes reference to certain clauses in the January 1979 revision of the Fifth Edition of the Conditions. It is nevertheless necessary, where the Second Edition of the CESMM is used in conjunction with that Edition of the I.C.E. Contract, to insert "CESMM, Second Edition" in the appropriate blank line in the Appendix to the Form of Tender. This is because Clause 57 of the Conditions provides that except where a statement or description expressly shows to the contrary, the Bill of Quantities shall be deemed to have been prepared in accordance with the CESMM 1976 or such later edition as may be stated in the Appendix to the Form of Tender.

The CESMM document contains eight numbered Sections. The first seven Sections are each divided into Paragraphs. Section 8 "Work Classification" is divided into twenty five main classifications, termed "Classes". A classification table incorporating rules which state how work shall be described and measured in the Bill of Quantities is provided for each Class and is particular to the Class in which it is given. The rules have equal status with rules in any other part of the document. The Paragraphs of Sections 1 - 7 of the CESMM contain rules and statements of general application. Throughout the document, rules and statements which must be observed if the provisions of the CESMM are not to be infringed are distinguished by the use of the word "shall". Those which use the words "should" or "may" denote they are recommendations or options and the provisions of the CESMM will not be infringed if they are not followed. Paragraph 5.6 refers to the percentage to be "entered" by the Contractor when tendering. Otherwise the document is consistent in the use of the words "given" and "inserted". "Given" when used in relation to the Bill of Quantities means given in the Bill before it is issued to tender. "Inserted" means inserted by the tenderers after the Bill has been issued to tender.

Regard must be given to the general matters set out in the Paragraphs when applying the Work Classification. In the present Chapter the gist of each Paragraph in the Sections of the CESMM is given, with added Commentary, as an essential preliminary to the discussion of individual Classes in subsequent Chapters. Reference should be made to CESMM for the printed text of the Sections.

---

\* *"Conditions of Contract for use in connection with Works of Civil Engineering Construction" issued and approved by the Institution of Civil Engineers and the Federation of Civil Engineering Contractors and also the Association of Consulting Engineers.*

*DEFINITIONS*

<u>COMMENTARY</u>

The meaning assigned to a word or expression in Section 1, will apply throughout the CESMM, except where the context otherwise requires. It will apply, also whenever the word or expression is used in the Bill of Quantities, unless the Bill assigns it a different meaning and includes Preamble amending the CESMM accordingly.

1.1

'Conditions of Contract', means the document defined in th paragraph referenced, commonly known as the I.C.E. Contract (fifth edition) (June 1973) (revised January 1979).

1.2

Words and expressions which are defined in the Conditions of Contract are to be taken as having the same meaning when they are used in the CESMM.

1.3

Words and expressions which are expressed with initial capital letters when they are defined in the CESMM and the Conditions of Contract should be expressed with initial capital letters when they are used in the Bill of Quantities.

References to <u>clauses</u> in the CESMM, "are references to clauses numbered in the Conditions of Contract". References to <u>paragraphs</u> in the CESMM, are references to paragraphs numbered in sections 1 to 7 of the CESMM.

1.4

The definition of the word "<u>work</u>" as given in the paragraph referenced may be said to include all the Contractor has to do. It should not be confused with the word "Works" as defined in the Conditions of Contract.

1.5

'Expressly required'. The CESMM provides that certain work is subject to measurement only when expressly required. Such work will not qualify to be measured unless it is specifically prescribed in the Contract or specifically ordered by the Engineer.

1.6

'Bill of Quantities' is defined as "a list of items giving brief identifying descriptions and estimated quantities . . ."

1.7

Item descriptions in the Bill are not required to fully describe the work, they are required to clearly identify it so that its nature and extent can be ascertained from the drawings and specification. (See Paragraph 5.11 of the CESMM).

'Daywork' means the method of valuing work at the cost of the labour on the basis of time spent and the cost of materials used and the plant employed.

1.8

Provision for daywork, if required, is made in the Bill of Quantities in accordance with Paragraphs 5.2, 5.6 and 5.7 of the CESMM.

'Work Classification'. The Work Classification used in the CESMM is that set out in Section 8 of the document. It is explained in Paragraph 3.1 of the CESMM. What it defines is stated in Paragraph 2.7 of the CESMM.

1.9

The CESMM provides for what might be described as the starting
and finishing surfaces in excavation and boring items to be
identifiable from the item descriptions. (See Paragraph 5.21
of the CESMM and Commentary on that Paragraph). To simplify
the application of the requirement, the CESMM adopts a
nomenclature for four surfaces.

'Original Surface'. This is the surface of the ground of the
Site as it exists when the Contractor enters upon it to
carry out the work of the Contract.                                  1.10

'Final Surface'. This is the surface at which excavation and
boring is to finally finish as shown on the Drawings. Work
below this Surface such as soft spots, is described as
'below the Final Surface'.                                           1.11

'Commencing Surface'. This is defined in relation to an item
in the Bill of Quantities, as 'the surface of the ground
before any work covered by the item has been carried out'.
In relation to several items given to divide different
materials in similar work in the same hole, the Commencing
Surface for each of the several items is the surface of the
ground before any of the several items are carried out,
provided work in separate stages is not expressly required.
See Figs. 1 and 2. The Commencing Surface may be the
Original Surface or it may be another surface somewhere
between the Original Surface and the Final Surface, or it
may be a filled surface above the Original Surface.                  1.12

'Excavated Surface'. This is defined in relation to an item
in the Bill of Quantities, as 'the surface to which
excavation included in the work covered by the item is
carried out'. In relation to several items given to divide
excavation in different materials in similar excavation in
the same hole, the Excavated Surface for each of the several
items is the surface to which excavation is carried out when
all the several items have been excavated, provided work in
separate stages is not expressly required. See Figs. 1 and
2. The Excavated Surface may be the Final Surface or it may
be another surface somewhere between the Final Surface and
the Original Surface.                                                1.13

'A hyphen between two dimensions'. This means a range
of dimensions which includes all dimensions exceeding the
first dimension but not exceeding the second.                       1.14

## *GENERAL PRINCIPLES*

The general Principles as set out in Section 2 of the CESMM,
provide some rules but they are mainly general statements.

## Title, Application and Extent

The title of the document is confirmed as the "Civil
Engineering Standard Method of Measurement". The title may be
abbreviated to "CESMM". It is intended for use in conjunction
with the I.C.E. Conditions of Contract (fifth edition) in
connection with civil engineering work.                             2.1

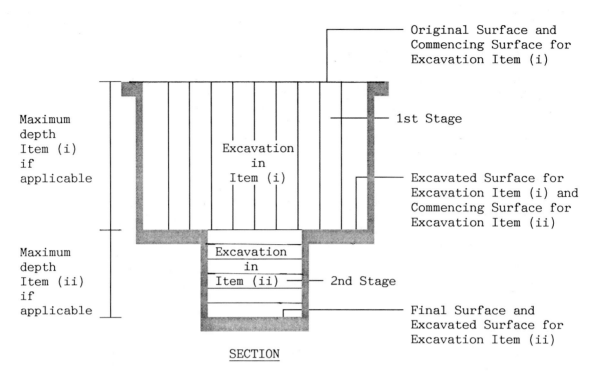

SECTION

Fig. 1. Illustration of the application of nomenclature for the four
       Surfaces (defined in CESMM Paragraphs 1.10 to 1.13 inclusive), where
       excavation in separate stages is expressly required.

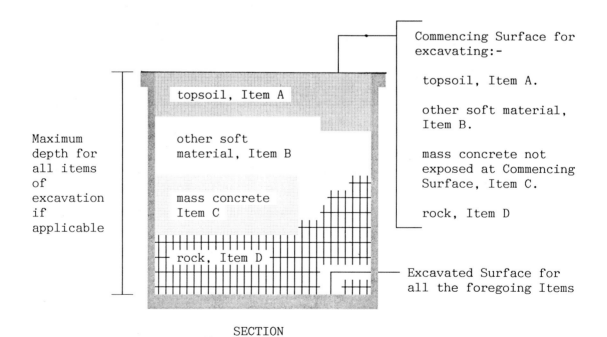

SECTION

Fig. 2. Application of Definition Rules, CESMM Paragraphs 1.12 and 1.13.
       Separate Items are required for each classification of material to
       be excavated. Items do not identify intermediate Surfaces, where
       excavation in separate stages is not expressly required.

## Title, Application and Extent (cont.

Work other than civil engineering construction, for which the CESMM is not appropriate, shall be itemised in sufficient detail to enable tenderers to price it adequately. Where such work is measured, the method of measurement shall be stated in the Preamble to the Bill of Quantities in accordance with Paragraph 5.4 of the CESMM.

2.2

## Objects of the CESMM

In defining the objects of the CESMM, the Paragraph referenced provides the rules that the Bill of Quantities shall be prepared and priced and the quantities of work shall be expressed and measured all in accordance with the CESMM.

2.3

It is permissible to deviate from the above rules subject to the provisions of Paragraph 5.4 of the CESMM being observed.

## Objects of the Bill of Quantities

The Bill of Quantities provides information of quantities to enable tenders to be prepared and provides a means of valuing work after the Contract is placed, all as stated in the Paragraph referenced.

2.4

Items in the Bill of Quantities should "distinguish different classes of work". This is achieved by itemising the work in accordance with the CESMM. For work of the "same nature carried out in different locations or in any other circumstances", the person compiling the Bill should adjudge the cost characteristics of location or circumstances and provide items in the Bill of Quantities which separate different considerations of cost.

2.5

The CESMM suggests that consistent with the foregoing itemisation requirements, the Bill of Quantities should be as simple and brief as possible.

2.5

Expressly required means as shown on the Drawings, described in the Specification or ordered by the Engineer. Paragraph 2.6 states that all work which is expressly required should be covered by the Bill of Quantities. This means the inclusion in the Bill of items for all work, whether temporary or permanent, shown on the Drawings or described in the Specification which is to be carried out to the extent directed by the Engineer.

2.6

The rules which Work Classification provides for the purpose of preparing quantities for work, govern the division of work into items, the information to be given in item descriptions, the units for the quantities and the measurement of work to calculate the quantities.

2.7

Work Classification is briefly described in Paragraph 3.1 of the CESMM. It is applied in accordance with Section 3 of that document. See subsequent Commentary.

## APPLICATION OF THE WORK CLASSIFICATION

COMMENTARY

Work Classification is the system introduced by the CESMM for the purpose of preparing and presenting the quantities of work. It governs the division of work into items, the information to be given in item descriptions, the units for the quantities and the measurement of work to calculate the quantities. Its general application is outlined in Section 3 of the document.

### Item Descriptions

The Work Classification sets out groups of not more than eight phrases, termed "descriptive features", in each of three "divisions" to create a classification table for each of the twenty five Classes into which the Work Classification Section of the CESMM is divided. An outline of what is included and/or excluded follows the Class title. Rules are given alongside the classifications in the table of each Class.                3.1

The Class appropriate to a component of work is selected by reference to the title of the Class and to the "Includes" and the "Excludes" given preceding the classification table.

Item descriptions are compiled by combining listed descriptive features. Each item description is made up of one descriptive feature from each division taken from between the same pair of horizontal lines in the classification table of the appropriate Class. In some cases these descriptions need to be amplified by additional description. See "Additional Description Rules", Paragraph 3.9 of the CESMM.

Item descriptions need not use precisely the words of the Work Classification. It is, nevertheless, sensible to do so except where it would result in the duplication of information. It is unnecessary to include standard descriptive features in item descriptions which give the same information in greater detail. For example, the item description "Douglas fir decking, thickness 63 mm...", would be adequate without stating that the decking is softwood and that it is in the thickness range 50 - 75 mm (Refer to Class O of the CESMM).

### Mode of Description

Item descriptions given in the Bill of Quantities for Permanent Works are required by the CESMM to identify the component of the Works and not the tasks to be carried out. The descriptive features in the Work Classification are phrased accordingly and their use in item descriptions will ensure compliance with the Paragraph referenced.               3.2

Item descriptions for work specifically limited must state the limitation. To conform with this provision, an ad-hoc qualification identifying the applicable limitation is added to the standard description. For example where the item is to cover fixing but not the supply of steel plate flooring, an appropriate item description, limiting the item for "Plate flooring", Class N, CESMM, for this requirement, would be "Steel plate flooring, as specification clause 'X', excluding supply and delivery of flooring and fixing components to Site".               3.3

### Separate Items

An item for a component of work comprises not more than one feature from each division of any one Class. Each item is given separately in the Bill of Quantities. Two or more items may not be grouped into one item.

3.4

### Units of Measurement

The unit of measurement in which the quantities are to be given for an item in the Bill of Quantities is that stated for the item in the Work Classification. The unit stated against a descriptive feature in the Work Classification will apply to all items to which the feature applies.

3.5

### Measurement Rules

Measurement rules are listed for each Class on the right hand page of the classification table. They not only give the conditions under which work is to be measured, but indicate also the method by which quantities are computed if other than in accordance with Paragraph 5.18 of the CESMM.

3.6

### Definition Rules

Words and expressions used in the Work Classification and in a Bill of Quantities prepared in accordance with the CESMM, have the meaning assigned to them in the Definition Rules which are listed in the classification table for each Class.

3.7

### Coverage Rules

Coverage rules listed in the classification tables amplify identified standard item descriptions by stating the work which is deemed to be included in the items. They are not intended to state all work included in an item. They do not preclude the work being made the subject of a Method-Related Charge.

3.8

### Additional Description Rules

Item description compiled by taking one descriptive feature from each division, as provided in Paragraph 3.1 of the CESMM, must be amplified by any additional description required by any provision of Section 5 of the CESMM or any applicable additional description rule in the CESMM Work Classification. Separate items in the Bill of Quantities must distinguish each difference created by any additional description attached to otherwise similar items.

3.9

Where required by an additional description rule, a particular dimension shall be stated in item descriptions in place of any range of dimensions given in the descriptive features of the item in the classification tables.

3.10

### Applicability of Rules

Rules applicable to all items in a particular Class are given in the classification tables of the CESMM on the right hand page above the double line. Those below this line apply to particular groups of items as shown by the classification table.

3.11

*THE SECTIONS OF THE CESMM*

*CODING AND NUMBERING OF ITEMS*

COMMENTARY

The CESMM provides code numbers for the items in the Work Classification. The system of coding is explained in Section 4 of the document.

## Coding

The code number for an item consists of the Class letter and the numbers of the descriptive features in the first, second and third divisions of the Work Classification, in that order. For example, E412 is the code number for "General excavation, topsoil, maximum depth 0.25 - 0.5 m" (Refer to Class E - CESMM).

4.1

For reference purposes, the CESMM uses the symbol * to denote all numbers in a particular division.

4.2

## Item Numbers

The code numbers given in the CESMM, may be used as item numbers in the Bill of Quantities. Whether they are so used is optional. Bills of Quantities are usually divided into Parts. When code numbers are used as item numbers in the Bill, items are listed in order of ascending code number within each Part, except where it is thought convenient to locate out of the general order a group of items under a heading, the items in each group are listed in order of ascending code number within the group. Distinction between items of similar code number in different Parts of the Bill can be made by prefixing the code number with the Part number and a full stop. Distinction between items of similar code number under different group headings can be made by adding as a suffix a full stop and a constant number at the end of the code numbers in a particular group. For example in the code 3.E623.2.1, the prefix 3 indicates Part 3 of the Bill, the following letter and three digits is the CESMM code. The suffix .2 indicates additional description (See Paragraph 4.7) and the final .1 indicates the chosen suffix for all items in a particular group.

4.3

Code numbers used as item numbers are not part of the item descriptions. Items are interpreted on the wording of the descriptions. An incorrect code number does not cause a correct description to be incorrect. A correct code number does not cause an incorrect description to be correct.

4.4

## Coding of Unclassified Items

Where an item includes a feature which the Work Classification does not list, the digit 9 is used in the applicable division position in the code number. For example, U925 would be the code number for the item "Refractory brickwork, thickness 215 mm, vertical facing to concrete". (Refer to Class U - CESMM).

4.5

For an item to which a division of classification does not apply or for which the Work Classification lists less than three divisions of classification, the consequent absence of a descriptive feature in the item is denoted by the use of the digit 0 in the applicable division in the code number. For example, E210 is the code number for the item "Excavation for cuttings, topsoil". (Refer to Class E - CESMM).

4.6

## Numbering of Items with Additional Description

To distinguish items which have the same code number but have additional description, or different additional description, a suffix number is attached to the code number. Application of this convention is shown in Example 1.2, Chapter 1.                                                   4.7

## *PREPARATION OF THE BILL OF QUANTITIES*

Section 5 of the CESMM contains rules and recommendations regarding the preparation and presentation of the Bill of Quantities, including its format and content.

## Measurement of Completed Work

The rules of measurement given in the CESMM when applied to the preparation of the Bill of Quantities for a Contract apply equally to the measurement of the completed work on that Contract.                                                      5.1

## Sections of the Bill of Quantities

The Bill of Quantities is required to be divided into the sections listed in the Paragraph referenced as follows:-

    A.     List of principal quantities

    B.     Preamble

    C.     Daywork Schedule

    D.     Work items (grouped into parts)

    E.     Grand Summary                                   5.2

Each section of the Bill is usually identified by the capital letter as indicated for the section in the list above. Section D groups "Work Items" into Parts. Each Part is usually numbered. (See Paragraph 5.8 of the CESMM and subsequent Commentary). If not required Section C - Daywork, may be omitted. (See Paragraphs 5.6 and 5.7 of the CESMM and subsequent Commentary).

## List of Principal Quantities

The list of principal quantities provided in Section A of the Bill of Quantities will consist of a brief schedule of the overall quantities of the adjudged principal components of the Works. (An Example is given in Fig. 3.). It will not usually show separately the quantities for individual Parts. Whilst the aim is to provide a reasonably accurate indication of overall requirements, it is of no contractual significance if there are differences between the list and the detailed quantities.                                                  5.3

SECTION A. - LIST OF PRINCIPAL QUANTITIES

| | |
|---|---|
| Provisional Sums | 55000 £ |
| Prime Cost Items | 10000 £ |
| Excavation | 650 m3 |
| Filling | 200 m3 |
| Concrete - mass in situ | 110 m3 |
| Pipelines - 975 and 1200 mm concrete pipes | 975 m |
| Manholes | 15 nr |
| Tunnels - 1500 mm concrete bolted segments | 45 m |
| Shafts - 5280 mm concrete bolted segments | 15 m |

Fig. 3. Example of a List of Principal Quantities for an imaginary contract.

SECTION C. - DAYWORK SCHEDULE

The Contractor shall be paid for work executed on a Daywork basis at rates and prices calculated by adding the percentage additions stated in the "Schedule of Dayworks carried out incidental to Contract Works" issued by the Federation of Civil Engineering Contractors to the rates and prices contained in the aforementioned "Schedules" and making further adjustment as follows:-

| | | |
|---|---|---|
| Schedule 1 Labour | addition/deduction* | of ...+ per cent |
| Schedule 2 Materials | addition/deduction* | of ...+ per cent |
| Schedule 3 Plant | addition/deduction* | of ...+ per cent |
| Schedule 4 Supplementary charges++ | addition/deduction* | of ...+ per cent |

* Appropriate deletion to be made by the Contractor when tendering.

+ Percentage to be entered by the Contractor when tendering.

++ Supplementary charges shall not include the charges referred to in the notes and conditions 2 (ii), 4 and 7 of Schedule 4.

Payment shall be made under the conditions and using the rates and prices contained in the edition of the aforementioned Schedules current at the date of the execution of the Daywork.

Fig. 4.  Example of Daywork Schedule in accordance with sub-paragraph (b) of Paragraph 5.6 of the CESMM.

Preamble

Work not covered by the CESMM is sometimes required to be
included in the Bill of Quantities. If this work is measured,
the Preamble must state the methods of measurement and/or any
amendments to the CESMM which have been adopted when preparing
the Bill of Quantities for the work and which are to apply
when it is re-measured. Bill items for Contractor designed
work and work open to Contractor suggested alternatives will
usually leave out detail which the CESMM requires to be
provided. In such cases the CESMM is amended by abbreviation.
Preamble must state the extent of all work affected by all
amendments to the CESMM.                                          5.4

A definition of rock must be given in the Preamble where
the Bill of Quantities includes items for excavation, boring
or driving in rock.                                              5.5

The terms in which rock is to be defined are not given in
the CESMM. Preferably definition gives geological description
or rock types in the terms used to describe the materials in
the borehole logs or reference conditions and classifies them
according to weathering indices or mechanical properties, such
as strength, fracture spacing, bedding characteristicts, etc.
The objective of the classification is to provide a means of
identifying particular strata which will qualify, under the
Contract, to be measured as rock or a particular class of
rock.

The function of the Preamble is not restricted to that
outlined for it in Paragraphs 5.4 and 5.5 of the CESMM. Even
when no deviation is made from the CESMM, circumstances arise
in the practical application of its provisions which suggest
that certain conventions and item coverage, which might in the
circumstances not otherwise be clear, should be explained in
Preamble for the guidance of tenderers.

Daywork Schedule

The CESMM provides that the Daywork Schedule, if any, included
in the Bill of Quantities shall take either of two forms,
viz:-

(a)  a specially prepared list as described in sub-
     paragraph (a) of Paragraph 5.6 of the CESMM, or           5.6(a)

(b)  a statement on the lines of sub-paragraph (b) of
     Paragraph 5.6 of the CESMM, bringing into use the
     stated "Schedules of Dayworks" issued by the
     Federation of Civil Engineering Contractors, and
     providing for tenderers to insert the percentage
     addition or deduction which they require to apply
     to the rates and prices (after the percentages in
     the Schedules have been applied) in the
     "Schedules of Dayworks" for each of the stated
     elements of Daywork. (See Fig.4).                          5.6(b)

Daywork Schedule (cont.

Because of the considerable work involved in setting out
definitions and conditions for a Daywork Schedule in the form
at (a) above, the use of such a Schedule is normally
restricted to circumstances where a satisfactory means of
valuing work executed on a daywork basis could not be achieved
by a Daywork Schedule which makes use of approved published
Schedules of Daywork.

The form indicated at (b) above is that which is commonly
used. (See Example Fig.4).

Provisional sums for work executed on a Daywork basis may
be given in the Bill of Quantities. When this is done, each
element of Daywork forms the subject of a separate item giving
an associated provisional sum. The sum being an estimate of
the amount which might reasonably be expected to be expended
on the element. The items with their associated provisional
sums would be given in the Bill of Quantities in Class A -
General Items. (See Items A411, A413, A415 and A417 of the
CESMM). Each of these items would be followed by an item for
adjustment, if the Daywork Schedule used is of the form
indicated in (b) previously. The item for adjustment would
provide for the appropriate percentage addition or deduction,
inserted in the Daywork Schedule by the Contractor, to be
applied to the associated provisional sum of the preceding
item in calculation of the price to be included in the amount
of the Bill of Quantities. (See Table 3.05 and page (4) of
Example AE.1. Chapter 3).                                    5.7


## Work Items

### Division of the Bill of Quantities into Parts

It is customary to divide the Bill of Quantities into
Parts. The recommendation implied by the CESMM is that the
Bill should be arranged in numbered Parts to distinguish
between those parts of the work which for any reason is
thought likely to give rise to different methods of
construction or considerations of cost. Class A - General
Items will usually be given as a separate Part of the Bill,
although it may sometimes be considered more helpful for
General Items specifically allied to one Part to be given in
that particular Part. Throughout the Bill of Quantities, items
within each Part must be arranged in the general order of the
Work Classification.                                        5.8

Parts are created for sections of the Works. A Part may
include several Classes. Within the Parts, the work may be
such that it requires items to be sub-divided (See Paragraph
5.10 of the CESMM).

The Parts into which the Bill of Quantities is divided
is decided by the person responsible for the preparation of
the Bill on the basis of their own judgment.

### Headings and Sub-headings

A heading must be given to each Part of the Bill of
Quantities. Within each Part items may be grouped under
sub-headings. Headings and sub-headings form part of the item
descriptions to which they apply. They must be repeated at the
start of each new page which lists items to which they apply.
In the Bill of Quantities, a line must be drawn across the
item description column below the last item to which each
heading or sub-heading applies.                                5.9

The heading given to a Part of the Bill of Quantities
will indicate the section or element of the Works covered by
the particular Part.

Creating a sub-heading, consisting of what otherwise
would be repetitive features in several item descriptions,
contributes to the brevity of the Bill of Quantities.

An example of the use of headings and sub-headings, also
the application of the rule in Paragraph 5.9 of the CESMM
which requires a line to be drawn across the item description
column, is illustrated in Fig. 5.

### Extent of Itemisation and Description

Work must be described and given in items as provided in the
Work Classification. Where work for any reason is thought
likely to give rise to special methods of construction or
consideration of cost, the CESMM suggests that which causes
the work to be considered special may be identified by
providing additional description and items, beyond the
requirements of the Work Classification.                       5.10

The person responsible for the preparation of the Bill of
Quantities will decide, using their own judgment, where to
provide additional description and items, as referred to in
the preceding paragraph. Additional description and items
would not be provided to identify that which would have little
or no cost effect.

### Descriptions

"Descriptions (in the Bill of Quantities) shall identify the
work covered by the respective items". The extent and nature
of the work is to be ascertained from the other
Tender/Contract documents read in conjunction with the Work
Classification.                                                5.11

Subject to Paragraph 3.2 of the CESMM, item descriptions
prepared in accordance with the Work Classification are
sufficient provided they clearly identify the work they
represent. It is appropriate to provide further itemisation
and additional description where they would not otherwise
clearly identify the work. See also Commentary on Paragraph
5.13 given subsequently.

PART 5. WALLS - SERVICE AREAS

| Number | Item description | Unit | Quantity | Rate | Amount £ | p |
|---|---|---|---|---|---|---|
| | BRICKWORK, BLOCKWORK AND MASONRY. | | | | | |
| | Engineering brickwork in Class B bricks as Specification clause 4.3, Type A mortar as Specification clause 4.7. | | | | | |
| U321 | Thickness 215 mm, vertical straight walls. | m2 | | | | |
| U360 | Piers, cross-sectional dimensions 900 x 328 mm. | m | | | | |
| | Surface features. | | | | | |
| U371.1 | Copings; brick on edge, with tile creasing, Drawing 27B. | m | | | | |
| U371.2 | Copings; brick on end, cross-sectional dimensions 328 x 215 mm. | m | | | | |
| U378 | Fair facing; Specification clause 4.22. | m2 | | | | |
| | Ancillaries. | | | | | |
| | Damp proof courses, to BS 743, type E. | | | | | |
| U382.1 | Width 215 mm. | m | | | | |
| U382.2 | Width 328 mm. | m | | | | |
| U387 | Built in pipes cross-sectional area not exceeding 0.05 m2. | nr | | | | |

COMMENTARY

The line drawn across the description column beneath Item Code U378 denotes the end of the items to which the sub-heading "Surface features" relates, but leaves both the sub-heading "Engineering brickwork, etc." and the main heading "BRICKWORK, BLOCKWORK AND MASONRY" operative.

The line drawn across the description column beneath Item Code U382.2 denotes the end of the items to which the sub-heading "Damp proof courses etc." relates, but leaves the sub-headings "Ancillaries" and "Engineering Brickwork etc." and the main heading "BRICKWORK, BLOCKWORK AND MASONRY" operative.

The three lines drawn across the description column beneath Item Code U387 denotes the end of the items to which the sub-headings "Ancillaries", "Engineering brickwork, etc." and the main heading "BRICKWORK, BLOCKWORK AND MASONARY" relates.

Fig. 5.    Illustration of lines drawn across description column as required by Paragraph 5.9 of the CESMM.

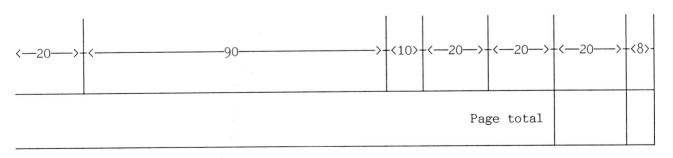

Page total

Fig. 6. Column widths in mm of Bill paper as suggested in Paragraph 5.22 of the CESMM.

COMMENTARY

Description (cont.

An appropriate Drawing or Specification reference may be given in an item description in place of any detail of description required to be given in accordance with the Work Classification. Such a reference must identify precisely where the omitted information may be found on the Drawing or in the Specification.                                                    5.12

Additional description stating location or other physical features shown on the Drawing or described in the Specification must be given where an item description compiled in accordance with the Work Classification would be insufficient to clearly identify the work it represents.      5.13

Ranges of Dimensions

The Work Classification provides for the dimensions of some components to be given within stated ranges. The description of an item may state the actual dimension in place of the range where all the components in the item are of one dimension.                                                        5.14

Items stating a range of dimensions cover only components they identify of the dimensions shown on the tender drawings and/or described in the specification. They do not cover components having other dimensions even though they are within the same range. Components may sometimes be itemised giving actual dimensions where, to facilitate valuation of variations it is thought desirable to have a Contract rate for a component of actual dimensions, thus avoiding having to agree a rate from a break down of an item which includes several components of different dimensions.

Prime Cost Items

The expressions "Prime Cost Item" and "Nominated Sub-contractor" when used in the CESMM, will have the meanings given in clauses 58(2) and 58(5), respectively, of the I.C.E. Conditions of Contract.

Prime Cost Items must be provided in the Bill of Quantities for all work which is to be carried out by Nominated Sub-contractors, whether or not the Nominated Sub-contractor is to carry out work on the Site. The Prime Cost Item given in the Bill of Quantities will consist of an identifying description with an associated sum. The sum being an estimate of the cost of the work to be carried out by the Nominated Sub-contractor. Each Prime Cost Item given in the Bill of Quantities must be followed by:-                       5.15

    (a)   an item, providing for the Contractor to insert a sum for labours in connection with the Prime Cost Item, which unless the Contract expressly requires otherwise, will include only the work stated in sub-paragraph (a) (i) of Paragraph 5.15 of the CESMM when the Nominated Subcontractor is to carry out work on Site, and only the work stated in

/cont.

Prime Cost Items (cont.

        sub-paragraph (a) (ii) of the same Paragraph when
        the Nominated Subcontractor is not to carry out work
        on site, and                                          5.15(a)

(b)  an item providing for the Contractor to insert as a
      percentage of the Prime Cost Item all other charges
      and profit.                                           5.15(b)

Where the Contractor is required to provide for the
Nominated Sub-contractor labours other than or in addition to
those indicated in Paragraph 5.15 of the CESMM, the precise
requirements must be prescribed in the Contract. They must be
stated in the descriptions of items designated "special
labours" given separately from the standard "labours" items.
See Table 3.06, Chapter 3.

Where the Contractor is to use any goods, materials or
services supplied by a Nominated Sub-contractor, the Bill of
Quantities will need to provide items for the Contractor's
work in using them. This could be done in the Bill of
Quantities in one of the following ways:-

(i)   Insofar as the CESMM is appropriate for the work it
      can be measured and billed in accordance with the
      Work Classification, subject to Paragraphs 3.3 and
      5.16 of the CESMM. For Paragraph 3.3 see previous
      Commentary. For Paragaph 5.16 see subsequent
      Commentary which gives that reference.

(ii)  Where the CESMM is not appropriate to the
      measurement of the work it can be itemised as
      provided in Paragraph 2.2 of the CESMM. See previous
      Commentary which gives that Paragraph reference.

(iii)  The work can be made the subject of a Provisional
      Sum.

The procedures as (i) to (iii) above would be appropriate
also to any Contractor's work in connection with the work
carried out by a Nominated Sub-contractor, as well as to that
which uses the materials, etc., the Nominated Sub-contractor
supplies.

The items for the Contractor's work dealt with as (i)
above, can be given in the Bill of Quantities, suitably
identified in their appropriate position in the Class to which
they belong. It is considered, however, that they are better
grouped under an identifying heading at the end of the Class
to which they belong or in a separate Part of the Bill created
for the purpose. Items for Contractor's work dealt with as
(ii) above can be grouped under an identifying heading at the
end of any Class considered allied to that to which they
belong or in a separate Part of the Bill created for the
purpose. Where Provisional Sums are given for the Contractor's

Prime Cost Items (cont.

work as (iii) above, they are the equivalent of specified contingencies and would be given with associated identifying descriptions in the General Items of the Bill of Quantities in the same way.

Items or headings under which are grouped items for work for which the Contractor is to use goods or materials or services supplied by a Nominated Sub-contractor must make reference to the Prime Cost Item under which they are supplied.

5.16

Provisional Sums

For definition of the term "Provisional Sum" when used in the CESMM, see clause 58(1) of the I.C.E. Conditions of Contract.

Any provision for contingencies required to be made in the Bill of Quantities must be made by giving Provisional Sums and not by giving quantities of work in excess of expected requirements. Provisional Sums for any specified contingencies are given with associated identifying descriptions in the General Items of the Bill of Quantities. Any Provisional Sum for a general contingency must be given in the Grand Summary. (See Paragraph 5.25 of the CESMM and subsequent Commentary).

5.17

The CESMM outlaws the deliberate increasing of quantities beyond the computed total requirements as a means of providing for contingencies. The forbearance imposed by the CESMM in this respect does not mean that the quantities given should be the minimum quantities and that all variables should be the subject of Provisional Sums. Where there are components which have dimensions which may vary there is no reason why they should not be estimated so that quantities may be computed to give the expected total requirements. If this is done, it would be consistent with the rule established by Paragraph 5.18 of the CESMM, which states "quantities shall be computed ... from the Drawings" to judge the extent of the variables and show them on the Drawings to enable the total expected quantities to be computed as stated. Alternatively, in any case where variables are not shown and it is judged that more work than is shown on the Drawings is to be expected, the procedure would be to compute the quantities from the Drawings and give a Provisional Sum to cover the cost of the additional work which might reasonably be expected.

Quantities

The quantities given in the Bill of Quantities must be computed net from the Drawings, unless it is directed otherwise by a measurement rule in the CESMM. They will usually be rounded to whole units. Fractional quantities of 0.50 and over being rounded up to the next whole unit. Other fractional quantities being neglected. Nevertheless, the use of fractional quantities may be considered where quantities are small. The CESMM imposes no rule regarding rounding off

## Quantities (cont.

quantities. It suggests that fractional quantities are not
generally necessary and should not be given to more than one
decimal place.                                                          5.18

## Units of Measurement

The Paragraph referenced sets out the abbreviations used for
the units of measurement previously referred to in Paragraph
3.5 of the CESMM.                                                       5.19

The abbreviations use small case letters with no full
stops. This convention must be followed when they are used in
the Bill of Quantities.

## Work Affected by Water

Any body of open water, other than ground water such as a
stream, canal, river or body of tidal water which is either on
the Site or bounds the Site must be identified in the preamble
to the Bill of Quantities. A reference must also be given to a
drawing which indicates the boundaries and surface levels of
each body of water, or the ranges of fluctuations where the
boundaries and surface levels fluctuate.                                5.20

A typical preamble clause to satisfy the requirements of
Paragraph 5.20 for the imaginary Works of constructing a new
jetty in the tidal water of a harbour adjoining an old quay,
might read:-

### Existing Body of Open Water

The Site includes an area of Tinemouthend Harbour to the
South of the Old Quay. Drawing No. 22/86 indicates the
extent of the work sited in the Harbour and also the
anticipated boundaries and surface levels of high and low
water.

The CESMM imposes no requirement as to how boundaries and
levels are to be indicated and the drawing may present them in
any convenient form using any convenient datum.

Levels or some other measure related to any convenient
datum may be used to indicate the surface levels of bodies of
non tidal water. The drawing for bodies of non tidal water
would appropriately indicate in addition to adjoining surface
or ground levels the static water surface level, or where
appropriate the average dry weather and storm flow water
surface levels, the position of the levels and either the
dates on which they were taken or the source from which they
were obtained. In the case of bodies of tidal water it is
convenient for the fluctuation between high and low water to
be given respectively on the drawing in terms of the surface
levels of mean high water and mean low water ordinary spring
tides related to Ordnance Datum (Newlyn). The reference may be
given of the official chart from which the levels were taken.

The level of the bed of a body of water related to the
same datum used for the surface level of the water and the

COMMENTARY

Work Affected by of Water (cont.

    adjoining ground or surface should be given on the drawing
where it is of significance to the work which is to take place
in relation to the water. For example, where the bed of the
body of water would form the Commencing Surface for piling.

    Where it is considered that factors such as the nature,
location, importance and other special characteristics of work
in or adjoining open bodies of water are likely to give rise
to special methods of construction or consideration of cost,
it is a matter of good practice to implement the suggestion in
Paragraph 5.10 of the CESMM and provide further itemisation
and additional description to distinguish it from other work
not affected by these factors. In some cases it will be found
convenient to group the work in the Bill under locational or
other appropriate headings and to refer in the heading to the
identifying Preamble and drawing reference.

Ground and Excavation Levels

    Item descriptions for work which involves excavation, boring
or driving must identify the Commencing Surface when it is not
also the Original Surface. They must identify the Excavated
Surface where it is not also the Final Surface. The depths of
work given in the item descriptions in accordance with the
Work Classification must be measured from the Commencing
Surface to the Excavated Surface.                                          5.21

    Descriptions need not identify Surfaces by level. The
identification required as provided in the preceding paragraph
may be effected by stating in the item descriptions the position of the Commencing Surface or the Excavated Surface, as
the case may be, in relation to the Original Surface or the
Final Surface or to a surface of a component of the Works. The
Commencing Surface must in all cases be stated for piling (See
Rule A3 Class P of CESMM). Otherwise it is not necessary to
state a Commencing Surface or an Excavated Surface where these
are the Original Surface and the Final Surface, respectively.
Examples of the application of the rule given in Paragraph
5.21 are given in Fig. E2, and in the Measured Example in
Chapter 7.

Form and Setting Out

    The CESMM suggests the Bill of Quantities is reproduced on
paper of A4 size. It suggests also how paper on which to set
out work items should be ruled and headed. The ruling and
headings are shown in Figs. 5 and 6, with column widths in
millimetres superimposed on the suggested sheet.                           5.22

    Each page of the Bill of Quantities makes provision for
the amounts inserted to be brought to a total. See Fig. 6. A
Summary must be provided for each Part of the Bill of
Quantities. It must make provision which enables the amount of
each page to be brought into the Summary and cast to a total.
The Summary will indicate also that the total amount of the
Part is to be carried to the Grand Summary. (See Paragraph
5.24 of the CESMM). Paper ruled differently from that for the
work items will usually be used for Summaries. An example of a
Part Summary is shown in Fig. 7.                                           5.23

PART 1 - GENERAL ITEMS - SUMMARY

| | £ | p |
|---|---|---|
| Page 11 . . . | | |
| Page 12 . . . | | |
| Page 13 . . . | | |
| Page 14 . . . | | |
| TOTAL PART 1 - Carried to SECTION 'E' GRAND SUMMARY    £ | | |

Fig. 7.  Example of Part Summary prepared to comply with
Paragraph 5.23 of the CESMM.

SEA DEFENCE WORK AT TINEMOUTHEND

SECTION E - GRAND SUMMARY

| | £ | p |
|---|---|---|
| PART 1  General Items . . . . . . Page 15 . . | | |
| PART 2  Site Clearance . . . . Page 19 . . | | |
| PART 3  Sea Wall . . . . . . Page 28 . . | | |
| PART 4  Promenade Pavements . . . Page 32 . . | | |
| PART 5  Flood Walls . . . . . Page 39 . . | | |
| PART 6  Work to Outfall Sewer . . Page 46 . . | | |
| Total    £ | | |
| General Contingency Allowance | 25000 | 00 |
| Total    £ | | |
| Adjustment Item : Addition/Deduction* . . . . . | | |
| Tender Total    £ | | |

Signed . . . . . . . . . . . on behalf of . . . . . . . . .

Date . . . . . . . . . . .

* Delete as appropriate

Fig. 8. Example of a Grand Summary prepared to comply with
Paragraphs 5.24 to 5.27 (inclusive) of the CESMM.

## Grand Summary

The last section of the Bill of Quantities gives a Grand Summary. The Grand Summary must give a list of Parts (See paragraph 5.2 of the CESMM). It must provide a column in which which the amounts from the Part Summaries can be inserted and totalled. An example of a Grand Summary is given in Fig. 8.

5.24

## General Contingency Allowance

Any provision in the Bill of Quantities for a general contingency must be made the subject of a provisional sum. (See the last sentence of paragraph 5.17 of the CESMM). The sum must be given in the Grand Summary in a position immediately following that provided for the total of the amounts for the Parts (See Fig.8).

5.25

## Adjustment Item

An adjustment Item must be given in the Grand Summary. It must be the last item given in the Grand Summary. (See Fig.8). Provision shall be made for all amounts other than that for the Adjustment Item to be brought to a total immediately preceding the Adjustment Item. (See also Paragraphs 6.3 to 6.5 inclusive of the CESMM).

5.26

## Total of the Priced Bill of Quantities

The Grand Summary must make provision for all amounts in the Summary to be brought to a Tender Total. (See Fig. 8).

5.27

*COMPLETION, PRICING AND USE OF THE BILL OF QUANTITIES*

Rules and explanatory statements in relation to the completion and pricing of the Bill of Quantities by a Tenderer are set out in Section 6 of the CESMM.

## Insertion of Rates and Prices

Rates and prices are required to be entered in the rate column by the tenderer in pounds sterling with pence entered as decimal fractions of one pound.

6.1

Specific reference to the rate column in Paragraph 6.1 of the CESMM, indicates the intention that tenderers must insert a rate for each item intended to be priced. A lump sum inserted in the amount column for a group of bracketed items is not acceptable.

When the ICE Conditions of Contract (fifth edition) are used, items which a tenderer chooses to leave unpriced are deemed to be covered by the priced items. See Clauses 11(2) and 55(2) of the ICE Conditions of Contract.

## Parts to be Totalled

Tenderers are required to cast the extended prices to a total
for each Part of the Bill of Quantities and to carry the total
of each Part to the Grand Summary. This is facilitated by
giving a summary for each Part (See Figs. 7 and 8, page 28).          6.2

## Adjustment Item

A tenderer may insert a lump sum addition or deduction against
the Adjustment Item (given in the Grand Summary) in adjustment
of the total of the Bill of Quantities.                               6.3

Any amount inserted by the Contractor in respect of the
Adjustment Item constitutes a fixed lump sum adjustment. It
will be treated as such in the final settlement whether or not
the total value of work is more or less than that anticipated
in the Bill of Quantities, but see Commentary on Paragraph
6.5.

Instalments on account of the amount, if any, of the
Adjustment Item must be made in interim certificates. They are
made in the proportion that the amount referred to in clause
60(2)(a) of the Conditions of Contract bears to the total of
the Bill of Quantities before the addition or deduction of the
amount of the Adjustment Item. (A statement to this effect
must be made in the Preamble of the Bill of Quantities). Such
interim additions or deductions are made before the deduction
of retention. They must not exceed in aggregate the amount
inserted for the Item in the Bill. When for an interim
certificate the calculations by proportion show that the
aggregate of the instalments has reached or would exceed the
amount originally inserted, the amount certified in that
certificate and which would continue to be certified in
subsequent certificates would be the amount of the Adjustment
Item. When at the date of the issue of the Certificate of
Completion for the whole of the Works (See clause 48 of the
Conditions of Contract) the aggregate of the instalments has
not reached the amount of the Adjustment Item, the balance
must be added to or deducted from the monies then due.                6.4

Loosely defined the amount referred to in clause 60(2)(a)
of the Conditions of Contract represents the value the
Engineer attaches to the work items carried out at the time he
is preparing his certificate. The value of unfixed goods and
materials are excluded from the amount.

Where the Contract Price Fluctuations clause is
applicable, the Effective Value (i.e. the amount due to the
Contractor excluding any amounts based on actual cost or
current prices) to which the Baxter Formula* is applied,
includes any addition or deduction in respect of the
Adjustment Item.                                                      6.5

     * *The Contract Price Fluctuations clause used in*
       *appropriate cases with the I.C.E. Conditions of*
       *Contract provides for the use of the Baxter*
       *formula.*

Section 7 of the CESMM deals with Method-Related Charges.

Some cost elements within an inclusive price related to the in position quantity of finished permanent work may not vary in direct proportion to quantity. For example, such a price will include a cost element for the labour and materials reflected by the physical entity of the work left on Site. It will include also the cost element covering the bringing to Site, the setting up and the operation, maintenance and removal of plant, machinery and such like related to the method of executing the work. For similar work the former cost element can be said to vary in direct proportion to quantity, whereas the latter cost element may not.

The foregoing serves to illustrate cases can arise where there is just cause to question the logic and equity of a valuation made by taking the total units of the admeasured quantities of an item and multiplying them by the inclusive price per unit attached to the particular item in the Bill of Quantities. With the implied object of providing within the Contract a satisfactory means of adjustment and avoiding contention in such cases, the CESMM allows tenderers the option of sub-dividing prices. They may, subject to the provisions of Section 7 of the CESMM, introduce into the Bill of Quantities priced items covering the elements of cost which relate to methods of executing the work (Method-Related Charges) and price the quantities given in the Bill of Quantities at prices which excludes the element of cost covered by the Method-Related Charges elsewhere given.

Definitions

'Method-Related Charge' means an itemised sum as defined in the Paragraph referenced. Each Method-Related Charge will be either a :-

                                                              7.1(a)

'Time-Related Charge', which denotes a Method-Related Charge which covers work the cost of which is related to the time taken to carry it out. For example, an itemised sum inserted to cover the work of operating and maintaining a facility or service for a period of time.

                                                              7.1(b)

'Fixed Charge', which denotes a Method-Related Charge which is not a Time-Related Charge. For example, an itemised sum inserted to cover the work of bringing to Site and setting up a facility or service.

                                                              7.1(c)

Insertion by a Tenderer

The CESMM, without making it compulsory, permits tenderers to insert for any items they may choose, priced items of Method-Related Charges, insofar as they cover work which relates to methods of execution which are considered not to be proportional to quantity, the cost of which has not been

### Insertion by a Tenderer (cont.

allowed  in the prices inserted for the quantified items given          7.2
in the Bill of Quantities.

The Bill of Quantities when issued to tender will include
several  blank  pages  for tenderers to use if  they  wish  to
insert Method-Related Charges. The blank pages are included in
the General  items (Class A) section of the document. They are
ruled  and  headed in a manner similar to those on  which  the
work items  are  given.  The  pages will be  included  in  the
document  in a position which ensures that any  Method-Related
Charges  inserted  will  follow the order set out for  them  in
Class  A of the Work Classification. See also Paragraph 7.3 of
the CESMM and subsequent Commentary.

### Itemisation

Itemisation  of  Method-Related Charges should  follow,  where
possible,  the order of classification and other  requirements
as  set out in Class A. The item descriptions inserted  should
state  whether the item covered is a Time-Related Charge or  a
Fixed  Charge and separate items should be inserted for  each.
Tenderers,  if they so wish, may insert Method-Related Charges
to  cover  items of work other than those set out in Class  A,
subject to Paragraph 7.2 of the CESMM.                                   7.3

### Descriptions

Paragraph  7.4  of  the CESMM establishes the rules  that  the
description  inserted  in  the  Bill  of  Quantities for  a
Method-Related  Charge shall define precisely the work covered
and  shall  identify  the resources intended to be  used,  and
shall  identify  the  particular items of Permanent Works  or
Temporary  Works,  if any, to which the Method-Related  Charge
relates.                                                                7.4

### Contractor Not Bound to Adopt Method

The  Contractor  is  not bound to adopt the  intended  method
inserted  in  the description of an item for a  Method-Related
Charge.                                                                 7.5

### Charges Not to be Measured

"Method-Related     Charges    shall    not    be   subject   to
admeasurement".                                                         7.6

The  quantity  of  time taken for the work covered  by  a
Time-Related  Charge  and the quantity of work  and  resources
covered by a Fixed Charge is not subject to admeasurement.

Quantities  of  the time it is anticipated will be  taken
for the work covered by a Time-Related Charge are not required
to be  stated in the item description. The unit of measurement
for a Method-Related Charge is the sum. The inserted sum being
an amount for the work covered by the Charge and not a rate to
be used to determine the Charge by admeasurement.

Charges Not to be Measured (cont.

    Method-Related Charges are deemed to be the prices for
the purpose of Clauses 52(1), 52(2) and 56(2) of the I.C.E.
Conditions. Consequently, an appropriate adjustment to a
Method-Related Charge would be made where, in the opinion of
the Engineer, it had been made unreasonable or inapplicable
because:-

    (i)   the work to which the Charge related had
          been varied by his order (See Clause 52
          of the I.C.E. Conditions).

    (ii)  the quantities of work to which the Charge
          related, were upon admeasurement greater or
          less than those stated in the Bill of
          Quantities.

    · Otherwise than as stated above the sum inserted for any
Method-Related Charge is not subject to adjustment.

Payments

Method-Related Charges are certified and paid pursuant to
clauses 60(1)(d) and 60(2)(d) of the I.C.E. Conditions of
Contract, and a statement to this effect must be given in the
Preamble to the Bill of Quantities. The Contractor includes
his estimate of the Charges in his monthly statement (I.C.E.
Conditions clause 60(1)) and the Engineer certifies the
amounts of the stated Charges which in his opinion is due to
the Contractor. (I.C.E. Conditions 60(2))(a).                    7.7

    The amount due for work covered by a Fixed Charge is
taken as the same proportion of the total Charge as the work
done bears to the total work covered by the Charge. The total
of the work covered by a Fixed Charge should be apparent from
the item and the proportion can be determined by fact.

    From the viewpoint of administering the Contract it is
advantageous to separate Fixed Charges for setting up services
or facilities from those for their removal.

    There is nothing in the rules of the CESMM, which
prevents tenderers from including in Fixed Charges for the
establishment of plant and equipment, the capital cost or
depreciation cost intended to be charged in respect of them to
the Contract. Where such costs are included in a Fixed Charge,
the Contractor is entitled to be paid them, in a certificate
at the appropriate time, as soon as the plant and equipment
envisaged by the Fixed Charge is established. It is often
unacceptable that the Employer should finance the Contractor
in this way. Where this is the case, instructions to tenderers
should require that any allowance tenderers wish to make for
the capital cost of or the depreciation cost for any plant and
equipment in a Method-Related Charge, shall be included in a
Time-Related Charge and not as part of a Fixed Charge.

Payments (cont.

    The amount due for work covered by a Time-Related Charge is taken as the same proportion of the total Charge as the relevant period of operation bears to the estimated total period of operation. Note that the total period of operation needs to be estimated. If as the work proceeds the estimate of the total period of operation proves unrealistic it should be revised. Thus the denominator of the fraction which determines the proportion may change from time to time.

Payment When Method Not Adopted

    Provided the result is satisfactory and provided the Engineer has not ordered a change of method, the Contractor is ultimately paid the amount attached to the item inserted for a Method-Related Charge, whether or not the Contractor used the method described in the item.

    Where the method is changed, the timing of the payment of the Charge, or the unpaid balance of the Charge where the changed method is substituted for the inserted method during progress, is a matter for agreement between the Engineer and the Contractor. Failing such agreement the Charge or the unpaid balance, as the case may be, is treated as if it were an addition to the Adjustment Item (See 6.3 to 6.5, Section 6, this Chapter).

    Any change of method ordered by the Engineer would be dealt with as a variation and would be valued as provided in Clause 52 of the I.C.E. Conditions of Contract.

*7.8*

### WORK CLASSIFICATION

The application of the Work Classification set out in Section 8 of the CESMM, is explained in Section 3 of the document. (See Previous Commentary on Section 3 in this Chapter).

    Section 8 commences with an index of the twenty five Classes contained in the Section and subsequently gives a classification table with descriptive features and Rules for each Class.

    In subsequent Chapters of this book each Class, or a group of allied Classes, is made the subject of a separate Chapter. Within each, Tables are given which summarise in outline the Rules given in the Work Classification of the CESMM. The Tables refer only to the requirements imposed by the Rules in the Work Classification. The full rule for a particular item must take account of any appropriate requirements in Sections 1 - 7 of the CESMM in addition to those noted in the Tables. Commentary which discusses the detail of applying the requirements of the CESMM to practical measurement and bill compilation is given to complement the Tables.

# 3 General Items – CESMM Class: A

General items, Class A of the CESMM covers general obligations, site services and facilitites, Temporary Works, testing, Provisional Sums and Prime Cost Items. It also provides for the Contractor to include Method-Related Charges, if he so chooses.

---

Table 3.01  Class A Generally

---

Generally - The unit of measurement for the General Items shall be the sum, except where another unit of measurement is used in accordance with Rule A/M2 (Rule A/M1)

---

COMMENTARY

Class A Generally (refer to Table 3.01)

Unlike other Classes of the CESMM, a unit of measurement is not given against the descriptive features in the classification table. Except for certain items of "specified requirements" which may be quantified, the unit of measurement for the Class A items is the sum. (See subsequent Commentary on Specified Requirements).

---

Table 3.02  Contractual Requirements

| 1st Division | 2nd Division | |
|---|---|---|
| Contractual requirements | Give item for performance bond, if required | |
| | Give separate items for insurance:- | The standard features for insurance cover only insurances in accordance with clauses 21 and 23 of the I.C.E. Contract, unless otherwise stated (Rule A/C1) |
| | of the Works | |
| | of constructional plant | |
| | against damage to persons and property | |
| | The Contractor may insert Method-Related Charges in accordance with Paragraph 7.2 for additional insurances. (Footnote Class A). | |

---

COMMENTARY

Contractual Requirements (refer to Table 3.02)

The standard contractual requirements items for insurances given in the CESMM cover insurances required to be effected in accordance with the I.C.E. Contract (Clauses 21 and 23), unless otherwise stated. Any insurances required in addition to, or different in scope from, the insurances prescribed in the I.C.E. Contract, should form the subject of Special Conditions of Contract and additional description or additional items should identify the requirement of the Special Conditions.

Where the Contract provides for the Contractor to indemnify the Employer against stated risks but makes no provision for him to insure

COMMENTARY

Contractual Requirements (cont.

    against them, the Contractor may if he chooses, insure against the stated risks and include the cost of so doing as Method-Related Charges.

---

Table 3.03   Specified Requirements

---

| Generally | Give specified requirements items for work other than the Permanent Works where the Contract expressly states the nature and extent of such work (Rule A/D1) |
|---|---|
|  | State if specified requirements items are to be carried out after issue of Completion Certificate (Rule A/A1) |
|  | Give a quantity for an item where the value is to be ascertained and determined by admeasurement (Rule A/M2) |
|  | Item descriptions for work, which is not quantified, shall distinguish between:- |
|  | establishment and removal of services or facilities, and |
|  | continuing operation or maintenance (Rule A/A2) |

| 1st Division | 2nd Division | 3rd Division |
|---|---|---|
| Specified requirements | Accommodation for the Engineer's staff | State type of accommodation |
|  | Services for the Engineer's staff | State nature of service |
|  | Equipment for use by the Engineer's staff | State type of equipment |
|  | Attendance upon the Engineer's staff | Identify attendant |
|  | Testing of materials<br><br>Testing of the Works | Give items for all testing not given separately in other Classes (Rule A/M3)<br><br>State particulars of samples and methods of testing (Rule A/A3) |
|  | Temporary Works | Describe in accordance with 3rd Division or other appropriate feature |

COMMENTARY

Specified Requirements (refer to Table 3.03)

    Items classed as specified requirements are given in the circumstances stated in Rule A/D1 but not otherwise. (See "Generally" in the first panel of Table 3.03). Where the Contractor may himself decide the nature and

COMMENTARY

Specified Requirements (cont.

extent of work other than the Permanent Works, such work does not qualify to be itemised in the Bill of Quantities.

Specified requirements items which it is intended shall be subject to admeasurement are quantified in appropriate units of measurement. Otherwise the unit of measurement attached to Class A items is the sum and they are not subject to admeasurement.

Item descriptions for work classed as specified requirements shall state if the work is to be carried out after the issue of the Certificate of Completion. (Rule A/A1).

---

Table 3.04 Method-Related Charges

| Method-Related Charges | May be inserted by tenderers in accordance with Section 7 of the CESMM (Rule A/M4) |
|---|---|
| | Itemisation and descriptions shall be in accordance with CESMM, Paragraphs 7.3 and 7.4, respectively |
| | Items shall distinguish between Time-Related and Fixed Charges (Rule A/A4) |

---

Table 3.05 Provisional Sums

| 1st Division | 2nd Division | 3rd Division | |
|---|---|---|---|
| Provisional sums | Dayworks | Give a separate item each with its associated sum for:- | |
| | | Labour | sum |
| | | Materials | sum |
| | | Plant | sum |
| | | Supplementary charges | sum |
| | | Where a Daywork Schedule as alternative (b) of Paragraph 5.6 of the CESMM is included in the Bill of Quantities, following each of the sums for the foregoing, give an item for percentage adjustment in accordance with the 3rd Division features (Rule A/M5) | % |
| | | The percentage adjustment inserted by tenderer should correspond with that inserted in the Daywork Schedule | |
| | Other Provisional Sums | Give separate items identifying each of any specified contingencies required with their associated sums | sum |

COMMENTARY

Provisional Sums (refer to Table 3.05)

For "Dayworks" refer to Commentary 5.6 and 5.7, Chapter 2. For "Provisional Sums" refer to Commentary 5.17, Chapter 2. See also the items in the specimen of the Part of the Bill of Quantities given in the Example at the end of this Chapter.

Table 3.06   Prime Cost Items

| 1st Division | | |
|---|---|---|
| Prime Cost Items:- | Identify the work included in each prime cost item (Rule A/A5). Give the amount of the associated sum | sum |
| which include work on Site by a Nominated Sub-contractor | Following each prime cost item:- | |
| which do not include work on Site by a Nominated Sub-contractor | give an item for "Labours" (Rule A/M6) | sum |
| | give an item, if required for "Special labours" and state labours (Rule A/M6 and A/A6) | sum |
| | give an item for "Other charges and profit" (Rule A/M6) | % |

COMMENTARY

Prime Cost Items (refer to Table 3.06)

Refer to Commentary 5.15 and 5.16, Chapter 2. See also items in the Specimen of the General Items Part of the Bill of Quantities at the end of this Chapter.

EXAMPLE AE.1

Specimen of General Items Part of a Bill of Quantities

The Example which follows is the General Items Part of the Bill of Quantities for a small, imaginary pipeline contract. In practice a Part of a Bill ends with a Part Summary. This is omitted from the Example. For a specimen of a Part Summary, see Figure 7, Chapter 2.

| Number | Item description | Unit | Quantity | Rate | Amount £ | p |
|--------|-----------------|------|----------|------|----------|---|
| | GENERAL ITEMS. | | | | | |
| | Contractual requirements. | | | COMMENTARY | | |
| A110 | Performance bond. | sum | | Insurance items given here | | |
| A120 | Insurance of the Works. | sum | | cover only the insurances | | |
| A130 | Insurance of construction plant. | sum | | required by the I.C.E. Contract. For any addition- | | |
| A140 | Insurance against damage to persons and property. | sum | | al insurances, see Comment- ary following Table 3.02 in this Chapter. | | |
| | Specified requirements. | | | | | |
| | Accommodation for the Engineer's staff. | | | Items for specified re- quirements are given for | | |
| A211.1 | Establishment and removal of offices; as Specification clause 1.5. | sum | | work other than the Perma- ent Work, where the Con- | | |
| A211.2 | Maintenance of offices. | sum | | tractor is required to carry them out in a parti- cular way, or to a parti- | | |
| | Services for the Engineer's staff. | | | cular extent. See Table 3.03 and Commentary | | |
| A222.1 | Establishment and removal of 2 nr G.P.O. telephones. | sum | | following the Table in this Chapter | | |
| A222.2 | Maintenance of G.P.O. telephones (provisional sum for call charges elsewhere given). | sum | | | | |
| | Equipment for use by the Engineer's staff. | | | Establishment and removal of services and facilities are | | |
| A231.1 | Establishment and removal of office equipment; as Specification clause 1.5. | sum | | given in separate items from those for their continuing operation and maintenance. | | |
| A231.2 | Maintenance of office equipment. | sum | | See Table 3.03. | | |
| A232.1 | Establishment and removal of testing equipment; as Specification clause 1.7. | sum | | | | |
| A232.2 | Maintenance of testing equipment. | sum | | | | |
| A233.1 | Establishment and removal of survey- ing equipment; as Specification clause 1.8. | sum | | | | |
| A233.2 | Maintenance of surveying equipment. | sum | | | | |
| | (1)     To Part 1 Summary     Page total | | | | | |

| Number | Item description | Unit | Quantity | Rate | Amount £ | p |
|---|---|---|---|---|---|---|
| | GENERAL ITEMS (cont. | | | | | |
| | Specified requirements (cont. | | | | | |
| | Attendance upon the Engineer's staff. | | | | | |
| A242 | Chainmen. | h | 200 | | | |
| | Testing Materials. | | | | | |
| A250.1 | Concrete strength tests; as Specification clause 4.30 (4 cubes/test). | nr | 40 | | | |
| A250.2 | Pipe bedding material tests; as Specification clause 7.18. | nr | 5 | | | |
| | Testing of the Works. | | | | | |
| | Air testing, as Specification clause 7.4. | | | | | |
| A260.1 | Concrete pipes, nominal bore 900 - 1200 mm, length 170 m. | sum | | | | |
| | Water testing, as Specification clause 6.4. | | | | | |
| A260.2 | GRP pipes, nominal bore 300 mm, length 265 m. | sum | | | | |
| A260.3 | Concrete pipes, nominal bore 375 mm, length 253 m. | sum | | | | |
| | Temporary Works. | | | | | |
| | Pumping, as Specification clause 1.37. | | | | | |
| A276.1 | Establishment and removal of plant. | sum | | | | |
| A276.2 | Operation and maintenance of plant. | h | 200 | | | |
| | Fencing, as Specification clause 1.3. | | | | | |
| A279.1 | Establishment and removal. | m | 450 | | | |
| A279.2 | Maintenance. | sum | | | | |

COMMENTARY

Where the value of establishment and removal of testing facilities are insignificant a separate item is not given for them. Preamble would indicate that items for tests were to include for establishment and removal of the testing facilities.

Additional separate items would be given for establishment and removal of testing facilities where tests involved costly testing facilities. In this case testing items would state establishment and removal of testing facilities were measured separately.

In accordance with the general policy of the CESMM, items are not given for plant standing by. If any standing by of plant or delays occur for any reason which, under the Contract entitle the Contractor to extra payment, such payment must be determined as provided in the Contract Conditions.

Items quantified are subject to admeasurement

PART 1 : GENERAL ITEMS

| Number | Item description | Unit | Quantity | Rate | Amount £ | p |
|--------|------------------|------|----------|------|----------|---|
| | GENERAL ITEMS (cont. | | | | | |
| | Method-Related Charges. | | | | | |
| | Note:  To enable the Contractor to insert Method-Related Charges, if he wishes to do so, blank pages are included in the Bill of Quantities when it is issued to tender. (See Commentary 7.2, Chapter 2). | | | | | |
| | The Contractor should formulate descriptions as set out in Paragraph 7.3 and 7.4 of the CESMM. (See Commentary on these Paragraphs in Chapter 2). | | | | | |
| | Examples of imaginary insertions by the Contractor are given in manuscript below. | | | | | |
| | *Plant* | | | | | |
| | *Tractor & trailer for collecting pipes from compound & distributing.* | | | | | |
| A332.1 | *Bringing to Site & remove; Fixed.* | SUM | | | | |
| A332.2 | *Operate; Time Related.* | SUM | | | | |
| | *Temporary Works* | | | | | |
| | *Footpath diversion by Woodburn School, during construction of large bore sewer.* | | | | | |
| A351.1 | *Establish; Fixed.* | SUM | | | | |
| A351.2 | *Operate & maintain; Time Related.* | SUM | | | | |
| A351.3 | *Remove & reinstate existing; Fixed.* | SUM | | | | |
| | (3)            To Part 1 Summary      Page total | | | | | |

| Number | Item description | Unit | Quantity | Rate | Amount £ | p |
|--------|------------------|------|----------|------|----------|---|
| | GENERAL ITEMS (cont. | | | | | |
| | Provisional Sums. | | | | | |
| | Daywork. | | | | | |
| A411 | Labour. | sum | | | 3000 | 00 |
| A412 | Percentage adjustment to Provisional Sum for Daywork labour. | % | | | | |
| A413 | Materials. | sum | | | 1500 | 00 |
| A414 | Percentage adjustment to Provisional Sum for Daywork materials. | % | | | | |
| A415 | Plant. | sum | | | 1500 | 00 |
| A416 | Percentage adjustment to Provisional Sum for Daywork plant. | % | | | | |
| A417 | Supplementary charges. | sum | | | 2000 | 00 |
| A418 | Percentage adjustment to Provisional Sum for Daywork supplementary charges. | % | | | | |
| | Other Provisional Sums. | | | | | |
| A420 | Call charges Engineer's staff Site telephones. | sum | | | 200 | 00 |
| | Nominated Sub-contracts which include work on Site, Prime Cost Items. | | | | | |
| A510 | Air valves and installation. | sum | | | 1000 | 00 |
| A520 | Labours. | sum | | | | |
| A530 | Special labours; as Specification clause 8.3. | sum | | | | |
| A540 | Other charges and profit. | % | | | | |
| | Nominated Sub-contracts which do not include work on Site, Prime Cost Items. | | | | | |
| A610 | Screening chamber screens. | sum | | | 350 | 00 |
| A620 | Labours. | sum | | | | |
| A640 | Other charges and profit. | % | | | | |

|  | (4)      To Part 1 Summary      Page total | | | | | |

# 4 Ground Investigation – CESMM
## Class: B

Ground investigation covered by Class B of the CESMM includes trial holes, boreholes, samples, site and laboratory tests, instrumental observations and professional services in connection with ground investigation. Excavation which is not carried out for the purpose of ground investigation is excluded from Class B and is measured under Class E. Boring for piling is also excluded and is measured under Classes P and Q.

Table 4.01  Ground Investigation - Generally

The preparation and submission of records and results is deemed to be included in items for ground investigation (Rule B/C1)

Table 4.02  Trial Holes

| 1st Division | 2nd Division | | 3rd Division | |
|---|---|---|---|---|
| Trial holes<br><br>State minimum plan area at bottom of holes, or maximum length where to locate services (Rule B/A1) | Number in material other than rock | nr | State maximum depth range in accordance with 3rd Division features | State if expressly required to be excavated by hand (Rule B/A2) |
| | Number in material which includes rock | nr | | |
| | Depth in material other than rock | m | | |
| | Depth in rock | m | | |
| | Depth supported | m | | |
| | Depth backfilled | m | | State back-filling material |
| Trial holes | Removal of obstruc-tions | h | | |
| | Pumping at a stated minimum rate of extraction | h | | State any special method of de-watering expressly required (Rule B/A3) |

COMMENTARY

Ground Investigation, Generally (refer to Table 4.01)

Items for ground investigation include the preparation and submission of records and results. There is no specific provision for the packing, transporting and disposing of samples and test specimens. Whilst the specification will provide details of these, it is prudent to include preamble stating that items for samples and tests in ground investigation are deemed to include packing, transporting and disposing of samples, cores and test specimens as required by the Specification. There is no mention in Class B of removal of surplus excavated material. Surplus will result from

COMMENTARY

Ground Investigation, Generally (cont.

increased bulk and to a greater extent if the holes are backfilled with imported material. Preamble should therefore be included stating that items for the depths of trial holes and boreholes are deemed to include for disposing of surplus excavated material.

Trial Holes (refer to Table 4.02)

The items measured for trial holes include items for the number of holes and items, in linear metres, for their depths. In both cases the items state whether they are in material other than rock or in material which includes rock. The numbered items state also the maximum depth of the holes in ranges measured from the Commencing Surface. Holes otherwise similar but of different depths are grouped in separate items for each standard depth range. Other items which may be required for trial holes, together with the units of measurement and reference to the Rules are given in Table 4.02.

Table 4.03 Boreholes

| 1st Division | 2nd Division | 3rd Division | |
|---|---|---|---|
| Light cable percussion boreholes<br><br>Items for depth are deemed to include casings (Rule B/C2) | Number          nr | | State diameter of borehole bases (Rule B/A4) |
| | Depth           m | State maximum depth range as 3rd Division features. | |
| | Depth backfilled m | State backfilling material | |
| | Chiselling to prove rock or to penetrate obstructions      h | Measure only if expressly required (Rule B/M1) | |
| Rotary drilled boreholes<br><br>Classify as rotary drilled boreholes whether drilled by rig or attachment (Rule B/D1) | Number          nr | State when in con-tinuation of light cable percussion boreholes (Rule B/A6) | State minimum core diameter (Rule B/A5)<br><br>State angle of inclination when inclined (Rule B/A7) |
| | Depth without core recovery   m<br><br>Depth with core recovery    m | State maximum depth range as 3rd Division features<br><br>Measure maximum depth for classification from Commencing Sur-face of light cable percussion boreholes where in continuation (Rule B/D3) | |
| | Depth cased       m | | |
| | Depth backfilled m | State backfilling material | |
| | Core boxes       nr | State length of cores<br><br>State minimum core diameter (Rule B/A5) | State if not to be property of Employer (Rule B/D2) |

COMMENTARY

Boreholes (refer to Table 4.03)

Each of the two types of boreholes for which classifications are given in Class B, require that items are measured for the collected number and the collected depths, in linear metres, for each group of similar boreholes. Holes are grouped by diameter for each type unless it is decided to subdivide an item for a diameter to implement Paragraph 5.10 of the CESMM. The diameters given in the items for light cable percussion boreholes are the diameters at the base of the holes. For rotary drilled boreholes the core diameters are given. Depth items for each type of borehole state the maximum depth range (or depth where exceeding 40 m), as given in the 3rd Division features, of the deepest borehole of those grouped in an item. When measuring rotary drilled boreholes, items for depth without core recovery are given separately from those for depth with core recovery and where cores are recovered numbered items are given for core boxes, stating the length of cores. The depth of any casings required to rotary drilled boreholes is measured, in linear metres. Casings for light cable percussion holes are deemed to be included in the items. The type of material through which boreholes are sunk does not have to be stated. But items in operational hours are given for chiselling expressly required to prove rock or to penetrate obstructions in light cable percussion boreholes. Any backfilling of boreholes is measured by depth in linear metres and the items state the backfilling material.

Table 4.04   Samples

| 1st Division | 2nd Division | 3rd Division |
|---|---|---|
| Samples                              nr<br><br>State size, type and class of samples in accordance with BS 5930 (Rule B/A8) | From the surface or from trial holes | Undisturbed soft material<br><br>Disturbed soft material<br><br>Rock<br><br>Groundwater |
|  | From boreholes | Open tube<br><br>Disturbed<br><br>Groundwater<br><br>Stationery piston<br><br>Swedish foil<br><br>Delft<br><br>Bishop sand |

COMMENTARY

Samples (refer to Table 4.04)

Samples are classified as noted in Table 4.04 and separate items are given in the Bill of Quantities for the number of each kind of sample required. Item descriptions must state the size, type and class of sample in accordance with BS 5930. The Specification will need to relate to the BS and

COMMENTARY

Samples (cont.

to provide additional detail of the requirements as to samples and sampling. Item descriptions will usually refer to the appropriate clauses in the Specification. The Bill should make clear that the items for samples are deemed to include for all requirements as to samples and sampling as are set out in the Specification.

Table 4.05  Site Tests and Observations

| 1st Division | | Site tests and observation |
| --- | --- | --- |
| 2nd Division | | |
| 3rd Division | | |
| Permeability | h | State type and give particulars of tests (Rule B/A9) |
| Groundwater level | nr | State when measurements are to be taken (Rule B/A10) |
| Standard penetration | nr | State whether in light cable percussion or rotary drilled boreholes (Rule B/A11) |
| Penetration vane | nr | |
| Vane in borehole | nr | |
| Pressure meter | nr | |
| Plate bearing | nr | State whether in pits or boreholes (Rule B/A12) |
| Self-boring pressure meter | nr | |
| California bearing ratio | nr | |
| Static cone sounding | nr | State maximum depth of cone and where electric cones are used, the capacity of the machine (Rule B/A13) |
| In-situ density BS 1377 nrs 15a-15d | nr | |
| Mackintosh probe | nr | |
| Hand auger boreholes | nr | State minimum diameter and maximum depth of boreholes (Rule B/A14) |

COMMENTARY

Site tests, Observations and Laboratory tests (refer to Tables 4.05 and 4.06)

The features or references to the features which are used to classify site tests and observations, instrumental observations and laboratory tests are given in Tables 4.05 and 4.06. Many tests are identified in the features by BS reference. Additional detail to that contained in the BS, such as where and when tests and observations are to be carried out and other requirements

Table 4.06    Instrumental Observations and Laboratory Tests

| 1st Division | 2nd Division | 3rd Division | | | 3rd Division |
|---|---|---|---|---|---|
| Instrumental observations<br><br>State details of type of observations and of protective fences (Rule B/A15) | Pressure head | Standpipes | m | | |
| | | Piezometers | m | | |
| | | Install covers | nr | | |
| | | Readings | nr | | |
| | Inclinometers | Installations | m | State whether instruments are in special boreholes (Rule B/A16) | |
| | | Readings | nr | | |
| | Settlement gauges | Installations | *nr | Deemed to include the provision of special boreholes (Rule B/C3) | |
| | | Readings | *nr | | |
| | Resistivity<br><br>Seismic<br><br>Magnetometer<br><br>Self-potential<br><br>Gravimetric | Installations | *nr | | |
| | | Readings | *nr | | |
| Laboratory tests        nr | Classification | | | | State type of tests as 3rd Division features with BS reference as noted |
| | Chemical content | State standards required and con-taminents to be analysed for tests for contaminants (Rule B/A17) | | | |
| | Compaction<br><br>Consolidation | State number of increments and effective pressure for triaxial cell and Rowe cell tests (Rule B/A18) | | | |
| | Permeability | | | | |
| | Strength | State diameter and whether single, multistage or set of three speci-mens required for quick undrained triaxial tests (Rule B/A19)<br>State diameter, effective pressure and if multistage for consolidated triaxial tests (Rule B/A20)<br>State normal pressure and size of shearbox for shearbox test (Rule B/A21)<br>State compactive effort, surcharge and whether soaking is required for California bearing ratio tests (Rule B/A22) | | | |

* *No unit of measurement is given in the CESMM against these features. In practice they are enumerated and described.*

COMMENTARY

Site tests, Observations and Laborartory tests (cont.

the Engineer desires to impose need to be given in the Specification. Item descriptions may make reference to clauses in the Specification to make clear the scope of activities, etc., intended to be included in the testing and observation items.

Table 4.07    Professional Services

| 1st Division | 2nd Division | 3rd Division | |
|---|---|---|---|
| Professional services<br><br>Measure only where expressly required for analysis of records and results (Rule B/M2)<br><br>Deemed to include preparing and submitting reports and keeping records of time spent (Rule B/C4) | Technician                h<br><br>Technician engineer    h | | Measure only working hours, exclude hours spent travelling, taking meals, etc. (Rule B/M3) |
| | Engineer or geologist h | Graduate<br><br>Chartered<br><br>Principal or consultant | |
| | Visits to Site            nr<br><br>Overnight stays in connection with visits to Site          nr | | Deemed to include travelling, meals, accommodation and other incidental expenses (Rule B/C5) |

COMMENTARY

Professional Services (refer to Table 4.07)

Any professional services required for supervising and progressing the work are included in the Contract and items for ground investigation are deemed to include preparing and submitting records and results. Items for professional services as set out in Class B are measured only where it is expressly required that records and results shall be analysed. They are given in units of hours for the stated grade of personnel. The hours measured are working hours. Hours spent travelling, taking meals, etc., are not measured and are deemed to be included in the items for professional services.

Expressly required visits and overnight stays for expressly required professional services on Site are given as numbered items. The items are deemed to include travelling, meals, accommodation and other incidental expenses.

EXAMPLE BE.1

Specimen Bill of Quantities

The Example which follows is for the Work Items (excluding General Items) of a Bill of Quantities for an imaginary ground investigation contract.

A site plan indicating the location of the exploratory holes and a schedule setting out the probable depths of the holes are usually included with the tender documents which accompany the Bill of Quantities.

PART 2 : BANDWOOD SITE

| Number | Item description | Unit | Quantity | Rate | Amount | |
|---|---|---|---|---|---|---|
| | | | | | £ | p |
| | GROUND INVESTIGATION. | | | | | |
| | Trial holes. | | | | | |
| | Minimum plan area 2 m2 at bottom of holes. | | | | | |
| B112.1 | Number in material other than rock, maximum depth 1 - 2 m. | nr | 2 | | COMMENTARY | |
| B122 | Number in material which includes rock, maximum depth 1 - 2 m. | nr | 2 | | Items would refer to Preamble where it was | |
| B130.1 | Depth in material other than rock. | m | 7 | | intended that they should include the removal of surplus ex- | |
| B140 | Depth in rock. | m | 1 | | cavated material. See Commentary following | |
| B160.1 | Depth backfilled with excavated material. | m | 8 | | Table 4.02. | |
| | Maximum length 4 m, excavated by hand to locate services. | | | | | |
| B112.2 | Number in material other than rock, maximum depth 1 - 2 m. | nr | 2 | | | |
| B130.2 | Depth in material other than rock. | m | 3 | | | |
| B150 | Depth supported; supports left in. | m | 3 | | | |
| B160.2 | Depth backfilled with imported sand. | m | 3 | | | |
| | Rotary drilled boreholes. | | | | | |
| | Minimum core diameter 100 mm. | | | | | |
| B310 | Number. | nr | 10 | | | |
| B333 | Depth without core recovery, in holes of maximum depth 10 - 20 m. | m | 110 | | | |
| B343 | Depth with core recovery, in holes of maximum depth 10 - 20 m. | m | 50 | | | |
| B360 | Depth backfilled with PFA/cement grout. | m | 160 | | | |
| B370 | Core boxes, length of cores 1.2 m. | nr | 8 | | | |
| | (1)                To Part 2 Summary          Page total | | | | | |

| Number | Item description | Unit | Quantity | Rate | Amount £ | p |
|--------|------------------|------|----------|------|----------|---|
| | GROUND INVESTIGATION (cont. | | | | | |
| | Samples from boreholes, as BS 5930. | | | | | |
| B421 | Open tube; 100 mm diameter x 450 mm long, undisturbed, Class 1. | nr | 8 | | | |
| B422 | Disturbed samples; mass 5 kg., Class 3. | nr | 2 | | | |
| B423 | Groundwater; volume 1 litre. | nr | 10 | | | |
| | Site tests and observations. | | | | | |
| B512 | Groundwater level; taken each morning throughout Contract period. | nr | 20 | | | |
| B513 | Standard penetration; as BS 1377, in rotary drilled boreholes. | nr | 4 | | | |
| B515 | Vane in boreholes. | nr | 4 | | | |
| B527 | Hand auger boreholes, 150 mm diameter x 1200 mm deep. | nr | 3 | | | |
| | Instrumental observations. | | | | | |
| B612 | Pressure head, Piezometers, installations. | m | 20 | | | |
| B614 | Pressure head, Piezometers, readings. | nr | 10 | | | |
| | Laboratory tests, chemical content. | | | | | |
| B721 | Organic matter, BS 1377, nr 8. | nr | 6 | | | |
| B722 | Sulphate, BS 1377, nrs 9, 10. | nr | 6 | | | |
| B723 | pH value, BS 1377, nrs 11a, 11b. | nr | 2 | | | |
| | Professional services | | | | | |
| B832 | Engineer or geologist chartered. | h | 15 | | | |
| B833 | Engineer or geologist principal or consultant. | h | 7 | | | |
| B840 | Visits to the Site. | nr | 2 | | | |

# 5 Geotechnical and Other Specialist Processes – CESMM Class: C

The classification table for Class C provides descriptive features to formulate items for drilling holes and grouting by injection to alter the properties of soils and rocks, for diaphragm walls, for ground anchors and for sand, band and wick drains. Grouting within tunnels, shafts and other subterranean cavities (except that carried out from the ground surface) is excluded from Class C and is included in Class T. Grouting carried out from sewers is also excluded and is included in Class Y.

---

Table 5.01 Drilling, Grout Holes, Materials and Injection

---

Generally - Drilling deemed to be in material other than rock or artificial hard material unless otherwise stated (Rule C/D1)

Items deemed to include disposal of excavated material and removal of services (Rule C/C1)

Commencing Surface when admeasuring shall be that adopted when preparing the Bill of Quantities (Rule C/M1)

---

| 1st Division | | 2nd Division | 3rd Division |
|---|---|---|---|
| Drilling for grout holes:-<br><br>through material other than rock or artificial hard material<br><br>through rock or artificial hard material<br><br>Driving injection pipes for grout holes | State diameter of holes (Rule C/A1)<br><br>In stage grouting, drilling through previously grouted holes shall not be measured (Rule C/M3)<br>For holes expressly required to be extended see under 3rd Division | State zone of inclination as 2nd Division features (See Figure C1).<br><br>Measure depths of holes along the holes irrespective of inclination (Rule C/M2) | For each diameter:-<br><br>of hole or driving give items for depths in ranges as 3rd Division features     m<br><br>of hole previously grouted and expressly required to be extended, measure and classify as in rock or artifical hard material and give items for depths in ranges as 3rd Division features (Rule C/M3)     m |

| 1st Division | 2nd Division | | 3rd Division |
|---|---|---|---|
| Grout holes    nr<br><br>State diameter of holes (Rule C/A1) | Number of holes | Include number grouted previously and expressly required to be extended (Rule C/M3) | |
| | Number of stages | Measure only total number of stages expressly required (Rule C/M4) | |
| | Single water pressure tests | | |
| | Multiple water pressure tests | | |

Table 5.01 Drilling, Grout Holes, Materials and Injection (cont.

| 1st Division | 2nd Division | 3rd Division | |
|---|---|---|---|
| Grout materials and injection | Materials    t | State materials as 3rd Division features. i.e. :- Cement, pulverised fuel ash, etc<br><br>State type of grout materials (Rule C/A2)<br><br>Mass not to include mass of mixing water (Rule C/M5) | |
| | Injection | Number of injections    nr<br><br>    State those in stages and whether ascending or descending (Rule C/A3) | Measure total number expressly required (Rule C/M6) |
| | | Neat cement grout    t<br><br>Cement and stated filler grout    t<br><br>Chemical grout    t<br><br>Other stated grout    t | Mass not to in-include mass of mixing water (Rule C/M7) |
| | | Single packer setting nr<br><br>Double packer setting nr | |

COMMENTARY

Drilling, Grout Holes, Materials and Injection (refer to Table 5.01)

The main divisions when measuring work of grouting by injection, are drilling for or driving pipes for the grout holes, the number of grout holes, the mass of grout materials, the number of injections and the mass of grout injected.

Items for drilling for grout holes or for driving pipes for grout holes are classified and described according to their:- (i) diameter, (ii) zone of inclination as given in the 2nd Division features (See Figure C1.), and (iii) depth range (or depth where exceeding 40 m) as given in the 3rd Division features of the classification in Class C. Items give the total collected depth, in linear metres, of drilling or driving for grout holes which are of similar diameter, similar zone of inclination and within the same standard depth range. Item descriptions for drilling for grout holes distinguish between those which are drilled through rock or artificial hard material and those drilled through other material. Holes previously grouted and expressly required to be extended are classed as drilled through rock. Items identify the surface from which drilling or driving is to commence if it is not the Original Surface.

Items for the number of grout holes give the total number of holes involved in the drilling for or driving pipes for the grout holes. The total number of holes includes those previously grouted which are expressly required to be extended. Items are given for the total number of stages where the grout holes are expressly required to be executed in stages. Numbered items are given for any water pressure tests required in grout holes. Single tests are given separately from multiple tests. The diameter of the holes are stated in the item descriptions for all the foregoing numbered items.

COMMENTARY

Drilling, Grout Holes, Materials and Injection (cont.

| Number | Item description | Unit | Diagrams Illustrating Angles of Inclination appropriate to Items |
|---|---|---|---|
| | GEOTECHNICAL AND OTHER SPECIALIST PROCESSES. | | |
| | Drilling for grout holes, diameter 50 mm. | | |
| | Vertical downwards. | | |
| C113 | In holes of depth 10 - 20 m. | m | |
| C114 | In holes of depth 20 - 30 m. | m | |
| | Downwards at an angle 0 - 45 degrees to the vertical. | | |
| C122 | In holes of depth 5 - 10 m. | m | |
| C123 | In holes of depth 10 - 20 m. | m | |
| | Horizontal or downwards at an angle less than 45 degrees to horizontal. | | |
| C132 | In holes of depth 5 - 10 m. | m | |
| C135 | In holes of depth 30 - 40 m. | m | |
| | Upwards at an angle 0 - 45 degrees to the horizontal. | | |
| C144 | In holes of depth 20 - 30 m. | m | |
| C146 | In holes of depth 42 m. | m | |
| | Upwards at an angle less than 45 degrees to the vertical. | | |
| C152 | In holes of depth 5 - 10 m. | m | |
| C154 | In holes of depth 20 - 30 m. | m | |
| | Grout holes, diameter 50 mm. | | Angle $x$ = Less than 45 degrees |
| C410 | Number of holes. | nr | Angle $y$ = 45 degrees |

Fig. C1. Specimen item descriptions and angles of inclination appropriate to standard descriptive features for drilling for grout holes. Items assumed to be in material other than rock or artificial hard material. The number of stages would be given as an item following Item Code C410 where grout holes are expressly required to be executed in stages.

COMMENTARY

Drilling, Grout Holes, Materials and Injection (cont.

    Materials and injection are classified separately. Items for materials measure the constituent materials of the grout mixtures and give the mass for each material in tonnes. Item descriptions state the type of materials in amplification of the 3rd Division features given for materials in Class C. For example, the type of cement would be added to the standard feature of "cement". The mass of materials measured excludes the mass of mixing water.

    Items measured for injection, include the number of injections, the mass of grout injected, in tonnes, and the number of packer settings. The items measured for injections give the total number of injections expressly required. The descriptions for the number of injections state if they are in stages and distinguish between those in ascending stages (i.e. successive stages rising up the holes) and those in descending stages (i.e. successive stages descending down the holes). In items for the grout injected, the mass of grout mixture (excluding the mass of mixing water) is measured and given in tonnes. The grout mixtures are described in accordance with the 3rd Division classifications given for injection in Class C. Items are given for any packer settings required. Single packer settings are given separately from double packer settings (See Example CE.1 at the end of this Chapter).

    Specimen item descriptions are given at the side of the diagram, Figure C3, for materials and injection where the stratum is divided for grouting by injection in three separate stages working from the top downwards as shown in section in the diagram. For drilling holes, grout holes etc., see preceding Table, and Commentary.

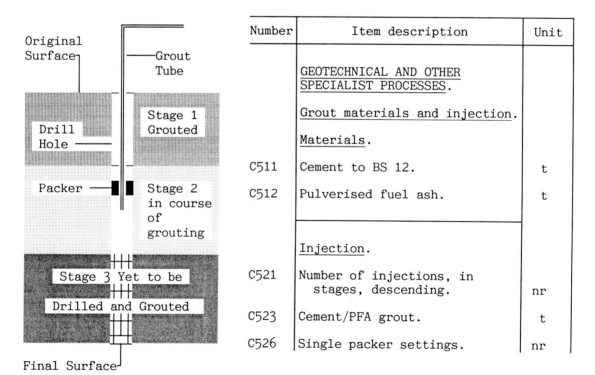

| Number | Item description | Unit |
|--------|------------------|------|
| | GEOTECHNICAL AND OTHER SPECIALIST PROCESSES. | |
| | Grout materials and injection. | |
| | Materials. | |
| C511 | Cement to BS 12. | t |
| C512 | Pulverised fuel ash. | t |
| | Injection. | |
| C521 | Number of injections, in stages, descending. | nr |
| C523 | Cement/PFA grout. | t |
| C526 | Single packer settings. | nr |

SECTION

Fig. C3.  Grout materials and injection in descending stages.

Table 5.02  Diaphragm Walls

Generally - "Diaphragm walls" are walls constructed using betonite slurry or other support fluid (Rule C/D2)

The Rules C/D1, C/C1 and C/M1 given against "Generally" in the first panel of Table 5.01 apply also to this Table

| 1st Division | 2nd Division | | 3rd Division |
|---|---|---|---|
| Diaphragm walls | Excavation:-<br><br>in material other than rock or artificial hard material    m3<br><br>in rock    m3<br><br>in artificial hard material    m3 | State thickness of walls (Rule C/A4)<br><br>State nature of artificial hard material (Rule C/A5)<br><br>Deemed to include preparing and upholding sides (Rule C/C2) | State maximum depth range as 3rd Division features<br><br>State actual depth where exceeding 30 m |
| | Concrete    m3<br><br>Items deemed to include for trimming the faces of walls and preparing tops to receive other work (Rule C/C3) | State thickness of walls (Rule C/A4)<br><br>State mix specification or strengths (Rule C/A6)<br><br>Measure depths from the cut-off levels expressly required (Rule C/M9)<br><br>Calculate volumes as in Rules F/M1 and F/M2 (Rule C/M9)<br><br>Class formwork for voids rebates and fillets as concrete ancillaries in Class G (Rule C/M8) | |
| | Bar reinforcement to BS 4449:-<br><br>mild steel    t<br><br>high yield steel    t | Include mass of stiffening, lifting and supporting steel cast in (Rule C/M10)<br><br>Take mass of steel as 7.85 t/m3 (Rule C/M11)<br><br>Deemed to include supporting reinforcement and preparing protruding reinforcement to receive other work (Rule C/C4) | State nominal size (i.e. cross-sectional size as BS 4449 and BS 4461) as 3rd Division features (Rule C/D3) |
| | Waterproofed joints    sum | | |
| | Guide walls    m | Measure to each side of diaphragm walls (Rule C/M12) | |

Table 5.03 Ground anchorages

The Rules C/D1, C/C1 and C/M1 given against "Generally" in the first panel of Table 5.01 apply also to this Table

| 1st Division | 2nd Division | | 3rd Division |
|---|---|---|---|
| Ground anchorages<br><br>State composition, location and working load and details of water and grouting tests and pregrouting and grouting (Rule C/A7) | Number in material other than rock or artificial hard material to a stated maximum depth.      nr | | Temporary<br><br>Temporary with single corrosion protection<br><br>Temporary with double corrosion protection<br><br>Permanent<br><br>Permanent with single corrosion protection<br><br>Permanent with double corrosion protection |
| | Total length of tendons in material other than rock or artifical hard material      m | Measure between outer ends of anchorages (Rule C/M13) | |
| | Number in material which includes rock or artificial hard material to a stated maximum depth      nr | | |
| | Total length of tendons in material which in- cludes rock or arti- ficial hard material      m | Measure between outer ends of anchorages (Rule C/M13) | |

COMMENTARY

Diaphragm Walls and Ground Anchorages (refer to Tables 5.02 and 5.03)

The standard descriptive features and the appropriate CESMM Rules for diaphragm walls and ground anchorages are noted or referred to in Tables 5.02 and 5.03. See measured Example at the end of this Chapter for Commentary on the measurement of diaphragm walls and ground anchorages.

Table 5.04 Sand, Band and Wick Drains

The Rules C/D1, C/C1 and C/M1 given against "Generally" in the first panel of Table 5.01 apply also to this Table

| 1st Division | 2nd Division | | 3rd Division |
|---|---|---|---|
| Sand, band and wick drains<br><br>Give separate items for:-<br><br>Sand drains<br><br>Band drains<br><br>Wick drains<br><br>State for each materials of which composed (Rule C/A8) | Number of drains      nr | | State cross- sectional dimension range:<br><br>n.e.100 mm<br><br>100-200 mm<br><br>200-300 mm<br><br>300-400 mm<br><br>400-500 mm<br><br>state if over 500 mm |
| | Number of pre- drilled holes      nr | Measure number express- ly required to be pre- drilled through over- overlying material (Rule C/M14) | |
| | Depth of overlying material      m | | |
| | Depth of drains of maximum depth: not exceeding 10 m      m | | |
| | 10 - 15 m      m | | |
| | 15 - 20 m      m | | |
| | 20 - 25 m      m | | |
| | State if over 25 m      m | | |

COMMENTARY

Sand Drains, Band Drains and Wick Drains (refer to Table 5.04)

    Although the three types "sand", "band" and "wick" drains are classified in the CESMM under a single 1st. Division feature, the Rules require that each type shall be separately identified in item descriptions and the materials of which they are composed stated. Items of stated type and cross-sectional dimensions are given for the number of drains. Items are also given, in linear metres, for the depth of the drains. They group together depths which fall within each particular 2nd Division maximum depth range in items separating and stating each appropriate maximum depth range (See Table 5.04). The depths of the drains are measured from the base of the holes to the top of the filter material in the drains. The items given for the drains are intended to cover their complete construction, including the columns of filter material, the holes to accommodate them, temporary casings or other means of upholding the sides of the holes and the disposal of the surplus excavated material resulting from the holes all in accordance with the requirements of the contract.

    Where it is expressly required that drains are constructed through material overlying the site of the drains, items classified according to the type of drains and their cross-sectional dimension range are given for the number of holes predrilled for the drains through the overlying material. Further items given in linear metres, for the collected total depth of the unfilled holes are measured from the top of the filter material to the Commencing Surface, and are classified "Depth of overlying material".

    Sand blankets related to the drains are measured as filling to stated depth or thickness (stating the material), as provided in Class E. Horizontal outlet drains are measured as provided in Classes I - L. These items, those for sand, band and wick drains and those for instrumental devices (Class B6**) installed with the drains, may be grouped under an identifying heading in a Part of the Bill of Quantities created to cover bulk excavation and filling.

    Specimen item descriptions (Fig. C2) below are for the sand drains shown in the diagram, they do not include the sand blanket or the embankment filling.

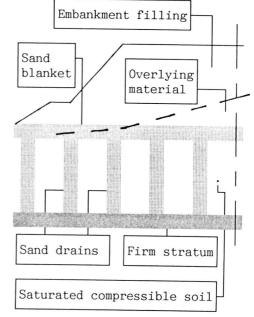

| Number | Item description | Unit |
|--------|------------------|------|
|  | GEOTECHNICAL AND OTHER SPECIALIST PROCESSES.<br><br>Sand drains, clean filter sand media, Specification clause 52.<br><br>Cross-sectional dimensions 400 - 500 mm. |  |
| C815 | Number of drains. | nr |
| C825 | Number of predrilled holes. | nr |
| C835 | Depth of overlying material. | m |
| C855 | Depth of drains of maximum depth 10 - 15 m. | m |

Fig. C2. Sand drains.

**PART SECTION**

MEASURED EXAMPLES

Two measured examples follow.

Grouting Subway Line from Surface Level - Example CE.1

The first measured example gives the dimensions for the grouting work on part of the line of a proposed subway, as shown on Drawing No. C/D/1 and explained in the text which follows.

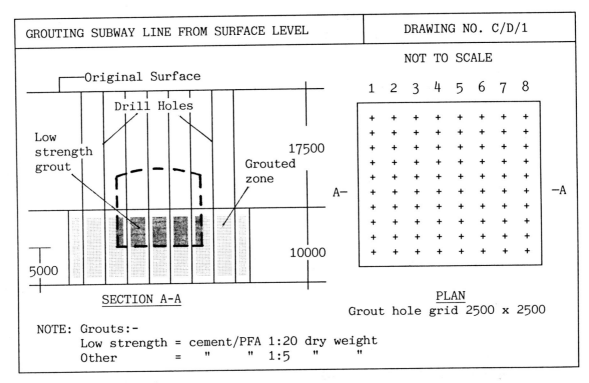

Drilling is assumed to be in material other than rock or artificial hard material. Injection is measured in two stages where there are two different mixes of grout in the same hole, but since the grouting is in ascending stages, the grout holes will be drilled the full depth in one operation and not in stages. It is assumed that the Specification calls for single water pressure tests to be carried out in two boreholes of each numbered grid line.

The specification may call for the flushing out of drill holes with water to clean out voids before grouting. It may also call for lining the drill holes with temporary casings where soft or unstable ground is encountered. The former is part of the injection process and is considered to be included in the items for injections. The latter is considered to be temporary work. Separate items are not required for either of these.

The quantity for the mass of grout injected is an estimate. It is made using an assumed voids ratio to calculate the void volume of the soil to be injected and converting this volume to mass in tonnes using assumed densities of 1.5 t/m3 and 1.0 t/m3 for grout including the mass of mixing water and the grout materials excluding the mass of the mixing water, respectively. The mass of each of the constituent materials making up the latter, as given in the items classified as "Materials", is calculated according to its proportion of the grout materials.

Diaphragm Walls - Example No. CE.2

The second measured example which follows gives the dimensions for diaphragm walls and ground anchors, as shown on Drawing No. C/D/2.

GROUTING SUBWAY LINE FROM
SURFACE LEVEL - DRG. NO C/D/1
EXAMPLE CE 1

|  |  |  |
|---|---|---|
|  |  | 17.50 |
|  |  | 10.00 |
|  |  | 27.50 |

Drilling for grout
holes 75 mm diam.

Vert. downwards.

10/8/ 27.50 — In holes of depth
20-30 m.　(C114

Grout holes.

10/8/ 1 — Number of holes.
(C410

8/ 2 — Single water press.
tests.　(C430

Vol. per m3 of groutd vol :-
grout assume voids ratio 0.6.
$= 1 \times \dfrac{0.6}{1.6} = 0.375 \ m3/m3$

dry matls assume water: solid
ratio 0.5. $= 0.375 \times \dfrac{1.00}{1.50} = 0.25 \ m3/m^3$

11/2.50 = 27.50
9/2.50 = 22.50

Groutd vol = 27.50 × 22.50 × 10.00
Total　 = 6187.50 m3

Total dry matls for injectn:-
6187.50 × 0.25 = 1546.87 m3
1547 @ 1.00 t/m3 = 1547 t

(1)

Grout matls and injectn.

Injectn.　Grid 1,2,7+8
10/2/ 2 — Number of injectns.
(C521.1

Grid 3,4,5+6
10/4/ 2 — Number of injectns;
in stages, ascending
(C521.2

10/2/ 2
10/4/ 2 — Single packer settgs.
(C526

1547 t — Ct. and PFA filler
grout.　(C523

11/2.50 = 27.50
4/2.50 = 10.00

Total groutd vol.　6187.50
Less low strength gro. vol:-
27.50 × 10.00 × 5.00 = 1375.00
Hi strength gro. vol = 4812.50

Mass matls - mixes by dry wght:-

|  | Ct. | PFA |
|---|---|---|
| $\dfrac{1547}{6188} \times \dfrac{1375}{21}$ = 16.37 × 20 = | | 327.40 |
| 16.37 × 1 = | 16.37 | |
| $\dfrac{1547}{6188} \times \dfrac{4812}{6}$ = 200.50 × 5 = | | 1002.50 |
| 200.50 × 1 = | 200.50 | |
|  | 216 87 | 1329.90 |

Materials

217 t — Ct. ord. P. to BS12.
(C511

1330 t — P.F.A. Spec. cl. 5.3
(C512

(2)

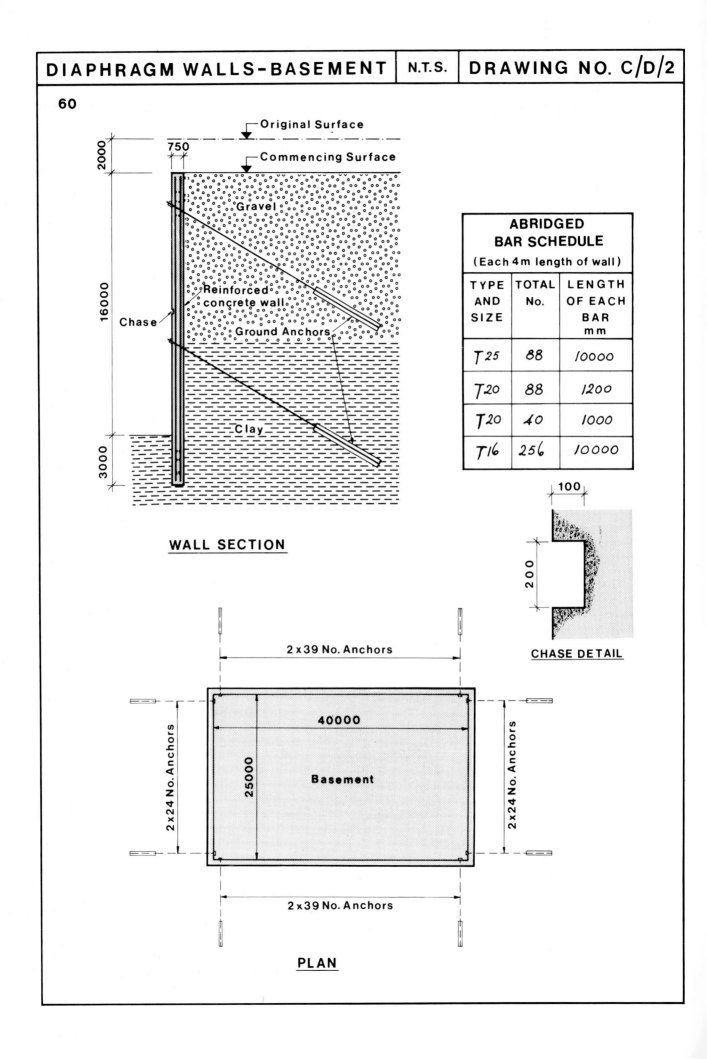

Original Surface

Commencing Surface

2000

750

16000

Gravel

Reinforced concrete wall

Chase

Ground Anchors

Clay

3000

**WALL SECTION**

## ABRIDGED BAR SCHEDULE
### (Each 4m length of wall)

| TYPE AND SIZE | TOTAL No. | LENGTH OF EACH BAR mm |
|---|---|---|
| T 25 | 88 | 10000 |
| T 20 | 88 | 1200 |
| T 20 | 40 | 1000 |
| T 16 | 256 | 10000 |

100

200

**CHASE DETAIL**

2 x 39 No. Anchors

2 x 24 No. Anchors

40000

25000

**Basement**

2 x 24 No. Anchors

2 x 39 No. Anchors

**PLAN**

DIAPHRAGM WALLS - DRG NO C/D/2
EXAMPLE CE2

Wall.

2/40.00 = 80.00
2/25.00 = 50.00
130.00
4/0.75 = 3.00
133.00

16.00
3.00
19.00

Diaphragm walls

| 133.00 | Excavn., max. depth |
| 0.75 | 15 - 20 m; wall thickn. |
| 19.00 | 0.75 m, Comm. Surf. |
| | top of wall. (C614 |

&

Conc.; strength
30 N/mm 2, wall thickn.
0.75 m.        (C640

| Sum | Waterproofed joints; |
| | Contractor designed, |
| | Spec. clause 3.6 (C670 |

| 2/133.00 | Guide walls; Contractor |
| | designed, Spec. clause 3.7, |
| | inc. excavn. (C680 |

(1)

Drawing No C/D/2 shows the the section after the basement is excavated. The dimensions for excavation and other work to the basement are not given in the Example.

The diaphragm wall would be constructed in panels in a trench using betonite support slurry and displacing the slurry with concrete placed by tremie. See diagram below and Table 5.02. The diagram does not show the reinforcement.

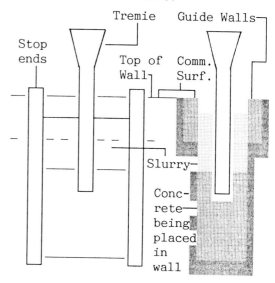

ELEVATION                SECTION

The details of the waterproofed joints and guide walls very often depend on the construction techniques adopted by the Contractor constructing the diaphragm walls and it is not unusual for the Contractor to be made responsible for their design. They are taken in the Example as "Contractor designed" on the assumption that the Specification sets out the Contractor's responsibilities and calls for them to be so designed.

The Example assumes that Preamble would be included in the Bill to the effect that items for guide walls are deemed to include their design and complete construction, including any excavation to accommodate them and their demolition and disposal when no longer required. The additional description "including excavation" makes clear that excavation for guide walls is not measured in that given by volume for the diaphragm wall.

## DIAPHRAGM WALLS - DRG No. C/D/1

Diaphragm walls (cont.

$$88 \div 4 = 22$$
$$40 \div 4 = 10$$
$$236 \div 4 = 64$$

High y. steel bar rfmt.
to BS 4449

| | |
|---|---|
| 133/22/10.00 | Nom. size 25 mm<br>× 3.854 Kg/m<br>————— Kg (C667 |
| 133/22/ 1.20<br>133/10/ 1.00 | Nom. size 20 mm<br>× 2.466 Kg/mm<br>————— Kg (C666 |
| 133/64/10.00 | Nom. size 16 mm<br>× 1.579 Kg/m<br>————— Kg (C665 |

Chase

$$130.00$$
$$4/0.10 = \underline{0.40}$$
$$130.40$$

| | |
|---|---|
| 130.40 | Conc. ancills.<br>Fmw no. fin.<br>For conc. components<br>of constant cross-<br>section; 3 sides hor.<br>chase 100 x 200 mm<br>c.s. dimensions in<br>face of diaphragm<br>wall (G184 |

(2)

COMMENTARY

Refer to the notes against the feature "Bar reinforcement" in Table 5.02 for details of itemisation and measurement of reinforcement.

The quantities and lengths of reinforcement are taken from the abridged bar schedule, which it is assumed includes stiffening, lifting and supporting steel for casting in. The waste calculations determine the number of bars per metre of wall, This number is used in conjunction with the length of wall in metres as the timesing factors applied to the length of the bars to calculate the total length of each size of bar. The dimensions are set down in a manner which allows the total length of bars to be multiplied by the mass per metre to calculate the mass for each bar size. The mass per metre of bar is calculated on the basis of steel being 7.85 t/m3. The mass for each bar classification would be reduced to tonnes for billing.

Formwork is here measured by length in one item (See Note at the foot of page 41 CESMM).

DIAPHRAGM WALLS - DRG No. C/D/2

Ground anchorages to diaphragm walls of basement, compesn as Spec. clause 3.17, workg. load 20 t. water & groutg. tests, pregroutg & groutg. as Spec. clause 3.20

$(2 \times 39) + (2 \times 24) = 126$

2/ 126

Number, perm. wi dble. corrasn. protect max. depth 15 m.    (C716

2/126/ 15.00

Total length of tendons, perm wi dble. corrasn. protect    (C726

2/ 126

Conc. ancills
Conc. acc. inserts, g anch. tendons groutd wi. ct. mor(1:2) into 75 mm diam. preformd. hole thro. 0.75m thickn r.c. diaph. walls (tendons m/s)  (G832

&

Fmw. ro fin. for voids small circ., depth 0.50 - 1m    (G172

2/ 126

Spec. rqmts. testg. of Wks. Testing perm. g. anchorages of diaph wall (wkg. load 20t) to 1.5 wkg load   (A260

(3)

COMMENTARY

The items which require to be given for ground anchors are set out in Table 5.03. The items in the Example use Specification references in preference to a detailed statement describing the features of the work as set out in Rule C/A7 of the CESMM. See left hand panel of Table 5.03.

The Example envisages that the tendons of each anchor will pass through the diaphragm wall in a preformed hole. In the circumstances, it is considered that the items for the number of anchors and the lengths of tendons do not qualify to be described as being in material which includes artificial hard material and they have been taken as being all in soft material.

Work related to the wall which falls to be classified in accordance with Classes other than C of the CESMM is measured in the Example. See items at the bottom of columns (2) and (3). Where the diaphragm walls are given under an identifying heading in the selected Part of the Bill of Quantities, these items would, preferably, be included with those of Class C under the heading rather than among the items of their Class outside the identifying heading. Where items of several Classes are listed under a heading, it is considered better if the heading is given in the Bill in capital letters rather than small case to avoid it being lost sight of by the Class description headings being in capital letters.

# 6 Demolition and Site Clearance – CESMM Class: D

Class D applies to the demolition and removal of subjects to be demolished or removed which are above the Original Surface. Work of this kind (other than the removal of tree roots) at or below the Original Surface is excluded from the Class and is measurable under Classes C, E, I, J, K, L, R, T, X or Y according to its classification.

The volume of a building or structure measured is that of the solid the part to be demolished would create above the Original Surface if it had no internal voids.

Where demolition abuts construction which is to remain, consideration must be given to the method of dealing with any support, protection, reinstatement and making good required to the remaining construction. Simple detachment one from the other may be covered by the Specification and a note in the Preamble of the Bill stating that prices for demolition are to include for such work and any incidental making good. More involved work of this kind, where it is considered a reasonable estimate of requirements can be made, may be given as measured items appropriately classified. Where it would be difficult prior to demolition to assess the nature and extent of the work to the existing it is appropriate to make it the subject of a Provisional Sum.

Where shoring is specified to support the remaining construction it is appropriate to consider that of a temporary nature as Temporary Works. That which is to be left in position on completion of the Contract being considered as part of the Permanent Works. Where the Contractor may himself select the means of complying with the requirements for temporary shoring, no items are given for it in the Bill of Quantities. Where temporary shoring is precisely specified and detailed it is given as items of specified requirements under Class A. The Engineer will usually design the shoring where it is to be left in position on completion of the Contract. Such shoring may be measured and given under an identifying heading in the Bill or it may be given as a Provisional Sum.

Where specific requirements are imposed in regard to hoardings, overhead platforms, fans or other temporary works related to the demolition, they need to be given as items of specified requirements under Class A.

Where work of diversion, removal, disconnection or sealing off of Statutory Authority's services is required in connection with demolition, this can only be undertaken by or under the order of the appropriate Authority. The Specification will usually require the Contractor to give the necessary notices and arrange for the work to be carried out. This is covered in the Bill of Quantities by giving a Provisional Sum for the work itself and for any related fees which may be repayable under Clause 26(1) of the I.C.E. Contract.

Table 6.01 indicates descriptive features and units of measurement and refers to the Rules in the CESMM. Commentary on Class D is included in the Measured Example at the end of this Chapter.

Table 6.01 Demolition and Site Clearance

| | | | |
|---|---|---|---|
| Generally - Items deemed to include disposal of materials arising (Rule D/C1) | | | |
| State when materials arising are to remain the property of the Employer (Rule D/A1) | | | |

**1st Division**

| | | | |
|---|---|---|---|
| General clearance | ha | Includes everything expressly required to be cleared except that for which separate items given (Rule D/D1) | |
| | | Includes stumps where hedges are removed (Rule D/C2) | |
| | | Identify area if not total area of Site (Rule D/A2) | |
| | | State backfilling material where holes left by removal of stumps are to be backfilled (Rule D/A3) | |

| 1st Division | | | 2nd Division | 3rd Division |
|---|---|---|---|---|
| Trees<br><br>Measure only when over 500 mm girth | nr | Measure girth one metre above ground (Rule D/D2)<br><br>Deemed to include removing their stumps (Rule D/C3) | State girth range as 2nd Division | State back- filling mat- erial where holes left by removal of stumps are to be backfilled (Rule D/A3) |
| Stumps | nr | Measure only stumps exceeding 150 mm diameter | State diam- eter range as 2nd Division | |
| Buildings<br>Other Structures | sum<br><br>sum | Identify buildings and other structures (Rule D/A4) | State predom- inant mater- ial:-<br>Brickwork<br><br>Concrete<br><br>Masonry<br><br>Metal<br><br>Timber<br><br>No predomin- ant material | State volume range as 3rd Division or actual volume when over 5000 m3<br><br>Volume stated is volume occupied above Original Surface (Rule D/D3) |
| Pipelines<br><br>Deemed to inc- lude demolit- ion of supports (Rule D/C4) | m | Measure when above ground and exceeding 100 mm bore.<br><br>Measure when in buildings and structures only when exceeding 300 mm bore (Rule D/M1) | State nominal bore range as 2nd Division | |

EXAMPLES DE.1 and DE.2

Measured Example (DE.1) - Specimen Bill (DE.2)

The measured Example which follows is for the site clearance and demolition shown on Drawing No. D/D/1. An example of the Bill of Quantities for the work is given as Example DE.2.

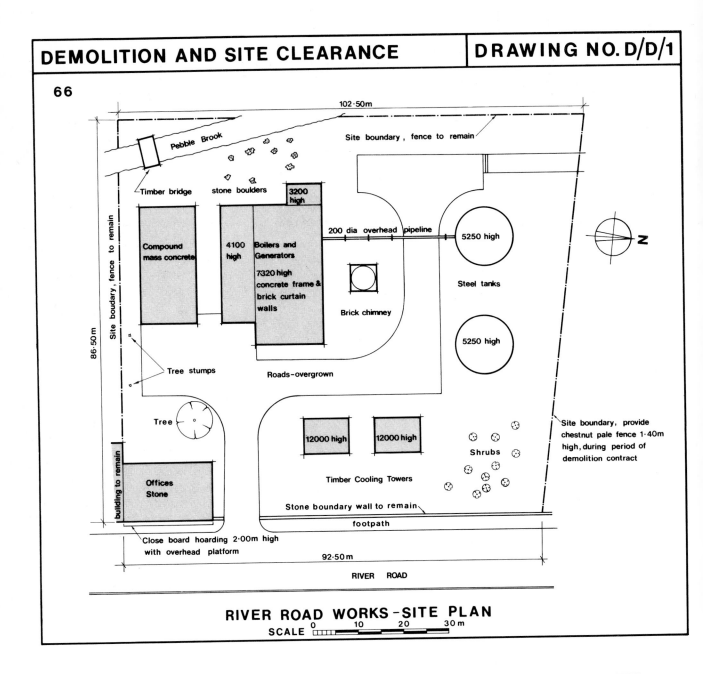

102·50m

Site boundary, fence to remain

Pebble Brook

Timber bridge   stone boulders

3200 high

4100 high   Boilers and Generators

Compound mass concrete

7320 high concrete frame & brick curtain walls

200 dia overhead pipeline

5250 high

Steel tanks

Brick chimney

5250 high

Tree stumps

Roads-overgrown

86·50m   Site boudary, fence to remain

Tree

Site boundary, provide chestnut pale fence 1·40m high, during period of demolition contract

12000 high   12000 high

Shrubs

building to remain

Offices Stone

Timber Cooling Towers

Stone boundary wall to remain
footpath

Close board hoarding 2·00m high with overhead platform

92·50m

RIVER ROAD

N

## RIVER ROAD WORKS – SITE PLAN
SCALE   0   10   20   30 m

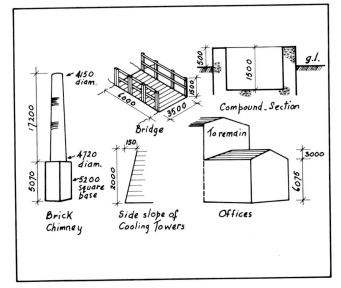

Brick Chimney
17200
5070
4150 diam.
4720 diam.
5200 square base

Bridge
1000
3500

Side slope of Cooling Towers
150
2000

Compound Section
500
1500
1500
g.l.

Offices
To remain
3000
6075

| PLAN DIMENSIONS OF BUILDINGS & STRUCTURES | | |
|---|---|---|
| Ref. | m | |
| Compound | 25.00 x 12.50 | See sketch. |
| Boils + Gen:- | | |
| main buildg. | 30.00 x 15.00 | |
| South annexe | 25.00 x 7.50 | |
| West annexe | 7.50 x 5.00 | |
| Chimney | 5.20 x 5.20 | See sketch |
| Steel tanks | 12.50 diam | both identical |
| Cooling towers | 10.00 x 7.50 | See sketch both identical |
| Offices | 20.00x 12.50 | See sketch |
| Bridge (stream) | 6.00 x 3.50 | See sketch |
| OTHER PARTICULARS | | |
| O/h. pipeline — length = 29.50 m | | |
| Tree (W. offices) = 1200 girth   (1m above g.l.) | | |
| Stumps ( „  „ ) = both 300 mm diam. | | |

## SITE SKETCHES AND NOTES

## EXAMPLE DE.1

Site clearance

|  |  |
|---:|---:|
|  | 102.50 |
|  | 92.50 |
| 2) | 195.00 |
|  | 97.50 |

| | | |
|---|---|---|
| 97.50 86.50 | 8433.75 | Gen. clearance inc. clearg o/grown roads, rem. u/growth, shrubs, stone boulds, rubbish + debris (Site area excludg areas of buildgs + strucs to be demolished) (D 100 |
| 25.00 12.50 | 312.50 | Ddt. ditto. (compound. |
| 30.00 15.00 | 450.00 | } boils. and generators |
| 25.00 7.50 | 187.50 | |
| 7.50 5.00 | 37.50 | |
| 5.20 5.20 | 27.04 | (chimney |
| 2/22/7/ 6.25 6.25 | 245.54 | 2) 12.50 6.25  (steel tanks |
| 2/10.00 7.50 | 150.00 | (coolg. towers |
| 20.00 12.50 | 250.00 | (offices |
| 37.50 5.00 | 187.50 | (stream |
| | 1847.58 | |
| | 6586.17 | |

Demolition, etc.

$$\frac{2 \times 12.00 \times 0.15}{2.00} = 1.80$$

|  |  |
|---:|---:|
| 10.00 × 7.50 | |
| 1.80 | 1.80 |
| 8.20 | 5.70 |
| 10.00 | 7.50 |

coolg. towers        2) 18.20 × 13.20

mean dimensions        9.10 × 6.60

(1)

On the premise that tenderers need to obtain the information they require to prepare their tender from an inspection of that which is to be demolished or cleared, the CESMM does not call for elaborate descriptions of the work. The descriptions are, however, required to identify the buildings and structures to be demolished. A site plan similar to Drawing No. D/D/1 will usually accompany the Bill of Quantities.

The item of general clearance is quantified in terms of the area of the site to be cleared and is given in the Bill of Quantities in hectares.

Where appropriate the removal of trees of a girth not exceeding 500 mm (trunk girth measured 1 m above ground level), the removal of stumps of trees not exceeding 150 mm diameter, the removal of pipelines which are above the ground and which do not exceed 100 mm nominal bore, the removal of hedges and their stumps and the removal of anything else which does not qualify to be separately itemised under Class D, but is expressly required to be removed would be described and included in the item of "General clearance".

The waste at the foot of Column (1) of the dimensions is the commencement of the preliminary calculations for use when calculating the volumes for subsequent items of demolition.

# DEMOLITION AND SITE CLEARANCE - DRG NO: D/D/1

Demolition, etc. (cont.

```
        4150
        4720
chimney  2) 8870
mean diam = 4435
mean radius 2218
```

## SCHEDULE OF VOLUMES

| | | Length | Width | Height | Vol (m3) |
|---|---|---|---|---|---|
| Compound. | | 25.00 | × 12.50 | × 0.50 = | 156.25 |
| Boils | | 30.00 | × 15.00 | × 7.32 = | 3294.00 |
| & | | 25.00 | × 7.50 | × 4.10 = | 768.75 |
| Generators | | 7.50 | × 5.00 | × 3.20 = | 120.00 |
| | | | | | 4182.75 |
| Chimney | $\frac{22}{7}$/ | 2.22 | × 2.22 | × 17.20 = | 266.42 |
| | | 5.20 | × 5.20 | × 5.07 = | 137.09 |
| | | | | | 403.51 |
| Tanks | $2/\frac{22}{7}$/ | 6.25 | × 6.25 | × 5.25 = | 1289.06 |
| C/towers | 2/ | 9.10 | × 6.60 | × 12.00 = | 1441.44 |
| Offices | | 20.00 | × 12.50 | × 6.08 = | 1520.00 |
| | $\frac{1}{2}$/ | 20.00 | × 12.50 | × 3.00 = | 375.00 |
| | | | | | 1895.00 |
| Bridge | | 6.00 | × 3.50 | × 1.50 = | 31.50 |

Sum — Strucs. concrete, vol. 156 m3; Compound adjoing. S. boundary, (D523

Sum — Buildgs. concrete fra & bkw. walls, vol. 4183 m3; Boils & Gen. (D497

(2)

The items for demolition assume the Specification calls for demolition down to the top of the lowest solid ground slab. It is assumed also, with the exception of the Compound, that the top of the lowest slab is at or above the Original Surface. The heights used to calculate the "volume occupied" are measured, therefore, from the top of the lowest ground slab.

The volume of the Compound is measured as Rule D/D3. The item given here covers only demolition down to the Original Surface. Removal of the concrete walls and slab below the Original Surface, if required, would be measured the nett volume of the concrete and be classified as "General excavation mass concrete maximum depth "X" m" (stating level at which exposed). See "Excludes" CESMM Class D.

Buildings and structures are identified in the item descriptions. See Rule D/A4.

Each item is for a specific building, structure or group. Consequently there will be but one volume in each item and the actual volume is stated in the item description in place of the range. See Paragraph 5.14 of the CESMM. See also previous Commentary on this Paragraph in Chapter 2.

It is a matter of personal preference whether a schedule of volumes is prepared or whether the dimensions for each building or structure are set down preceding each item.

There is no standard classification for the composite construction of the Boilers and Generators building. It is appropriate to use the digit 9 in the second division position in the Code to denote this. See Paragraph 4.5 of the CESMM.

## Demolition etc. (cont.

| | |
|---|---|
| Sum | Strucs. bkw., vol 404 m3; Chimney. (D514 |
| Sum | Group of two strucs., metal, vol 1290 m3; two Steel Tanks (D546 |
| Sum | Group of two strucs., timber, vol. 1441m3; two Cooling Towers. (D556 |
| Sum | Buildgs. masonry, vol. 1895 m3; Offices. (D436 |
| 1 | Trees of girth 1.20 m. (D220 |
| 2 | Tree stumps of diam. 300 mm. (D310 |
| 29.50 | Pipelines, nom. bore 200 mm. (D610 |
| | See Preamble |
| Sum | Strucs. timber, vol. 92 m3; Bridge over Pebble Brook. (D551 |

(3)

COMMENTARY

The unit of measurement for buildings and structures is the sum.

It is considered preferable where there are several identical buildings or structures in close proximity to group them in a single item, rather than give each as a separate item. See items in adjoining column.

Trees exceeding 500 mm girth (trunk girth measured 1 m above ground level), are given by number, stating the girth or the girth range.

Stumps of trees exceeding 150 mm diameter are given by number stating the diameter or the diameter range.

Pipelines which exceed 100 mm nominal bore which are above ground are measured linearly in metres stating the nominal bore or the nominal bore range. Items include for the demolition and removal of supports.

It is assumed in the Example that there are no pipelines exceeding 300 mm nominal bore within the buildings and structures to be demolished.

The actual girth of the tree, the actual diameter of the stumps and the actual nominal bore of pipeline each represent a single dimension in one item and are given in the item descriptions in place of the range. See Paragraph 5.14 of the CESMM.

Pebble brook would be identified in the Preamble of the Bill of Quantities. A reference would be given to a drawing indicating the boundaries of the brook and its water surface level. See Paragraph 5.20 of the CESMM

The Example includes only Class D items. Specified requirement items and items for the work to the remaining buildings have not been included.

| Number | Item description | Unit | Quantity | Rate | Amount £ | p |
|---|---|---|---|---|---|---|
| | DEMOLITION AND SITE CLEARANCE. | | | | | |
| D100 | General clearance; including clearing overgrown roads, removing undergrowth, shrubs, boulders, rubbish and debris. Site area excluding areas of buildings and structures to be demolished. | ha | 0.66 | | | |
| | Trees and stumps. | | | | | |
| D220 | Trees, girth 1.20 m. | nr | 1 | | | |
| D310 | Tree stumps, diameter 300 mm. | nr | 2 | | COMMENTARY | |
| | Buildings. | | | | The items of demolition in this Example, being for subjects of one volume or groups of subjects each of the same volume, state the actual volume in preference to the volume range given in Class D of CESMM (See Paragraph 5.14 of CESMM). | |
| D436 | Masonry, volume 1895 m3; Offices. | sum | | | | |
| D497 | Concrete frame and brickwork walls, volume 4183 m3; Boilers and Generators. | sum | | | | |
| | Structures. | | | | | |
| D514 | Brickwork, volume 404 m3; Chimney. | sum | | | | |
| D523 | Concrete, volume 156 m3; Compound adjoining South boundary. | sum | | | | |
| D546 | Two metal, volume 1290 m3; two identical Steel Tanks. | sum | | | | |
| D551 | Timber, volume 32 m3; Bridge over Pebble Brook. | sum | | | | |
| D556 | Two timber, volume 1441 m3; two identical Cooling Towers. | sum | | | | |
| | Pipelines. | | | | | |
| D610 | Nominal bore 200 mm. | m | 30 | | | |

# 7 Earthworks – CESMM Class: E

Earthworks covered by Class E includes excavation, dredging, filling, compaction, disposal and landscaping.

Excluded from the Class is excavation for:-

   site investigation (included in Class B)

   diaphragm walls and ground anchorages (included in Class C)

   drains, sewers and the like (included in Classes J,K,L and Y)

   piles (included in Classes P and Q)

   foundations for traffic signs (included in Class R)

   tunnels, shafts, headings and the like (included in Class T)

   foundations for fences and gates (included in Class X)

Excluded also is reinstatement following pipe laying (included in Class K)

---

Table 7.01 Excavation

| | |
|---|---|
| Excavation generally | Measure net from the Drawings with no allowance for bulking, shrinkage or waste. Take measurements on Site where boundaries between different materials are not shown on Drawings (Rule E/M1) |
| | Deemed to be material other than topsoil, rock or artificial hard material unless otherwise stated (Rule E/D1) |
| | Deemed to include upholding sides, for additional excavation for working space and for removing existing services (Rule E/C1) |
| | State Commencing Surface if it is not the Original Surface. State Excavated Surface if it is not the Final Surface (Rule E/A4) |
| | Measure from Commencing Surface used when preparing the Bill of Quantities when measuring completed work (Rule E/M2). |
| | Measure separately an isolated volume of rock or artificial hard material, only if in excavations less than 2 m wide its volume exceeds 0.25 m3 and elsewhere if its volume exceeds 1 m3 (Rule E/M8) |
| | State identity of body of open water as given in Preamble in items for excavating below the body of water (Rule E/A2) |
| | Measure volume of excavation below a body of open water as the volume which is below water when water is at its highest level (Rule E/M7) |

Table 7.01 Excavation (cont.

| 1st Division | | 2nd Division | 3rd Division |
|---|---|---|---|
| Excavation by dredging   m3 | State if measured from other than soundings (Rule E/M4)<br><br>State location and limits if not clear (Rule E/A1)<br><br>Measure completed work as by dredging whether or not it was so excavated (Rule E/M3) | Topsoil<br><br>Material other than than rock or artificial hard material<br><br>Rock<br><br>Stated artificial hard material exposed at the Commencing Surface<br><br>Stated artificial hard material not exposed at the Commencing Surface | |
| Excavation for cuttings   m3 | Includes excavation in or under embankments prior to placing filling (Rule E/D2) | | |
| Excavation for foundations   m3 | Measure volume either occupied or vertically above any part See Fig. E5. (Rule E/M6)<br><br>State if around pile shafts or for underpinning (Rule E/A3)<br><br>State location and limits if not clear (Rule E/A3) | | State maximum depth range:-<br><br>n.e. 0.25<br><br>0.25 - 0.5 m<br><br>0.5 - 1 m<br><br>1 - 2 m<br><br>2 - 5 m<br><br>5 - 10 m<br><br>10 - 15 m<br><br>State when exceeding 15 m deep |
| General excavations   m3 | For excavation for structures measure volume either occupied or vertically above any part. See Fig. E5. (Rule E/M6)<br><br>Borrow pits - Class excavation from within borrow pits as general excavation (Rule E/D3), and state it is from within borrow pits (Rule E/A5). Measure net volume as equal to net volume of filling for which used (Rule E/M9). Deemed to include removal and replacement of overburden or unsuitable material (Rule E/C2) | | |

COMMENTARY

Excavation (refer to Table 7.01)

Excavation is measured by volume and the quantities are given in the Bill of Quantities in m3. Descriptive features for excavation and a summary of the CESMM Rules are given in Table 7.01.

Excavation is measured net from the Drawings with no allowance for bulking, shrinkage or waste. The volume being that before the material is excavated. The convention adopted for the measurement of excavation to accommodate structures is illustrated later.

Excavation items do not include for disposing of the excavated material. Separate items are given for either using the excavated material for filling or for disposing of it otherwise, as the case may be. Additionally, items may require to be given for double handling where double handling of the excavated material is expressly required. See Commentary later on Excavation Ancillaries.

Unless otherwise stated in the item descriptions, all excavation is deemed to be in material, other than top soil, rock or artificial hard material.

It is not necessary to state a Commencing Surface or an Excavated Surface when they are the Original Surface and the Final Surface, respectively. The excavation in an item is, therefore, deemed to start at the Original Surface and finish at the Final Surface when a Commencing Surface or an Excavated Surface is not identified in the item description.

The item descriptions "Excavation for cuttings" or "Excavation for foundations", or "General excavation", without further wording, each denote by application of the provisions in the two preceding paragraphs, that the material to be excavated is material other than top soil, rock or artifical hard material and that the excavation in the item starts at the Original Surface and finishes at the Final Surface.

Items will separate excavation according to the standard classifications of the materials to be excavated. Horizontal bands of different material are not measured as stages of excavation, unless their excavation in stages is expressly required.

There is no requirement for excavation in running sand to be separately itemised and it will be classified as in natural material other than top soil or rock, unless the discretion afforded by paragraph 5.10 of the CESMM is exercised and it is decided to make the excavation in running sand the subject of separate items.

An isolated volume of rock or artificial hard material is not measured separately from the material in which it occurs, unless in excavation less than 2 m wide its volume exceeds 0.25 m3, or in other excavation its volume exceeds 1 m3.

*Excavations for Cuttings*

Excavation for cuttings is measured by volume and is given in m3 in the Bill of Quantities. The depth of excavation of cuttings is not required to be stated in the item descriptions. The implications of the unqualified item description, "Excavation of cuttings", is explained in the Commentary on Excavation generally.

COMMENTARY

Excavation (cont.

*Excavation for Cuttings (cont.*

Specimen item descriptions for the excavation for the cutting shown in cross-section in the diagram, Figure E1, are given at the side of the diagram. The specimen item descriptions assume (i) the excavation starts at the Original Surface and finishes at the Final Surface (ii) there is no top soil at the Original Surface. The quantity of excavation which would be attached to an item would be the volume of the particular class of material to be excavated.

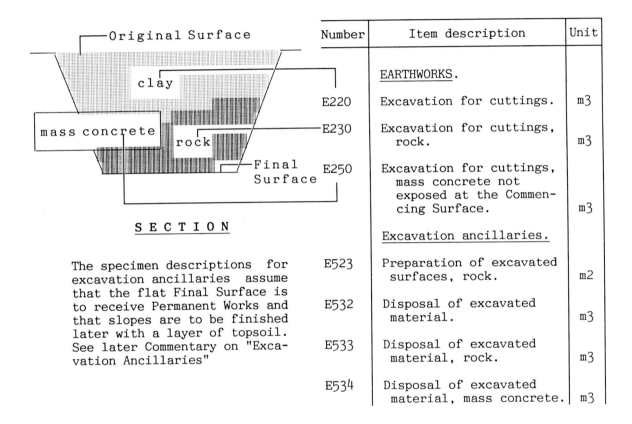

| Number | Item description | Unit |
|--------|------------------|------|
| | EARTHWORKS. | |
| E220 | Excavation for cuttings. | m3 |
| E230 | Excavation for cuttings, rock. | m3 |
| E250 | Excavation for cuttings, mass concrete not exposed at the Commencing Surface. | m3 |
| | Excavation ancillaries. | |
| E523 | Preparation of excavated surfaces, rock. | m2 |
| E532 | Disposal of excavated material. | m3 |
| E533 | Disposal of excavated material, rock. | m3 |
| E534 | Disposal of excavated material, mass concrete. | m3 |

S E C T I O N

The specimen descriptions for excavation ancillaries assume that the flat Final Surface is to receive Permanent Works and that slopes are to be finished later with a layer of topsoil. See later Commentary on "Excavation Ancillaries"

Fig. E1. Excavation for cuttings, not in stages.

The excavation of cuttings will sometimes require to be measured in stages. It is common experience for a specification to require that the bottom 150-300 mm of the excavation is left, to protect the formation, and excavated immediately prior to the laying of the base material. If this is an express requirement (rather than a condition of use of the bottom surface of the cutting by the contractor's construction traffic), it constitutes a stage of excavation for which a separate item must be given. Similarly, where there is top soil and it is specified to be excavated separately from other material, the excavation of the top soil is a stage of excavation for which a separate item must be given.

The item descriptions for each stage of excavation must identify the Commencing Surface or the Excavated Surface where these are not also the Original Surface or the Final Surface, respectively.

COMMENTARY

Excavation (cont.

*Excavation for Cuttings (cont.*

Specimen descriptions for the excavation for the cutting, expressly required to be excavated in stages, shown in cross-section in the diagram, Fig. E2 are given at the side of the diagram. The specimen item descriptions assume, (i) top soil 150 mm deep excavated as a separate stage (ii) remaining material is material, other than top soil, rock or artifical hard material (iii) the last 150 mm of excavation is left to protect the formation and is to be excavated as a separate stage.

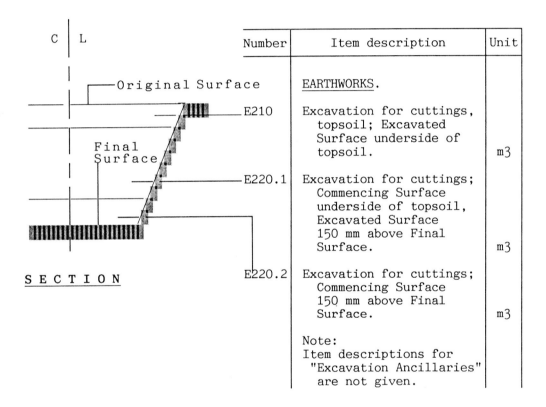

| | Number | Item description | Unit |
|---|---|---|---|
| | | EARTHWORKS. | |
| | E210 | Excavation for cuttings, topsoil; Excavated Surface underside of topsoil. | m3 |
| | E220.1 | Excavation for cuttings; Commencing Surface underside of topsoil, Excavated Surface 150 mm above Final Surface. | m3 |
| | E220.2 | Excavation for cuttings; Commencing Surface 150 mm above Final Surface. | m3 |
| | | Note: Item descriptions for "Excavation Ancillaries" are not given. | |

Fig. E2. Excavation for cuttings in stages.

*Excavation for Walls at Sides of Cuttings*

When walls are required at the sides of cuttings, there is a question of what dividing line to take between the excavation of the cutting and the excavation to accommodate the wall and footings.

It is suggested that the excavation to accommodate the wall and its backfilling is classified as general excavation, the depth of the excavation being taken down to the formation of the pavement abutting the face of the wall. The excavation below the pavement formation to accommodate the footings being classified as excavation for foundations. The suggested convention is illustrated in cross-section in the diagram, Fig. E3.

COMMENTARY

Excavation (cont.

*Excavation for Walls at Sides of Cuttings (cont.*

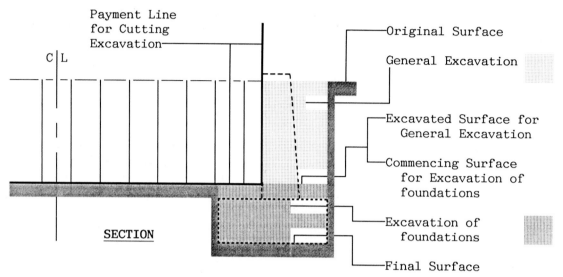

Fig. E3. Excavation for walls at sides of cuttings.

In this situation the limits of the excavation in any one item will not be clear in the Bill without some additional detail. This additional detail could be provided by a diagram on the drawings indicating the measurement convention used for measuring the excavation when preparing the Bill of Quantities. The CESMM requires that item descriptions for "Excavation for foundations" must state the location and limits of the excavation where this is not clear.

*Excavation Below Embankments*

Excavation in or under embankments carried out prior to placing filling is classed "Excavation for cuttings", and is given in m3. Where an embankment is to be constructed on steeply sloping ground, the surface to receive the embankment may be specified to be benched in steps or trenched. Whilst the excavation for the steps or trenches can be classified as "Excavation for cuttings", it should be identified either by reference to the particular location or by adding to the standard description, the phrase "benched in steps below embankments" or "trenched below embankments", as the case may be.

*General Excavation and Excavation of Foundations*

The classification "General excavation" covers excavation to reduce levels over areas and will also be used for excavation to reduce a site to the formation level of a structure. "Excavation for foundations" is that which accommodates foundations. The item descriptions for both these types of excavation must state the range of depth in which the maximum depth of the particular excavation work occurs. Both types are measured by volume and the unit of measurement is m3.

Item descriptions for "Excavation for foundations" state the location and limits of the excavation where they would otherwise not be clear. They state also if the excavation is around pile shafts or for underpinning. Excavation from within borrow pits is classed as "General excavation". For rules and details see last panel in Table 7.01.

COMMENTARY

Excavation (cont.

*General Excavation and Excavation of Foundations (cont.*

Specimen item descriptions for the excavation of foundations and to reduce the levels for the structure shown in cross-section in the diagram, Fig. E4., are given at the side of the diagram.

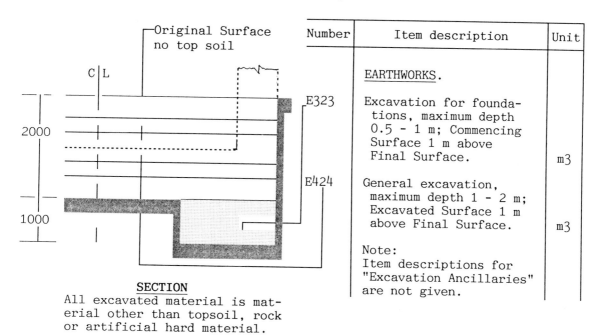

| Number | Item description | Unit |
|--------|------------------|------|
| | EARTHWORKS. | |
| E323 | Excavation for foundations, maximum depth 0.5 - 1 m; Commencing Surface 1 m above Final Surface. | m3 |
| E424 | General excavation, maximum depth 1 - 2 m; Excavated Surface 1 m above Final Surface. | m3 |
| | Note: Item descriptions for "Excavation Ancillaries" are not given. | |

**SECTION**

All excavated material is material other than topsoil, rock or artificial hard material.

Fig. E4. General excavation and excavation of foundations.

*Excavation for Structures and Foundations*

The volume measured for the excavation of a structure or foundation is the volume either occupied by or vertically above any part of the structure or foundation. (Rule E/M6 of the CESMM).

The application of this Rule to three situations is illustrated in the following cross-section diagrams. The boundaries of the excavation are shown by the lines of dashes.

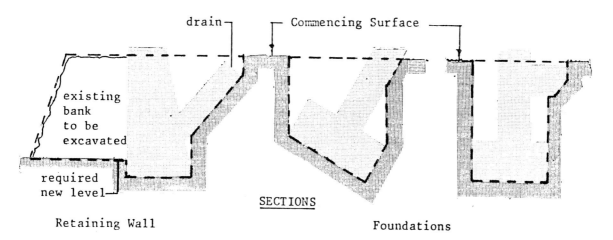

Retaining Wall                    Foundations

Fig. E5. Volume of excavation measured for structures and foundations.

COMMENTARY

Excavation (cont.

*Excavation below a Body of Water*

Item descriptions for excavations below a body of open water, which has been identified in the Preamble in accordance with paragraph 5.20 of the CESMM, must identify the body of water. The volume measured for the excavation below a body of water is the volume below the water when the water surface level is at the higher level of fluctuation, where the surface level fluctuates. When the work is admeasured, measurements are taken on the basis of the boundaries and levels of the water shown on the referenced drawings and not on the actual boundaries and levels which obtain. The Contractor could, however, have grounds for additional payment under clause 12 of the I.C.E. Conditions if totally unanticipated fluctuation in water levels occurred.

*Excavation by Dredging*

Excavation by dredging is measured from soundings unless it is otherwise stated in item descriptions. The quantities are the nett in situ volumes of the voids formed, given in m3. The volume is calculated from the areas to be excavated by dredging, as defined in the contract or as subsequently ordered, and depths measured from the surface of the bed of the river or other body of water, i.e. the Commencing Surface, as established from soundings, to the Final Surface. Where quantities are prepared from soundings an hydrographical survey will usually be provided and the dredging requirement will be plotted on the survey. Reference to this document in item descriptions will indicate the location and limits of the dredging, as required by Rule E/A1 of the CESMM.

An alternative method of measuring dredging is to measure the volume of dredged material from the hopper or barge in which the material is initially deposited. When dredging is measured from other than soundings, the method must be stated in the item descriptions.

Excavation classed as by dredging in the Bill of Quantities is admeasured as by dredging irrespective of the method of excavation adopted by the Contractor.

Excavation Ancillaries (refer to Table 7.02)

*Trimming of Excavated Surfaces*

Trimming of excavated surfaces is measured in square metres to surfaces which are to receive no Permanent Works. It is stated in item descriptions where the surfaces to be trimmed are:- (a) inclined at an angle 10 - 45 degrees to the horizontal (b) inclined at an angle 45 - 90 degrees to the horizontal (c) vertical. The material to be trimmed is given in the item description in accordance with the descriptive features. It is deemed to be material other than top soil, rock or artificial hard material unless otherwise stated.

*Preparation of Surfaces*

Preparation of surfaces is measured superficially in square metres to surfaces which are to receive Permanent Works except surfaces which are to receive filling or landscaping. The item covers merely preparing the surface to the required profiles and configurations. It would not include any material or additional operations, such as the application of weedkiller or a surface dressing. These would be given as separate items or, if preferred, may be given in the preparation item by added description. The material of the surface to be prepared is given in the item descriptions. It is deemed to be material other than topsoil, rock or artificial hard material unless otherwise stated.

Table 7.02   Excavation Ancillaries

---

Generally   State where excavation ancillaries are in connection
with excavation by dredging (Rule E/A6)

---

1st Division - Excavation ancillaries

| 2nd Division | | | 3rd Division |
|---|---|---|---|
| Trimming of excavated surfaces    m2 | Measure to surfaces which are to receive no Permanent Works, whether expressly required or not (Rule E/M10) | State if surfaces:- (a) inclined at 10-45 degrees to horizontal (b) inclined at 45-90 degrees to horizontal (c) vertical (Rule E/A7) | Describe materials in accordance with 3rd Division features. State precise nature of artificial hard material. Deemed to be carried out on material other than topsoil, rock or artificial hard material, unless otherwise stated (Rule E/D5) |
| Preparation of excavated surfaces    m2 | Measure to surfaces which are to receive Permanent Works, whether expressly required or not, except filling, landscaping and surfaces where formwork has been measured (Rule E/M11) | | |
| Disposal of excavated material    m3 | Volume is calculated from the total net volume of excavation less the total net volume of excavated material used for filling (Rule E/M12) Means disposal off Site unless otherwise stated (Rule E/D4) State location of disposal area when disposed of on Site. (Rule E/A8) | | |
| Double handling of excavated material    m3 | Measure only if expressly required. Volume is that of void in stockpile (Rule E/M13) | | |
| Dredging to remove silt    m3 | Measure only when expressly required that silt which accumulates after the Final Surface has been reached shall be removed (Rule E/M14) | | |
| Excavation of material below Final Surfaces and replacement with stated material    m3 | State precise nature of replacement material | | |
| Timber supports left in    m2 Metal supports left in    m2 | Measure area of supported surface for which the supports are expressly required to be left in (Rule E/M15) | | |

---

Excavation Ancillaries (cont.

*Preparation of Surfaces (cont.*

It is stated in the item descriptions where the surfaces to be prepared
are:- (a) inclined at an angle 10 - 45 degrees to the horizontal (b)
inclined at an angle 45 - 90 degrees to the horizontal (c) vertical.

COMMENTARY

Excavation Ancillaries (cont.

*Disposal of Excavated Material*

Separate items from those for excavation must be given either for the disposal of the excavated material or for its use as filling as the case may be. The volume of disposal of excavated material given in the Bill is the net volume of excavation less the net volume of the excavated material used for filling. Quantities are given in m3.

*Double Handling of Excavated Material*

A separate item for double handling excavated material is measured only when double handling is expressly required. Consequently, excavation and filling items are deemed to include all double handling that may be necessary to carry out the earthworks. The inclusion in the Bill of Quantities of a separate item for double handling excavated material is not decided on whether it would be impossible not to, or whether it is sensible, convenient or practical to stockpile and double handle excavated material, these are matters which are left for the Contractor to decide and allow for accordingly. The measurement of double handling of excavated material is decided by the dictates of the specification or the order of the Engineer.

Double handling of excavated material is measured by volume and is given in the Bill of Quantities in m3. Rule E/M13 of the CESMM requires that the volume shall be that of the void formed in the stockpile. Consequently, when calculating the volume of double handling of excavated material for the quantities in the Bill of Quantities, if the calculations start with the in place volume of the filling for which the material is to be used, an allowance will need to be made for the difference in bulk of the material in the stockpile and its bulk when used as filling.

When calculating the volume of material for double handling on the site the volume of the stockpile will need to be measured both before and after the material has been removed.

*Dredging to Remove Silt*

Dredging to remove silt is applicable only to silt which accumulates after the Final Surface has been reached and is expressly required to be removed.

The quantities for the Bill of Quantities will require to be estimated because the amount which will accumulate will not be known until measured on completion.

*Excavation of Material Below Final Surface*
*and Replacement with Stated Material*

Soft spots below the formation are among the items to which the classification in the above heading will apply. The precise nature of the replacement material must be given in the item description. The unit of measurement is cubic metres.

*Supports Left In*

Timber supports and metal supports which are expressly required to be left in are measurable items and are each given separately. The areas given in the items are those of the surfaces supported given in square metres. The dictates of the specification or the order of the Engineer decides when the items are to be measured and included in the Bill of Quantities.

Table 7.03  Filling

| 1st Division | | |
| --- | --- | --- |

| Filling | The volume of filling is measured net from the Drawings with no allowance for bulking, shrinkage or waste (Rule E/M1)<br><br>Deemed to include compaction (Rule E/C3)<br><br>State compaction requirements when different compaction requirements are specified for the same material (Rule E/A10)<br><br>State limitations when rate of deposition is limited (Rule E/A11) | |

| 2nd Division | | | The volume of imported filling is the difference between the net volume of filling and the net volume of excavated material derived from work in Classes E and T used for filling (Rule E/M19) |
| --- | --- | --- | --- |
| To structures | m3 | Measure only to extent that the volume filled is also measured as excavation in accordance with Rule E/M6 (Rule E/M16) | |
| Embankments | m3 | | |
| General | m3 | | |
| To stated depth or thickness | m2 | State compacted thickness.  The classification applies to filling of a uniform depth, such as a drainage blanket, topsoiling, etc. (Rule E/D8)<br><br>State materials (Rule E/A12)<br><br>State if upon surfaces inclined at 10-45 degrees, inclined at 45-90 degrees to horizontal or vertical (Rule E/A13) | Bulk filling in layers is not classed as to stated thickness (Rule E/D8)<br><br>No deduction from the volume of filling for that left from temporary roads and incorporated with approval (Rule E/M17) |

Additional filling due to settlement or penetration into underlying material is measured only if its depth exceeds 75 mm (Rule E/M18)

3rd Division - Filling material - Deemed to be non-selected excavated material unless otherwise stated (Rule E/D6)

| Excavated topsoil | | Where in water and quantities cannot be measured satisfactorily, measure in transport vehicles (Rule E/M21) |
| --- | --- | --- |
| Imported topsoil | | |
| Non-selected excavated material other than topsoil or rock | | |
| Selected excavated material other than topsoil or rock | | |
| Imported natural material other than topsoil or rock | State materials (Rule E/A9) | |
| Excavated rock | Class as excavated rock only if filling of rock expressly required at stated locations. State location (Rule E/D7) | Where in soft areas measure volume in transport vehicles (Rule E/M20) |
| Imported rock | | |
| Imported artificial material | State material (Rule E/A9) | Where in water and quantities cannot be measured satisfactorily, measure in transport vehicles (Rule E/M21) |

## Table 7.04  Filling Ancillaries

### 1st Division - Filling ancillaries

| 2nd Division | | | 3rd Division | |
|---|---|---|---|---|
| Trimming of filled surfaces | m2 | Measure to surfaces which are to receive no Permanent Works, whether expressly required or not (Rule E/M22) | State in accordance with 3rd Division features, the surface material on which carried out<br><br>Surfaces deemed to be other than topsoil, rock or artifical hard material unless otherwise stated (Rule E/D9)<br><br>Where carried out on artificial hard material state precise nature of material | State if surfaces:-<br><br>(a) inclined 10 - 45 degrees to horizontal<br><br>(b) inclined 45 - 90 degrees to horizontal<br><br>(c) vertical (Rule E/A14) |
| Preparation of filled surfaces | m2 | Measure to surfaces which are to receive Permanent Works, whether expressly required or not, except surfaces to receive filling, landscaping and surfaces where formwork has been measured (Rule E/M23) | | |
| Geotextiles | m2 | State type and grade of materials (Rule E/A15) | | |

### COMMENTARY

### Filling (refer to Table 7.03)

Filling is measured as equal in volume to that of the solid which represents the size and shape of the filled volume. The filled volume is taken as equal to the excavated volume (measured before excavation), where the material excavated is used for filling. Additional filling needed because of settlement of or penetration into the surface upon which the filling is placed is measured where the depth of settlement or penetration exceeds 75 mm.

Item descriptions are required to state the compaction requirement where different compaction requirements are specified for the same material. The classification "to stated thickness" is not applicable to bulk filling compacted in layers. Any limitation on the rate of deposition of filling is stated in item descriptions.

Filling material is deemed to be non-selected excavated material unless otherwise stated in the item descriptions. Excavated rock for use as filling is measured only when its use as filling at stated locations is expressly required. The Contractor may use rock for filling if the Specification allows, but he will only be paid at the rate for soft material, unless filling with rock is expressly required.

When filling with material excavated on site is measured, the filling requirement must be matched in volume by excavation. If there is an insufficient volume of excavation to meet the filling requirement, the deficit will, obviously, need to be obtained from another source.

COMMENTARY

Filling (refer to Table 7.03) (cont.

During the measurement process it is not always possible to gauge what the outcome will be when the volume of filling with excavated material is balanced against that of the excavation. A procedure must be instituted or a measurement convention adopted to indicate the position before the excavation and filling items are billed. The procedure used in Example EE.1 is to measure all material for disposal when measuring the excavation initially. A volume of equal to that of any filling with excavated material is deducted from the disposal of excavated material initially measured when filling is measured. If this convention is followed any deficit of excavated material for filling is disclosed by a negative quantity arising when disposal of excavated material is cast to a total for billing. An alternative procedure is to measure the excavation and measure the filling which is in excavated material leaving them to be totalled and compared when all is measured. The comparison will indicate the volume of disposal of excavated material or the volume of filling to be re-classified as imported as the case may be.

Filling described as "to stated thickness" is measured in m2 (See Commentary later). Otherwise all filling is measured by volume and is given in the Bill of Quantities in m3.

*Filling to Structures*

The classification "filling to structures" covers filling to voids excavated for structures and foundations and also filling within, around and over structures. The diagram in Figure E6 illustrates situations where, if required to be filled as shown, the filling would be classified as "to structures". The banks marked (a) may suggest the classification "embankments" but banking up of this description is considered to be correctly classified as to structures.

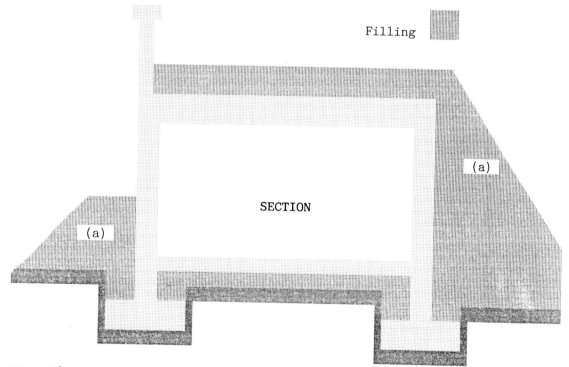

Fig. E6. Filling to structures.

COMMENTARY

Filling (cont.

*Filling to Structures (cont.*

The volume of filling in an excavated void is restricted to the volume of excavation, measured in accordance with Rule E/M6, which the filling replaces. For example, if reference is made to the sections of the foundations in Figure E5, if the whole excavated void which is not occupied by the concrete is required to be backfilled, then the cross-section of filling is the blank areas within the lines of dashes, notwithstanding that the contractor may, or may have no option but to, excavate working space. It will be noted from the two diagrams referred to above that, from the practical aspect, the voids as measured to the right of the concrete, are inaccessible for filling. Nevertheless, the measurement rules of the CESMM must apply and it will be for the contractor to allow for working space or other means of backfilling. In such circumstances it would be reasonable to indicate location of the filling in the item description.

*Embankments*

Embankments are measured by volume and the unit of measurement is m3. The measured volume will include any designed volume for long term settlement. The classification embankments applies not only to those for roads and railways but also those in dam construction.

Specimen item descriptions for the embankment shown in cross-section in the diagram Fig. E7. are given at the side of the diagram.

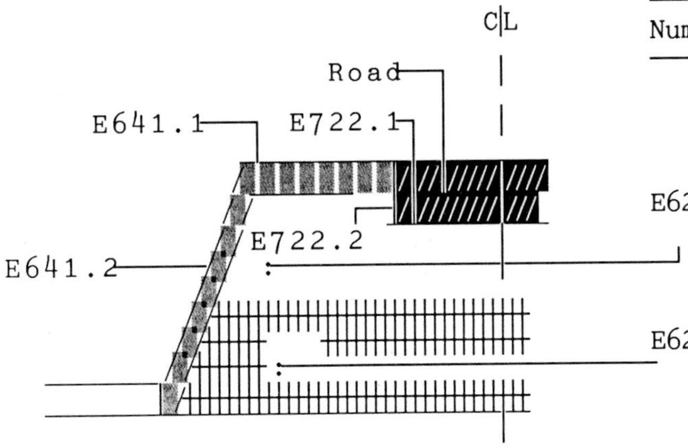

| Number | Item description | Unit |
|--------|------------------|------|
| | EARTHWORKS. | |
| | Filling. | |
| E624 | Embankments, selected excavated material other than topsoil or rock. | m3 |
| E626 | Embankments, excavated rock; horizontal layer between CS"*" and CS"*", Drawing No. X. | m3 |
| E641.1 | Thickness 150 mm, excavated topsoil. | m2 |
| E641.2 | Thickness 150 mm, excavated topsoil; upon surfaces inclined at an angle 45 - 90 degrees to the horizontal. | m2 |
| | Filling ancillaries. | |
| E722.1 | Preparation of filled surfaces. | m2 |
| E722.2 | Preparation of filled surfaces; vertical. | m2 |

**S E C T I O N**

The specimen item descriptions assume that rock as filling is expressly required at the stated location.

Fig. E7. Embankments.

COMMENTARY

Filling (cont.

*Embankments (cont.*

Any instrumentation expressly required for tests, or for monitoring settlement in embankments would be dealt with either as measured items in a similar manner to items Code 6** Class B of CESMM or be given as specified requirements items or provided for by the inclusion of a provisional sum in Class A of the Bill of Quantities.

*Filling to Stated Thickness*

The classification "to stated thickness", applies to filling of a required thickness, such as a uniform bed of hardcore under a ground slab of a structure, a layer of drainage material to form a drainage blanket, and the like.

The classification takes precedence over the other Second Division classifications, it not being required to state whether the filling so described is in relation to embankments, structures, etc.

Filling of this classification is measured superficially in m2 and the thickness is stated in the item descriptions. The actual thickness having been thus stated it is unnecessary to include the standard phrase "to stated thickness" in the description. Descriptions must state where the work is upon surfaces which are:- (a) inclined at an angle of 10-45 degrees to the horizontal (b) inclined at an angle of 45-90 degrees to the horizontal (c) vertical.

*General Filling*

General filling is that to make up levels over areas and in situations which would not be appropriately classified under the other Second Division descriptive features. The unit of measurement is m3.

Filling Ancillaries (refer to Table 7.04)

Item descriptions for filling ancillaries identify work upon inclined surfaces. See Table 7.04 for classification of angles of inclination.

Trimming and the preparation of surfaces of filling are deemed to be carried out upon material other than topsoil, rock or artifical hard material unless otherwise stated in item descriptions.

*Trimming of Filled Surfaces*

Trimming of filled surfaces is measured in m2 to surfaces which are to receive no Permanent Works.

*Preparation of Filled Surfaces*

Preparation of filled surfaces is measured in m2 to surfaces which are to receive Parmanent Works, except surfaces which are to receive filling or landscaping and surfaces for which formwork is measured.

*Geotextiles*

Geotextiles are measured by area in m2. The area is measured gross, inclusive of the area of the specified laps. Item descriptions state the type and grade of the material.

Table 7.05  Landscaping

| 1st Division - Landscaping - Deemed to include fertilizing, trimming and preparation of surfaces (Rule E/C4) | | |
| --- | --- | --- |
| 2nd Division | | 3rd Division |
| Turfing | m2  State if pegged or wired (Rule E/A16) | State if upon surfaces inclined at an angle exceeding 10 degrees to the horizontal (Rule E/A17) |
| Hydraulic mulch grass seeding | m2 | |
| Other grass seeding | m2 | |
| Plants | nr  State species and size | |
| Shrubs | nr | |
| Trees | nr | |
| Hedges | m   State species, size and spacing<br><br>Measure developed length along centre line (Rule E/M24) | State whether single or double row in accordance with the 3rd Division features |

COMMENTARY

Landscaping (refer to Table 7.05)

The features of classification for landscaping include turfing, grass seeding, plants, shrubs, trees and hedges. They are set out in Table 7.05 which gives also the units of measurement and a summary of the appropriate CESMM Rules. Items for landscaping are deemed to include fertilizing, trimming and preparation of surfaces. The requirements for such treatments should be made clear in the Specification.

*Turfing*

Turfing is measured by area and is given in m2. Item descriptions state when turfing is upon surfaces inclined at an angle exceeding 10 degrees to the horizontal. Item descriptions state where turfing is to be pegged or wired. Distinction is made between turfing carried out with imported turves and those obtained from the Site.

*Hydraulic Mulch and Other Grass Seeding*

Grass seeding is given in m2. Item descriptions state when seeding is upon surfaces inclined at an angle exceeding 10 degrees to horizontal. The specification for hydraulic mulch grass seeding will usually require that this type of seeding is carried out in accordance with the recommendations issued for the particular process and item descriptions make reference to the appropriate clauses.

COMMENTARY

Landscaping (cont.

*Plants, Shrubs, Trees and Hedges*

The specification or drawing will usually indicate the botanical names of the species and these are the names stated in the item descriptions. Preamble or additional description should make clear the associated work such as pits, staking, ties, etc., which is intended to be included in the items.

Unless other particular feature is required, the size of shrubs is given in terms of height above ground.

Trees, in addition to their botanical names, will usually be described as "half-standard", "standard", "heavy standard", "semi mature", etc., and each of these types will be defined in the specification in terms of nominal height above ground, height to the first branch and diameter at a given height above ground.

Hedges are measured in linear metres, on their centre line, to their developed length. This means that the measured length will be from the first to the last hedge plant in the row, to which will be added half the distance between the hedge plants for each end. Separate items are given for hedges with single rows of plants and for those with double rows of plants.

*Specimen Item Descriptions for Landscaping*

| The specimen item descriptions in the adjoining column assume the Specification clauses describes:- | Number | Item description | Unit |
|---|---|---|---|
| | | EARTHWORKS. | |
| | | Landscaping. | |
| the turfing and whether or not the turves are to be obtained from the Site, | E810 | Turfing; upon surfaces inclined at an angle exceeding 10 degrees to the horizontal, as Specification clause "*". | m2 |
| the seeding and associated work | E830 | Grass seeding; upon surfaces inclined at an angle exceeding 10 degrees to the horizontal, as Specification clause "*". | m2 |
| the shrubs and associated work and how height is measured, | E850 | Shrubs, Buxus sempervirens, 600 mm high; as Specification clause "*". | nr |
| the trees and associated work and the size of a "standard" tree, | E860 | Trees, Quercus robur, standard; as Specification clause "*". | nr |
| the hedge plants and associated work, the spacing of the plants and how height is measured. | E871 | Hedges, Fagas sylvatica, 600 mm high, single row; as Specification clause "*". | m |

NOTE: "Buxus sempervirens" = Common Box.
      "Quercus robur"      = Common Oak.
      "Fagus sylvatica"    = Common Beech.

EXAMPLE No. EE.1

Measured Example

The Example of "taking off" which follows illustrates conventions and the application of the provisions of the CESMM to the measurement of the earthworks for the Cutting and Embankment shown on Drawing No. E/D/1. The cross-sections in the Example are of fairly regular shape and the ordinary trapezoidal rule is used for the calculation of areas and volumes. The Example does not include the measurement of the road.

*Initial Calculations for Dimensions*

For the measurement of a cutting and filling operation of the kind in the Example, numerous waste calculations need to be made before a meaningful start can be made to set down the dimensions in the dimension column of the sheets. It would cause lengthy written work on the dimension sheets if measurements were taken and entered for small sections of the operations. It is best to make a schedule of initial waste calculations, setting out the calculated depths, slope lengths and the like, in a form convenient for reference and to proceed on the dimension sheets when results from the schedules can be collected and formulated into as few as possible entries against the items.

Confusion will result if the method of setting down the initial calculations does not allow an easy identification of the depth or other measurement of a particular part of the work.

In working the example the initial calculations are made and set out in the form shown on Plate EP.1. Set out in this manner, particular measurements are easily located as the "taking off" proceeds. If the schedule is referred to when measurement work for the final account is proceeding on the site it will also be simple to check the dimensions which were used to calculate the Quantities.

The sheet for the schedule is ordinary analysis paper, ruled with the requisite number of vertical columns. The first four steps in the procedure of preparation are as follows:-

1. Enter appropriate cross-section reference.

2. Enter road level given at the centre line of the cross-section.

3. Calculate the road levels at the sides, i.e. take 2.5% of half the constant width (14 m divided by 2). Add resultant to the centre level for the right. Deduct resultant from centre level for the left. Enter on schedule.

4. Deduct existing ground levels from road levels. The resultant "D" = depth. A negative resultant indicates cut. A positive resultant indicates fill.

| 1 | 2 | 3 | 4 | 5 | 6 | 7 | 8 | 9 | 10 | 11 |
|---|---|---|---|---|---|---|---|---|----|----|
| CS80 | | | | | | | | | | |
| | | Rd.levs | 12.08 | | 12.25 | | 12.43 | | | |
| | | Xg.G.L. | 15.20 | | | | 15.35 | | | |
| | | D = | -3.12 | | | | -2.92 | | | |

EXAMPLE No. EE.1

Measured Example (cont.

*Initial Calculations for Dimensions*

Continuing the explanation of the procedure of preparation of the schedule of Initial Calculations, the further steps are as follows:-

5. Calculate SB = spread of banks, by multiplying "D" by the Cotangent of the angle at the foot of the banks (Cotangent of 30 degrees = 1.73205). Enter the figures across the vertical columns 3 & 4 and 8 & 9.

6. Enter "CW" - constant width. Thicken lines to form panels to distinguish horizontal measurements from those for depths, slope lengths etc.

7. Add spread of banks to "CW". Enter overall width. (Top for cuttings, bottom for embankments).

8. Add 6 & 7 above together and divide by 2 to calculate mean width. Enter mean width.

9. Add together "D" on left and "D" on right and divide by 2, to calculate "AVD" - average depth. Enter average depth.

10. Multiply ("AVD" by the Cosecant of 30 degrees) to calculate average slope length. (Cosecant of 30 degrees = 2.0000). Draw sloping lines and enter slope lengths.

| 1 | 2 | 3 | 4 | 5 | 6 | 7 | 8 | 9 | 10 | 11 |
|---|---|---|---|---|---|---|---|---|---|---|
| | | | | AVS | | AVS | | | WIDTHS | |
| | | SB= | 5. 40 | (5) | | | 5. 06 | (5) | 24.46(7 | top |
| CS80 | (1) | CW= | | | 14.00 | (6) | | | 14.00(6 | bottom |
| | | Rd levs | 12.08 | (3) | 12.25 | (2) | 12.43 | (3) | (19.23) | (8 mean |
| | | Xg GL's | 15.20 | (4) | | | 15.35 | (4) | | |
| | | D= | 3.12 | (4) | 3.02 | | 2.92 | (4) | | |
| | | | | | | AVD | (9) | | | |
| | | | | | | | | | | |

When the schedule is completed to the extent shown above all waste calculations for CS80 have been entered. The same procedure is then followed for CS60 and so on until all the wastes for all cross-sections have been entered. The distance between cross-sections are then entered in the vertical column 2 and the position of the zero contour is calculated all as shown on Plate EP.1. All is then organised for recording the items and dimensions on the dimension sheets. It should be remembered that in this case the finished sizes are recorded on the schedule.

Approach to the Taking of Dimensions

From an inspection of the Drawing, an initial break down of the work into the following parts or elements is considered convenient for the purpose of measurement:- (i) excavation, (ii) filling, and (iii) work to surfaces. The Example deals with the work in that order, completing the measurements of the items within each part or element before proceeding to the next. It being considered that this is a methodical sequence of measurement.

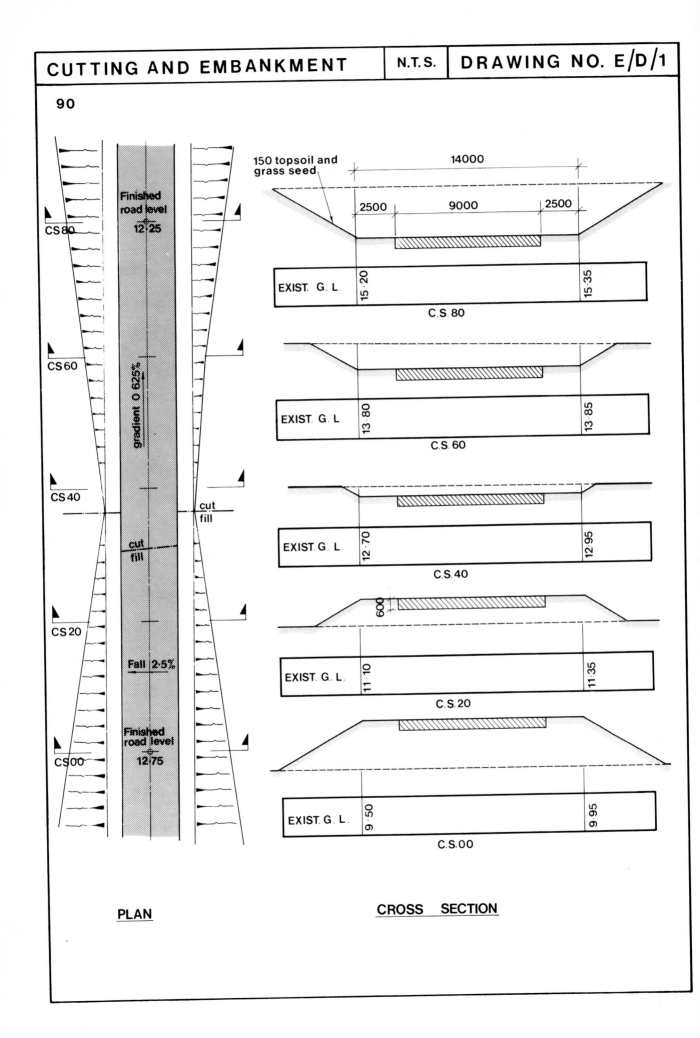

| CUTTING AND EMBANKMENT | N.T.S. | DRAWING NO. E/D/1 |

**PLAN**

**CROSS SECTION**

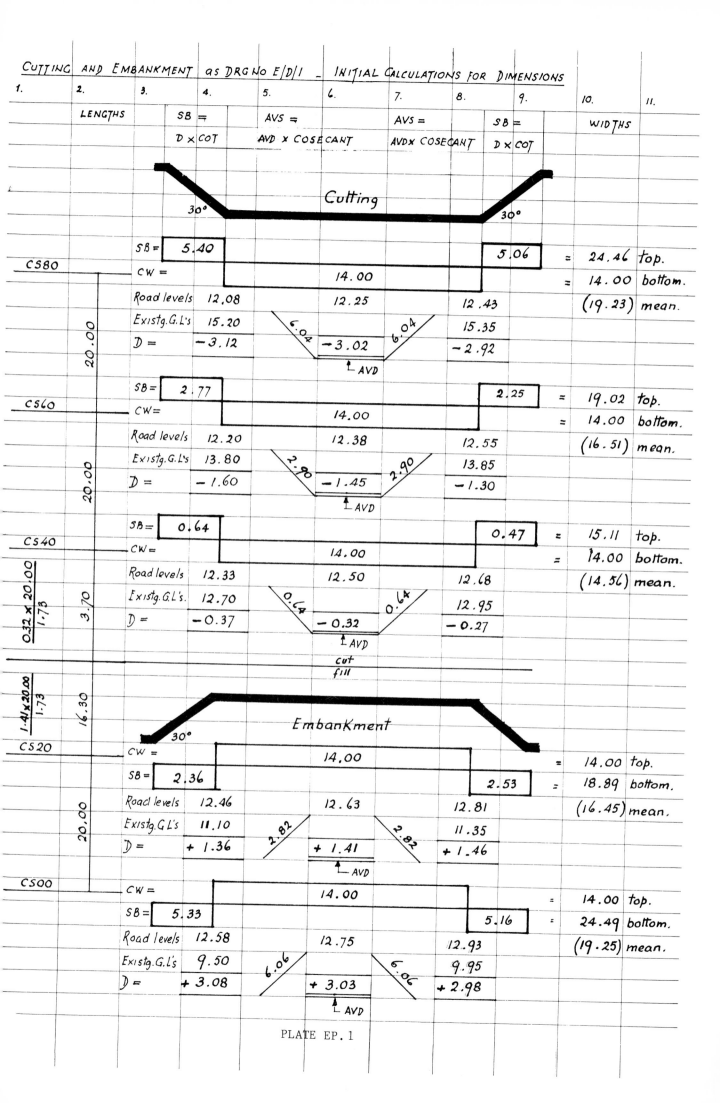

CUTTING AND EMBANKMENT as DRG No E/D/1 – INITIAL CALCULATIONS FOR DIMENSIONS

| 1. | 2. | 3. | 4. | 5. | 6. | 7. | 8. | 9. | 10. | 11. |
|---|---|---|---|---|---|---|---|---|---|---|
| | LENGTHS | | SB =<br>D × COT | | AVS =<br>AVD × COSECANT | | AVS =<br>AVD × COSECANT | SB =<br>D × COT | WIDTHS | |

**Cutting**

30°   30°

**CS80**

| SB = | 5.40 | | | | | 5.06 | = | 24.46 | top. |
| CW = | | | 14.00 | | | | = | 14.00 | bottom. |
| Road levels | 12.08 | | 12.25 | | 12.43 | | | (19.23) | mean. |
| Existg. G.L's | 15.20 | | 6.04 | 6.04 | 15.35 | |
| D = | −3.12 | | −3.02 | | −2.92 | |

AVD   20.00

**CS60**

| SB = | 2.77 | | | | | 2.25 | = | 19.02 | top. |
| CW = | | | 14.00 | | | | = | 14.00 | bottom. |
| Road levels | 12.20 | | 12.38 | | 12.55 | | | (16.51) | mean. |
| Existg. G.L's | 13.80 | | 2.90 | 2.90 | 13.85 | |
| D = | −1.60 | | −1.45 | | −1.30 | |

AVD   20.00

**CS40**

| SB = | 0.64 | | | | | 0.47 | = | 15.11 | top. |
| CW = | | | 14.00 | | | | = | 14.00 | bottom. |
| Road levels | 12.33 | | 12.50 | | 12.68 | | | (14.56) | mean. |
| Existg. G.L's | 12.70 | | 0.64 | 0.64 | 12.95 | |
| D = | −0.37 | | −0.32 | | −0.27 | |

AVD   3.70

0.32 × 20.00 / 1.73

cut
fill

1.41 × 20.00 / 1.73     16.30

**Embankment**

30°

**CS20**

| CW = | | | 14.00 | | | | = | 14.00 | top. |
| SB = | 2.36 | | | | | 2.53 | = | 18.89 | bottom. |
| Road levels | 12.46 | | 12.63 | | 12.81 | | | (16.45) | mean. |
| Existg. G.L's | 11.10 | | 2.82 | 2.82 | 11.35 | |
| D = | +1.36 | | +1.41 | | +1.46 | |

AVD   20.00

**CS00**

| CW = | | | 14.00 | | | | = | 14.00 | top. |
| SB = | 5.33 | | | | | 5.16 | = | 24.49 | bottom. |
| Road levels | 12.58 | | 12.75 | | 12.93 | | | (19.25) | mean. |
| Existg. G.L's | 9.50 | | 6.06 | 6.06 | 9.95 | |
| D = | +3.08 | | +3.03 | | +2.98 | |

AVD

PLATE EP. 1

EARTHWKS – CUTTS & EMBANKS. DRG. E/D/1

EXAMPLE EE.1

Strip topsoil

| | | |
|---|---|---|
| CS 80 | ½/ 24.46 = | 12.23 |
| CS 60 | 19.02 = | 19.02 |
| CS 40 | ½/ 15.11 = | 7.56 |
| | | 38.81 |

| | | |
|---|---|---|
| CS 40 | ½/ 15.11 = | 7.56 |
| 0 | ½/ 14.00 = | 7.00 |
| | | 14.56 |

| | | |
|---|---|---|
| 0 | ½/ 14.00 = | 7.00 |
| CS 20 | ½/ 18.89 = | 9.45 |
| | | 16.45 |

| | | |
|---|---|---|
| CS 20 | ½/ 18.89 = | 9.45 |
| CS 00 | ½/ 24.50 = | 12.25 |
| | | 21.70 |

| | | |
|---|---|---|
| 20.00 | | |
| 38.81 | | Excavn. for cutts., |
| 0.15 | 116.43 | topsoil; Excavd. Surf. |
| | | 150 mm below Orig. |
| 3.70 | | Surf.  E210 |
| 14.56 | | |
| 0.15 | 8.08 | ⌐ (CS40-0 |
| 16.30 | | Excavn. ancills. |
| 16.45 | | disposal of excavd. |
| 0.15 | 40.22 | matl. topsoil (CS0-20 |
| 20.00 | | E531 |
| 21.70 | | |
| 0.15 | 65.10 | (CS 20-00 |
| 2/ 43.70 | | 2/20.00 = 40.00 |
| 0.04 | | 3.70 |
| 0.15 | 0.52 | 43.70 |
| | 230.35 | (overlap top cuttings |

(1)

(1.)

The ordinary trapezoidal rule (half the sum of the first and last ordinates plus the sum of the intermediate ordinates multiplied by the distance between the ordinates) is used for the areas which is cubed by the depth of the excavation. It is possible to enter the dimensions in the manner shown, only when there is a constant depth of excavation.

The dimensions in the waste column are taken from the Initial Calculations Sheet and are the nett finished widths of the cutting and embankment at existing ground level. To conform precisely to the Specification requirement of providing a uniform 150 mm depth of top soil to the new slopes, the widths of the excavation of top soil should be increased by the overlap of sloping and horizontal at the top of the cutting, as shown in the following diagram.

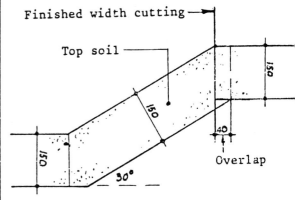

(150 x Sec 30 degrees) - 150 = 23 mm

23 x Cot 30 degrees = 40 mm overlap

The overlap, although it will tail out between CS40 and the zero contour, is taken as a constant width for the full length of both sides of the cutting and rather than complicate matters by adjusting the main widths, the small extra is given as a separate set of dimensions at (1).

Cutts.

Bulk dig

150 × 1.1547 = 173
                150
                 23

23 × 1.732 = 40

| 2/.04 = | 19.23 | 16.51 | 14.56 | 14.56 |
|---|---|---|---|---|
| | .08 | .08 | .08 | .08 |
| | 19.31 | 16.59 | 14.64 | 14.64 |

| ½/ | 20.00 | | Excavn. for cutts. Comm. |
|---|---|---|---|
| | 19.31 | | Surf. u/s. topsoil; Excavd. |
| | 3.02 | 583.16 | Surf. 450mm above Fin. |
| | | | Surf.        (CS 80 |
| | 20.00 | | E220.1 |
| | 16.59 | | |
| | 1.45 | 481.11 | + |
| ½/ | 20.00 | | (CS 60 |
| | 14.64 | | Excavn. ancills. |
| | 0.32 | 46.85 | disposal of excavd. |
| ½/ | 3.70 | | matl.    (CS 40 |
| | 14.32 | | E532       14.64 |
| | 0.32 | 8.48 | 14.00 |
| | | | 2 )28.64 |
| | | 1119.60 | 14.32 |
| | | | (CS40 - 0 |

Addn. depth road

0.32 + 0.45 = 0.77

$$\frac{0.77 \times 20.00}{1.73} = 8.90$$

          3.70
          5.20

| 2/ | 20.00 | | Excavn. for cutts., |
|---|---|---|---|
| | 9.00 | | Comm. Surf. 450 mm |
| | 0.45 | 162.00 | above Final Surf. |
| | 3.70 | | E220.2 |
| | 9.00 | | |
| | 0.45 | 14.99 | + |
| ½/ | 5.20 | | Excavn. ancills. |
| | 9.00 | | disposal of excavd. |
| | 0.45 | 10.53 | matl. |
| | | | E332 |
| | | 187.52 | |

(2)

COMMENTARY

An adjustment in waste is made to the finished width to bring it to the width of the bulk excavation. This is necessary because of the difference indicated in the diagram in the Commentary to the Dimensions in Column (1).

The depth of excavation is measured to the formation to receive the top soil of the verges at the sides of the roads. It is the same as the finished depth. The 150 mm top soil removed compensating for the 150 mm to be placed at the bottom.

The dimensions are set down, length x average width x average depth. The last two dimensions in each set being those for the areas of the cross-section. The weighting being, 1 for the first and last cross-section and 2 for the intermediate cross-sections,

It will be noted that the descriptions state an Excavated Surface or a Commencing Surface because the excavation starts or finishes at other than the Commencing Surface or Final Surface, respectively.

The description added to the standard descriptions generates a dotted on suffix number.

The last item in the adjoining column is the additional depth to accommodate the road, as shown in the following diagram. The zero contour line changes position because of the additional depth.

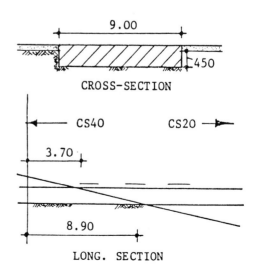

CROSS-SECTION

LONG. SECTION

## Embanks.

```
        16.37        16.45  19.25
        14.00  2/.04: 0.08   0.08
      2)30.37        16.37  19.17
        15.19
```

| | | |
|---|---|---|
| ½/ | 16.30 | |
| | 15.19 | |
| | 1.41 | 174.56 |
| ½/ | 20.00 | |
| | 16.37 | |
| | 1.41 | 230.82 |
| ½/ | 20.00 | |
| | 19.17 | |
| | 3.03 | 580.85 |
| | | **986.23** |

{ Fillg., embanks. sel. excavd. matl. oth. than topsoil or rock.
E 624     (CS 0-40

     or     (CS 20

{ Ddt. Excavn., ancills. disposal of excavd. matl.    (CS 00
E 532

## Sinkg. for road

```
        20.00
         8.90
        11.10
```

| | | |
|---|---|---|
| ½/ | 5.20 | |
| | 9.00 | |
| | 0.45 | 10.53 |
| | 11.10 | |
| | 9.00 | |
| | 0.45 | 44.96 |
| | 20.00 | |
| | 9.00 | |
| | 0.45 | 81.00 |
| | | **136.49** |

{ Ddt. Fillg., embanks. sel. excavd. matl. a.b.
E 624

     or

{ Add. Excavn ancills. disposal of excavd. matl.
E 532

(3)

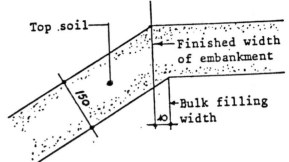

<u>Bottom of cutts to</u>
<u>receive sub-base</u>

| | | |
|---|---|---|
| | 2/20.00 = | 40.00 |
| | | 3.70 |
| | | 5.20 |
| | | 48.90 |

| 48.90 | | |
|---|---|---|
| 9.00 | 440.10 | |

Excavn. ancills, prepn.
of excavd. surfs.

E522.1

<u>Sides of sub-base</u>

| 2/ | 48.90 | |
|---|---|---|
| | 0.45 | 44.01 |

Excavn. ancills, prepn.
of excavd. surfs.
vertical.

E522.2

<u>Surfs. embanks to</u>
<u>receive sub-base</u>

| | | |
|---|---|---|
| | | 80.00 |
| | | 48.90 |
| | | 31.10 |

| 31.10 | | |
|---|---|---|
| 9.00 | 279.90 | |

Fillg. ancills., prepn.
of filld. surfs.

E722.1

<u>Sides of sub-base</u>

| 2/ | 31.10 | |
|---|---|---|
| | 0.45 | 27.99 |

Fillg. ancills., prepn
of filld. surfs.
vertical.

E722.2

The preparation of surfaces might conventionally be measured when the dimensions of the road were being taken. The actual detail of the Permanent Works in contact with the earthworks would be more apparent from the roadwork drawings and dimensions could be generated from the dimensions of the road.

Preparation of surfaces is measured to both excavated and filled surfaces. It is measured to both horizontal and vertical surfaces which are to receive Permanent Works. It is possible that at the edges, the filling would be overfilled and cut back to the vertical surface. These edges are classified as the preparation of filled surfaces and not as excavated surface as the method of preparation might suggest.

The Rules in Class E of CESMM require the preparation of vertical surfaces to be identified in item descriptions. This makes it necessary to dot on a suffix number to the Code number of both the standard description and the amplified description.

It is assumed that the requirements of the specification are merely to prepare the formation and that a surface dressing or other work to the formation is not called for. Had this not been the case, the surface dressing or other work would be given as separate items, or if preferred, could be included with the preparation item by adding the description of the work to the standard description.

(4)

Verges + tops cutts.

4/20.00 = 80.00

| | | |
|---|---|---|
| 2/ | 80.00 | |
| | 2.50 | 400.00 |
| 2/ | 43.70 | |
| | 0.04 | 3.50 |
| | | 403.50 |

{ Fillg, thickn. 150mm, excavd. topsoil  E641.1 (top bank

+

Ddt. Excavn. ancills., disposal excavd. matl., top soil  E531

Cub x 0.15 = 60.53 m3

+

Add Landscapg., grass seeding  E830.1

Slopes to cutts CS80-0

| | | | |
|---|---|---|---|
| 2/½/ | | 20.00 | |
| | | 6.04 | 120.80 |
| 2/ | | 20.00 | |
| | | 2.90 | 116.00 |
| 2/½/ | | 20.00 | |
| | | 0.64 | 12.80 |
| 2/½/ | | 3.70 | |
| | | 0.64 | 2.37 |
| | | | 251.97 |

{ Fillg. thickn 150mm., excavd. topsoil, surfs. 10 - 45 degrees to horiz.  E641.2

+

Ddt Excavn ancills., disposal excavd. matl., topsoil.  E531

Cub. x 0.15 = 37.80 m3

+

Add Landscapg. grass seedg., surfs e. 10 degrees to horiz  E830.2

(5)

COMMENTARY

The first set of dimensions in the adjoining column are for the verges at the sides of the road. The second set covers the replacement of top soil to the overlap at the top of the banks to the cutting. The dimensions for the overlap are obtained from those for excavation.

The material resulting from top soil excavation was previously measured for disposal. The Ddt items for disposal reduces the volume previously measured by the volume required to be used for filling.

The filling with topsoil is measured superficially, whilst the disposal of excavated topsoil is measured cube. Rather than write out fresh dimensions for the disposal, the instructions to cube the areas attached to the items by the depth of the topsoil is given in the description column for each item requiring to be cubed.

The slope lengths are taken from the Initial Calculation Sheet. As there are two sides to the cutting the dimensions are timesed by 2/.

The procedure for entering the dimensions for the areas of the slopes uses the slope length at the cross-sections multiplied by the length between the cross-sections with weighting of ½/ for the ends and 1/ for the intermediates and is illustrated diagramatically below.

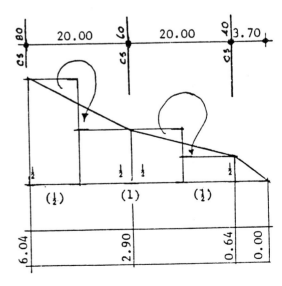

97

Slopes to embanks.

| | | |
|---|---|---|
| 2/½/ | 16.30 | |
| | 2.82 | 45.97 |
| 2/½/ | 20.00 | |
| | 2.82 | 56.40 |
| 2/½/ | 20.00 | |
| | 6.06 | 121.20 |
| | | 223.57 |

Fillg. thickn. 150 mm,
excavd. top soil surf
10 - 45 degrees to
horiz.          E 641.2

The dimensions at the Sections are entered, following the same procedure as explained in the Commentary to Column (5) of the Dimensions.

Ddt. Excavn. ancills.
disposal of excavd.
matl. topsoil. E 531
Cub × 0.15 = 33.54 m3

Topsoiling is measured according to the classification "stated thickness". Different suffix numbers are dotted on to the Code number to distinguish that on flat from that on inclined surfaces.

Add Landscapg.
grass seeding. surfs.
e. 10 degrees to horiz.
          E 830.2

NOTES: The dimensions in this Example have been squared for the purpose of preparing the Specimen Abstract, on Page 7 in Chapter 1.

In practice dimensions are lined through when they are abstracted as illustrated in the adjoining Column 6. For clarity this is not done elsewhere in the Example. The line of dashes represents the lining through of the person who checked the abstracting.

A Bill of Quantities for the work measured in the Example is given on Page 8 of Chapter 1.

(6)

# 8 In Situ Concrete, Concrete Ancillaries and Precast Concrete – CESMM Classes: F, G and H

Classes F, G and H of the CESMM cover concrete structures and general concrete work with certain exceptions.

Class F relates exclusively to in situ concrete. Formwork and reinforcement for in situ concrete, post-tensioned prestressing and sundry ancillaries for in situ concrete are included in Class G. Precast concrete units are covered by Class H. References are made subsequently to the work specifically included in and excluded from each Class. The text of this Chapter deals with each Class individually in alphabetical order of the Class references.

### *IN SITU CONCRETE - CESMM CLASS F*

No specific "Includes" are listed at the head of the Class F classification table in the CESMM. The Class covers in situ components for structures and other forms of in situ concrete construction with the exception of those specifically excluded. The "Excludes" at the head of the Class F classification table in the CESMM lists the following:-

> In situ concrete for:-
> > capping of boreholes (included in Class B)
> > diaphragm walls (included in Class C)
> > excavation ancillaries (included in Class E)
> > granolithic and other applied finishes (included in Class G)
> > drainage and pipework (included in Classes K and L)
> > piles (included in Classes P and Q)
> > roads, pavings and kerbs (included in Class R)
> > tunnel and shaft linings (included in Class T)
> > foundations for fences and gates (included in Class X)

The rules in Class F require items for the provision of concrete to be given separately from those for the placing of the concrete. Both provision and placing are measured by volume and are given in the Bill in m3.

Rules regarding deductions from the volumes of concrete and the volumes to be ignored are outlined in Table 8.01. These rules apply to both the provision and placing of concrete and are set out in Rules F/M1 and F/M2 of the CESMM. The diagram Fig. F1. shows sections of beams and illustrates features to which the terms used in Rules F/M1 and F/M2 could apply. The terms could apply to features like those illustrated but of different profile and/or in different positions.

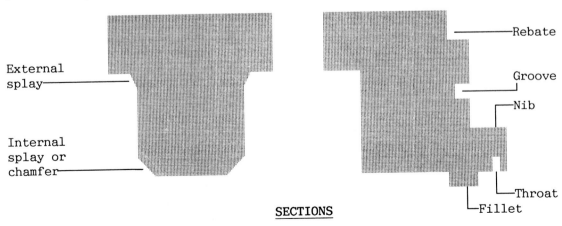

External splay

Internal splay or chamfer

Rebate

Groove

Nib

Throat

Fillet

SECTIONS

Fig. F1.  Terms used in Rules M1 and M2 of Class F of the CESMM

Table 8.01   Concrete Generally

No deduction from the volume of concrete for the volume occupied by:- (a) reinforcement and metal sections (b) prestressing components (c) cast in components each not exceeding 0.1 m3 in volume (d) rebates, grooves, throats, fillets, chamfers or internal splays each not exceeding 0.01 m2 in cross-sectional area (e) pockets and holes defined as large or small voids in accordance with Rule D3 of Class G, (f) joints or joint components between adjacent volumes of concrete (Rule F/M1)

The volume of concrete in nibs or external splays each not exceeding 0.01 m2 in cross-sectional area is not measured (Rule F/M2)

Table 8.02   Provision of Concrete

Classify in accordance with BS 5328 (Rule F/D1). State the specification of the concrete mix in accordance with BS 5328, or state a mix reference given elsewhere in the Contract (Rule F/A1)

Designed mixes are those where the mix proportions are selected by the Contractor (Rule F/D2)

Ordinary prescribed mixes are those where the mix complies with BS 5328: Section 2 (Rule F/D3)

Special prescribed mixes are those where the mix proportions are specified in the Contract (Rule F/D3)

| 1st Division | 2nd and 3rd Divisions |
|---|---|
| Provision of concrete:<br><br>Ordinary prescribed mix   m3 | Classify as BS 5328. State: Grade (as 2nd Division), type of cement and size of aggregate (as 3rd Division) and type of aggregate |
| Provision of concrete:<br><br>Designed mix                      m3 | Classify as BS 5328. State: Grade (as 2nd Division), type of cement and size of aggregate (as 3rd Division), minimum cement content (where higher than in Table 6 of the BS), and the type of aggregate |
| Provision of concrete:<br><br>Special prescribed mix   m3 | State the mix proportions in kg. of each constituent. State also the type of cement and size of aggregate (as 3rd Division), the minimum cement content (where higher than in Table 6 of the BS), and the type of aggregate |

COMMENTARY

Provision of Concrete (Refer to Table 8.02)

The details which need to be stated or identified in an item description for the provision of concrete are the same as the requirements to be specified as provided in BS 5328. An outline of the details to be stated in the item descriptions are given in Table 8.02. The grade of concrete is the same as the "characteristic compressive strength" in BS 5328, i.e. crushing strength in N/mm2 at 28 days.

In practice, rather than list all the details required by the CESMM in the items, it will usually be found convenient to describe the various mixes or to refer to and give details of them as BS 5328 in the Specification and to tabulate them and allocate each particular mix a reference. The item descriptions will then need only to quote the Specification reference. For example - Provision of concrete, Type D20, as Specification clause "X"- m3". The code number for this item would use the CESMM numbers appropriate to the type of concrete, its grade and aggregate size given in the Specification.

Table 8.03  Placing of Concrete

Generally  - The location of concrete members in the Works may be stated  in item  description  for  placing concrete where  special characteristics  may affect  the method and rate of placing concrete (NOTE at foot of Page 39  of CESMM)

State  where  concrete  (other than blinding) is expressly  required  to  be placed against an excavated surface (Rule F/A2)

1st Division

Mass

Reinforced

Prestressed   Includes prestressed which is also reinforced (Rule F/D4)

| 2nd Division | | 3rd Division |
|---|---|---|
| Blinding      m3 | | State 3rd Division thickness range<br><br>Use minimum thickness for classif- ication of blinding (Rule F/D5) |
| Bases, foot- ings, pile caps and ground slabs m3 | Measure beams attached to ground slabs as part of slab, except where the beams are expressly required to be cast separately (Rule F/M4) | State 3rd Division thickness range<br><br>Thickness for classification of ground slabs shall exclude addit- ional thickness of integral beams (Rule F/D6) |
| Suspended     m3 slabs | Measure beams attached to suspended slabs as part of slab, except where the beams are expressly required to be cast separately (Rule F/M4)<br><br>Class suspended slabs less than one metre wide as beams (Rule F/D7) | State 3rd Division thickness range<br><br>Thickness for classification of suspended slabs shall exclude additional thickness of integral beams and other projections (Rule F/D6) |
| Walls         m3 | Measure columns and piers attached to walls as part of wall, except where the columns and piers are expressly required to be cast separately (Rule F/M3)<br><br>Class walls less than one metre wide as columns (Rule F/D7) | State 3rd Division thickness range<br><br>Thickness for classification of walls shall exclude additional thickness of integral columns, piers and other projections (Rule F/D6) |

Table 8.03  Placing of Concrete (cont.

| 2nd Division | | | 3rd Division |
|---|---|---|---|
| Columns and piers | m3 | Not applicable to columns and piers attached to walls, except those expressly required to be cast separately from walls (Rule F/M3). See Walls | State 3rd Division cross-sectional area range |
| Beams | m3 | Not applicable to beams attached to slabs, except those expressly required to be cast separately from slabs (Rule F/M4) | State 3rd Division cross-sectional area range for other than special beam sections.  Describe special beam sections as following paragraph:- |
| Casings to metal sections | m3 | Not applicable to casing of metal sections integral with walls and slabs except those expressly required to be cast separately (Rule F/M3 and F/M4).  See Walls and Slabs. | Special beam sections - Beams are classed as special beam sections where their cross-section profiles are rectangular (or approximately) over less than four fifths of their length or where of box or other composite section (Rule F/D8). State cross-sectional dimensions or state type or mark number for which dimensions are given on a Drawing (Rule F/A3) |
| Other concrete forms | m3 | | State (a) principal dimensions of components or (b) type or mark number where principal dimensions are given on the Drawings, or (c) state location where principal dimensions are given on the Drawings (Rule F/A4) |

COMMENTARY

Placing of Concrete (Refer to Table 8.03)

Item descriptions for placing concrete state whether the concrete is mass concrete, reinforced concrete or prestressed concrete. Prestressed concrete which is also reinforced is classed as prestressed.

The descriptions will also state the element in which the concrete is placed in accordance with the Second Division descriptive features and, except for the classifications "special beam sections" and "other concrete forms", will give the dimension ranges of the components as provided in the Third Division of the classification table, Class F of the CESMM. For the details given at Third Division level of the classifications "special beam sections" and "other concrete forms", see Table 8.03.

It is a matter of good practice to state in the item descriptions the location of concrete components where special characteristics may affect the method and rate of placing, as noted at the foot of Page 39 of the CESMM.

COMMENTARY

Placing of Concrete (cont.

*Blinding*

The thickness used for the classification of blinding is the minimum thickness. See Rule F/D5 of the CESMM. The Rule should be implemented in relation to blinding in a particular location and not to blinding as a whole. For example, if say 75 mm thick blinding occurs in one location and say 200 mm thick in another, each would be itemised and given according to its particular thickness range. Interconnected blinding of varying thicknesses would be classified according to the minimum thickness.

*Bases, Footings, Pile Caps and Ground Slabs*

The placing of concrete in the several elements bases, footings, pile caps and ground slabs are grouped in a single descriptive feature. The volume of all three elements of the same thickness range are added together in one item, unless further itemisation is considered advisable in accordance with Note at the foot of Page 39 of the CESMM.

Beams integral with ground slabs are measured as part of the slab unless it is expressly required that the beams are to be cast separately.

*Suspended Slabs*

In the absence of an express requirement that the beams are to be cast separately, the volume measured for the placing of concrete in a suspended slab will include the volume of beams integral with the slab. It will also include the volume of any other projections integral with the slab which are considered to involve complexity of placing no greater than that of the slab. Projections considered to involve complexity of placing greater than that of the slab would be appropriately classified and be given separately. For notes on classification thickness and slabs less than one metre in width see those against the feature in Table 8.03.

*Walls*

The volume measured for the placing of concrete walls will include the volume of any columns and piers integral with the wall unless it is expressly required that the columns and piers are cast separately. The thickness classification will be that of the wall excluding the thickness of any attached columns or piers. Walls less than one metre long are classed as columns. Item descriptions for walls of special profile will usually include a drawing reference.

*Columns and Piers*

The classification "columns and piers" is appropriate for independent members. It is not applicable to columns and piers attached to walls unless they are expressly required to be cast separately from the walls.

Column caps may be classed as columns or as "other concrete forms". In either case they are identified as column caps in the item descriptions. Alternatively, column caps may be measured as part of the slab to which they are attached.

COMMENTARY

Placing of Concrete (cont.

### *Beams*

The classification "beams" does not apply to beams integral with slabs, unless they are expressly required to be cast separately from the slabs.

The classification "special beam section" is defined in Rule F/D8 of the CESMM. See the details given against the classification under 3rd Division in Table 8.03.

### *Casing to Metal Sections*

The sections cased are identified in the item descriptions, i.e. stanchions, beams, grillages, etc. The classification does not apply to the casing of metal sections which is integral with walls or slabs, unless the casings are expressly required to be cast separately from the walls or slabs.

### *Other Concrete Forms*

Particular details are given in the item descriptions for components classified as "other concrete forms". These are set out in Rule F/A4 of the CESMM. See the details given against the classification under 3rd Division in Table 8.03.

The classification is appropriate for use where (i) a component would not be correctly described by a standard descriptive feature, or where (ii) a combination of work items form a member which it would be more practical to treat as composite.

### *Tapering and Sloping Members*

Tapering members whose thickness or cross-sectional area extends into more than one thickness or cross-sectional area range are divided into separate items for each standard thickness or cross-sectional area range, respectively. Additional description may be given stating members are tapered or sloping.

Where the taper or slope is thought to complicate the placing of the concrete, members may be treated as special, with descriptions giving actual thickness and cross-sectional areas in place of the standard ranges. The digit 9 would then be used in the appropriate position in the Code number to indicate the non-standard features.

Where there is doubt as to whether a sloping member should be classed a beam or a column, the classification "other concrete forms" is appropriate, or it can be classed as either a column or a beam according to judgement. In the latter case it may be considered helpful to give the location of the members or state a drawing reference.

### *CONCRETE ANCILLARIES - CESMM CLASS G*

Concrete ancillaries in Class G covers formwork and reinforcement for in situ concrete, to the extent that they are not listed in the "Excludes" at the head of the classification table. The Class includes joints in in situ concrete, post tensioned prestressing and accessories for in situ concrete. It excludes post tensioned prestressing which is included in Class H. Reference to work included in Class G is made in the "Excludes" at the head of the classification tables in Classes F, H, M, N, O, S, T and W.

Table 8.04   Formwork

---

**1st Division**

---

Formwork:

  rough finish

  fair finish

  other stated
  finish

  stated
  surface
  features

Formwork is deemed to be to plane areas exceeding 1.22 m wide unless otherwise stated (Rule G/D2)

Measure for all final surfaces of in situ concrete requiring support during casting, unless otherwise stated in the CESMM (Rule G/M1)

Measure to upper surfaces exceeding 15 degrees to the horizontal and to other upper surfaces where expressly required (Rule G/M3) State where formwork is to upper surfaces except where not exceeding 10 degrees to the vertical (Rule G/A2)

Formwork is not measured to the following concrete surfaces:-

    (a)   edges of blinding not exceeding 0.2 m wide or deep

    (b)   joints and associated rebates and grooves

    (c)   temporary surfaces formed at Contractor's discretion

    (d)   surfaces expressly required to be cast against an excavated surface

    (e)   surfaces less than 45 degrees to the horizontal where the concrete is cast against an excavated surface (Rule G/M2)

State where formwork is to the surfaces of blinding (Rule G/A3)

State where formwork is to be left in   (Rule G/A1)

---

| 2nd Division | | 3rd Division | |
|---|---|---|---|
| Plane horizontal | 85 - 90 degrees to the vertical (Rule G/D1) | State width ranges: | |
| Plane sloping | 10 - 85 degrees to the vertical (Rule G/D1) | not exceed- | |
| Plane battered | 0 - 10 degrees to the vertical (Rule G/D1) | ing 0.1 m | m |
| Plane vertical | 0 degrees to the vertical (Rule G/D1) | 0.1 - 0.2 m | m |
| Curved to one radius in one plane | State radius (Rule G/A4a) | 0.2 - 0.4 m | m2 |
| | | 0.4 - 1.22 m | m2 |
| | | exceeding 1.22 m | m2 |
| Other curved to stated radii         m2 | One radius in two planes (spherical). state radius (Rule G/A4b)  Varying radius (conical) state maximum and minimum radii (Rule G/A4c) | | |

Table 8.04   Formwork (cont.

| 1st Division | 2nd Division | 3rd Division |
|---|---|---|
| Formwork<br><br>rough finish<br><br>fair finish<br><br>other stated finish<br><br>stated surface finish | For voids      nr<br><br>No deduction from the area of other formwork obscured by forms for "large" or "small" voids and for projections and intrusions and inserts (Rule G/M6) | State whether to large or small voids:<br><br>Large = 0.1 - 0.5 m2 area, or where circular 0.35 - 0.7 m diameter (Rule G/D3)<br><br>Small = not exceeding 0.1 m2 area, or where circular not exceeding 0.35 m diameter (Rule G/D3)<br><br>Measure depth to the adjacent surface of concrete (Rule G/D3) Classify as 3rd Division depth ranges. State actual depth where exceeding 2 m<br><br>Measure in detail when larger than "large voids" (Rule G/M4) |
| | For concrete components of constant cross-section    m<br><br>This classification may be used to measure formwork by length in one item instead of by area in items for the separate surfaces, where formwork is for components of constant cross-section (See Note at foot of Page 41 of CESMM) | Beams     State the principal cross-section dimen-<br>Columns   sions of the component and its mark<br>Walls     number, location or other unique ident-<br>Other     ifying feature<br>members  (Rule G/A5)<br>(Describe<br>members)  State when to curved components and radii (Rule G/A6) |
| | The details to be stated in item descriptions for "Projections" and "Intrusions" include those set out in G/A5 (see penultimate panel in 3rd Division above) except that the cross-sectional dimensions need not be stated (Rule G/A5) | Projections Classify nibs and exter-<br>           nal splays not exceeding<br>Intrusions 0.01 m2 cross-sectional<br>           area as "Projections"<br>State if   (Rule G/D4) Classify<br>"project-  rebates, grooves, in-<br>ions"or   ternal splays, throats,<br>"intrus-   fillets and chamfers not<br>ions" are  exceeding 0.01 m2 as<br>curved    "Instrusions" (Rule<br>and state  G/D5)<br>radii<br>(Rule     Measure "Projections"<br>G/D4)    and "Intrusions" in detail when they exceed 0.01 m2 cross-sectional area (Rule G/M5) |

Fig. F2. Plane formwork, classifications and angles of inclination in accordance with Rule G/D1 of the CESMM.

COMMENTARY

## Formwork (refer to Table 8.04)

Formwork is measured to the surfaces stated in Rule G/M1 of the CESMM. See the 1st Division panel of Table 8.04. It is not measured to temporary surfaces formed at the discretion of the Contractor. It is not measured to the surfaces of blinding not exceeding 0.2 m wide or deep, or to the remaining surfaces as noted in the 1st Division panel of Table 8.04.

Formwork to upper surfaces of concrete is measured where they are inclined at an angle exceeding 15 degrees to the horizontal and to other upper surfaces where formwork is expressly required. Item descriptions state it is to upper surfaces except where the surfaces are inclined at an angle not exceeding 10 degrees to the vertical.

Unless it is expressly required that the concrete is to be cast against the excavated surface, formwork is measured to the surfaces of concrete (except blinding concrete) against excavated surfaces, other than where it is against surfaces inclined at an angle less than 45 degrees to the horizontal.

The CESMM requires that item descriptions shall state where formwork is to blinding concrete. It also requires that it shall be stated in the item descriptions where it is required that formwork is left in.

All formwork is classified at 1st Division level according to the finish or features it is to produce on the surface of the concrete. Commentary follows which is particular to the further levels of classification.

### Formwork to Plane Surfaces

Item descriptions for formwork to the plane surfaces of concrete describe the formwork as horizontal, sloping, battered or vertical, each indicating defined angles of inclination as noted in Table 8.04. See also Fig. F2. Descriptions state also the appropriate Third Division width range for formwork not exceeding 1.22 m wide. Quantities for formwork in the ranges not exceeding 0.2 m wide are given in linear metres. Those for formwork in the ranges exceeding 0.2 m wide are given in m2. It is not necessary to state the width when it exceeds 1.22 m wide. Width is taken as the least of the two dimensions of the formwork.

### Curved Formwork

"Formwork curved to one radius in one plane" is described as quoted. Separate items are given for each different radius and the radius is stated in item descriptions. Width ranges and units of measurement are set out in Table 8.04.

Formwork for curved surfaces other than that to one radius in one plane is classed as "other curved". Item descriptions state the shape of such surfaces and state the radius or radii, as the case may be, in accordance with Rule G/A4 of the CESMM. Separate items are given for each different shape. Formwork of this classification is measured by area and is given in m2, irrespective of width. See last panel of Table 8.04 on Page 104.

Where formwork is for curved surfaces of a component which is of constant cross-section, it is considered preferable to measure it by length in accordance with the alternative method given in the Note at the foot of Page 41 of the CESMM, rather than to measure the surfaces as outlined above. See note against "For concrete components of constant cross-section" in Table 8.04. See also subsequent Commentary.

COMMENTARY

Formwork (cont.

*Formwork for Voids*

The classification "formwork for voids" is applicable to the formwork required to form holes, pockets and the like within the limits of area or diameter stated in Rule G/D3 of the CESMM. Voids are described as either large or small voids as defined in Rule G/D3 of the CESMM. The formwork for them is given as numbered items and no deduction is made from other formwork for the area obscured by the forms for large and small voids. Descriptions will usually state the types of voids, e.g. pockets, sumps, etc. Separate items are given for each type. Further itemisation with particular identifying descriptions may be given, where in the interest of clarity or of distinguishing meaningful cost differences it is considered necessary to do so. Measurement conventions and other details are given against the descriptive feature in Table 8.04. Formwork for voids larger than those classed as large voids in Rule G/D3 is measured in detail in accordance with the rules for formwork generally, as provided in Rule G/M4 of the CESMM.

*Formwork for Concrete Components of Constant Cross-Section*

The classification "formwork for concrete components of constant cross-section" may be used instead of the other formwork classifications where the formwork for a component or part of a component is of constant girth and profile when viewed in cross-section. See Note at foot of Page 41 of the CESMM. The alternative it provides is instead of measuring items for the formwork for each of the surfaces of the component the combined surfaces may be given as one item measured by length subject to Rule G/A5 of the CESMM. The Rule requires particular information to be included in the item description. See notes against the classification in Table 8.04.

Items of formwork classified and given in accordance with the alternative, convey more clearly the nature of the formwork and the extent of repetition than would be apparent from a series of items measured and given in accordance with other formwork classifications. In practice when taking measurements of formwork for concrete components of constant cross-section for the preparation of the Bill, awareness of the advantages of measuring the formwork by length in accordance with the alternative leads to it being used wherever practical as the preferred method of measurement.

It is of advantage to use the alternative and measure by length as one item the formwork for rebates, grooves and fillets, where otherwise those exceeding 0.01 m2 cross-sectional area, would be measured, in accordance with Rule G/M5 of the CESMM as a series of formwork items to the several surfaces. The alternative has broad application and may be used not only for formwork for components such as columns, beams and the like, but also for formwork for walls and that for features of all kinds, provided the formwork is of constant girth and profile.

Reinforcement (Refer to Table 8.05)

Item descriptions for reinforcement state the materials to be used and where there are alternative qualities, their quality. For steel reinforcement to BS, it is sufficient to state the BS reference of the reinforcement.

In the normal course, items in accordance with the CESMM for reinforcement for a structure given in the particular Part of the Bill appropriate to the structure, is considered sufficient to identify the reinforcement. This is not to say that situations do not arise where it is reasonable to provide additional itemisation to distinguish cost differences.

Table 8.05   Reinforcement

Generally - Mass of steel reinforcement shall be taken as 0.785 kg/m per 100 mm2 of cross-section (7.85 t/m3). Mass of other reinforcing material shall be specified (Rule G/M7). Deemed to include supporting reinforcement other than that supporting top reinforcement (Rule G/C1)

| 1st Division | | Reinforcement | | |
|---|---|---|---|---|
| 2nd Division | | | | 3rd Division |
| Mild steel bars to BS 4449 | t | State the cross-sectional size of bar defined in BS 4449 and BS 4461 as the nominal size (Rule G/D6) | | Classify according to nominal size of bars. Group together in one item bars of 32 mm or greater |
| High yield steel bars to BS 4449 or BS 4461 | t | State lengths to next higher multiple of 3 m where bars exceed 12 m in length before bending (Rule G/A7) | | |
| Stainless steel bars of stated quality | t | Include mass of steel supports to top reinforcement (Rule G/M8) | | |
| Reinforcing bars of other stated material | t | | | |
| Special joints | nr | State type of joint and type and size of bar (Rule G/A8) Applicable to welded, swaged or screwed joints in bars (Rule G/D7) | | |
| High yield steel fabric to BS 4483 | m2 | State type in accordance with BS 4483 (Rule G/A9) | Measure nett with no allowance for laps (Rule G/M9) | Classify according to range in kg/m2 |
| Fabric of other stated material | m2 | State the material, sizes and its nominal mass per m2 (Rule G/A10) | | State actual mass per m2 where it exceeds 8 kg/m2 and where only one mass per m2 in one item |

Reinforcement (cont.

For example helical reinforcement and reinforcement to special profile to suit the shape of a component would be so described and be given separately from reinforcement which involved only normal bending and hooking.

*Bar Reinforcement*

Bar reinforcement is measured by mass. Quantities give the calculated mass of the bars and that of any metal supports to top reinforcement. They exclude the mass of other supporting and tying reinforcement. For calculating mass, steel is taken as 7.85 t/m3, that of other reinforcement is taken as stated in the Contract.

Separate items are given for each different size of bar less than 32 mm. Bars of 32 mm or greater are grouped in one item. Item descriptions for bars exceeding 12 m long, before bending, state the length of the next higher multiple of 3 m. The quantities of bars are given in tonnes, usually rounded off to the nearest tonne. Where it is considered unsatisfactory to

COMMENTARY

Reinforcement (cont.

*Bar Reinforcement (cont.*

unsatisfactory to round off quantities, fractional quantities may be used. See Paragraph 5.18 of the CESMM.

Special joints such as welded, swaged or screwed joints in reinforcing bars are given as numbered items stating the type of joint and the nominal size of the bar.

*Fabric Reinforcement*

Fabric reinforcement is measured by area in m2. The area of additional fabric in laps is not measured. The CESMM gives no direction as to the size of openings it is appropriate to deduct. Applying a strict interpretation, the area given is the area of the fabric, excluding the additional area of laps, left in the finished work. A practical application is to make no deduction for an opening in the fabric which is of an area not greater than that of a large void as defined in Rule G/D3 of the CESMM. In the absence of a note in Preamble indicating the adoption of the convention mentioned in the preceding sentence, the Contractor must presume that fabric has been measured in strict accord with the provision of the CESMM.

Rule G/A9 of the CESMM requires that item descriptions for high yield steel fabric to BS 4483 state the type number accorded the particular fabric in the BS. Those for other fabric reinforcement are required to state material, sizes and nominal mass per square metre. Compliance with the Rule creates items which state or reflect actual mass per square metre in place of a Third Division range.

| *Specimen Item Descriptions for Reinforcement* | Number | Item description | Unit |
|---|---|---|---|
| The specimen descriptions envisage all reinforcement to be steel to BS. The sub-headings would state materials and quality if it was otherwise. | | CONCRETE ANCILLARIES. Reinforcement. Mild steel bars, BS 4449, grade 250. | |
| Because of its special nature, helical reinforcement is located and given separately from that requiring only the normal bending and hooking. | G512.1 | Diameter 8 mm. | t |
| | G512.2 | Diameter 8 mm; helical binding, columns E6 - E34. | t |
| Bars over 12 m long before bending, are given to the next higher multiple of 3 m. The bars in items Code G526.1 and 2 are 12 - 15 and 15 - 18 metres long, respectively. | | High yield steel bars, BS 4449, grade 460/425. | t |
| | G525 | Diameter 16 mm. | t |
| | G526.1 | Diameter 20 mm, length 15 m. | t |
| Each different type of fabric reinforcement of a particular nominal mass is given as a separate item in consequence of Rule G/A9 of the CESMM. See Table 8.05 | G526.2 | Diameter 20 mm, length 18 m. | t |
| | | High yield steel fabric, BS 4483. | |
| | G563 | Reference No. A252, nominal mass 3.95 kg/m2. | m2 |

Table 8.06   Joints

**1st Division**

Joints   Measure only at locations where joints are expressly required (Rule G/M10)

Deemed to include formwork (Rule G/C3)

| 2nd Division | | | 3rd Division | |
|---|---|---|---|---|
| Open surface | | "Formed surface" applies to joints requiring temporary support of the whole surface during casting. Other joints are classed as "Open surface" (Rule G/D8) | State width or depth range as 3rd Division features. | |
|   plain | m2 | | | |
|   with filler | m2 | | Measure width or depth between outer surfaces of concrete with no addition or deduction for grooves, rebates, etc. (Rule G/M11) | |
| Formed surface | | Deemed to include intermediate surface treatment where expressly required (Rule G/C2) | | |
|   plain | m2 | | | |
|   with filler | m2 | State dimensions and nature of components (Rule G/A11) | Widths or depths are average widths or depths (Rule G/D9) | |
| Plastic or rubber water-stops | m | Deemed to include cutting and joining and special fittings at angles and junctions (Rule G/C4) | Classify as 3rd Division width ranges | State dimensions and nature of components (Rule G/A11) |
| Metal water-stops | m | Measure length along centre line (Rule G/M11) | | |
| Sealed rebates or grooves | m | | | |
| Dowels | nr | | Plain or greased | |
| | | | Sleeved or capped | |

COMMENTARY

Joints (refer to Table 8.06)

The categories of items given for joints are those which relate to the joints, those which relate to any components required for the joints and any sealed grooves or rebates to the surface of the joints.

Items for joints are measured at locations where joints are expressly required with or without formwork and with or without filler material. Joints are measured by area in m2 and items are deemed to include formwork to the joints where it is required. The conventions used for measuring width for the purpose of calculating area and for classification purposes are given in Rule G/M11 of the CESMM. The classifications "open surface joints" and "formed surface joints" are defined in Rule G/D8 of the CESMM. Any filler material required to the joints is included in the description of the joints. The dimensions and the nature of the filler is stated in the descriptions. See Table 8.06 for notes on the CESMM Rules mentioned in this paragraph.

COMMENTARY

Joints (cont.

    Components other than filler are measured separately from the joints and include waterstops and dowels incorporated in joints and sealed rebates or grooves where required to the surface of the joints. In all cases the dimensions and nature of components are stated in item descriptions. Items for waterstops are deemed to include cutting, and joining and special fittings at angles and junctions. Waterstops and sealed rebates and grooves are measured in linear metres. Dowels are enumerated.

    Example FE.1., included subsequently in this Chapter, provides a measured example. In the Example the application of the provisions of the CESMM to the measurement of joints is illustrated.

---

Table 8.07  Post-tensioned Prestressing

| 1st Division | Post-tensioned prestressing | Deemed to include ducts, grouting and other components and tasks ancillary to prestressing (Rule G/C5) | |
|---|---|---|---|
| **2nd Division** | | | **3rd Division** |
| Horizontal internal tendons in in situ concrete | nr | Measure by number of tendons (Rule G/M12) | Measure lengths for classification as developed lengths of tendon between outer faces of anchorages (Rule G/D11) |
| Inclined or vertical internal tendons in in situ concrete | nr | Identify the concrete component to be stressed (Rule G/A12) | |
| Horizontal internal tendons in precast concrete | nr | State the composition of tendon and particulars of anchorage (Rule G/A12) | Classify according to appropriate length range as 3rd Division features. |
| Inclined or vertical internal tendons in precast concrete | nr | Classify profiled tendons in horizontal components as "horizontal tendons" (Rule G/D10) | |
| External jacking operations | nr | Measure by number of external jacking operations (Rule G/M12)  Identify the concrete component to be stressed (Rule G/A12) | |

---

COMMENTARY

Post-tensioned prestressing (Refer to Table 8.07)

Prestressing is measured by numbering the tendons, where tendons are used, and by numbering the externaljacking points where stress is induced by jacking only. Elaborate descriptions are not given. Item descriptions make reference to the Specification where the prestressing system and the stressing components are described and to the Drawings showing the concrete components and other details.

    An example follows of a Bill description for the post-tensioned prestressing of in situ concrete beams using tendons.

COMMENTARY

Post-tensioned Prestressing (cont.

*Specimen Item Descriptions for Post-tensioned Prestressing*

| | Number | Item descriptions | Unit |
|---|---|---|---|
| The item description uses the 1st and 2nd Division standard features and gives:- | | CONCRETE ANCILLARIES. | |
| the developed length of the tendons (Rule G/D11) expressed within a 3rd Division range | | Post-tensioned prestressing, as Specification clauses 18.1 to 18.10. | |
| the composition of the tendons (Rule G/A12) | G717 | Horizontal internal tendons in in situ concrete, length 25 - 30 m; of 7/12 mm diameter strands with anchorages as Specification clause 18.05; main beams M1 to M5 Drawing No 197/22. | |
| particulars of anchorages by specification reference (Rule G/A12) | | | |
| identity of components to be stressed (Rule G/A12) | | | nr |

Table 8.08  Concrete Accessories

1st Division  Concrete accessories

| 2nd Division | | 3rd Division |
|---|---|---|
| Finishing of top surfaces m2 | Measure only when separate finishing treatment required (Rule G/M13) | State surface finish as 3rd Division features |
| Finishing of formed surfaces         m2 | No deductions for openings not exceeding 0.5 m2 in area (Rule G/M14)  Items for applied finish are deemed to include, materials, surface treatment, joints and formwork (Rule G/C6) | State materials, thickness and surface treatment of applied finishing (Rule G/A13) |
| Inserts                Deemed to include the supply of inserts unless otherwise stated (Rule G/C7) | All components cast or grouted into in situ concrete, except reinforcement, structural metalwork, prestressing and jointing material, are classed as inserts (Rule G/D12)  Identify component and state its principal dimensions (Rule G/A14)  Identify inserts which:- (a) project from one surface of concrete (b) project from two surfaces of concrete (c) are within the volume of the concrete (Rule G/A15)  State where expressly required to be grouted into preformed openings and measure formwork to form openings (Rule G/M15). State grout materials and sizes of preformed opening (Rule G/A16) | Linear inserts   m  Other inserts   nr  Make no deduction from general areas of formwork for inserts. See (Rule G/M6) |
| Grouting under plates nr | State material (Rule G/A17) | State area range as 3rd Division features |

COMMENTARY

Concrete Accessories (Refer to Table 8.08)

*Finishing of Surfaces, Inserts and Grouting under Plates*

Items for finishing surfaces of concrete are measured where a worked finish (as opposed to that produced by casting the concrete against formwork designed to give the desired finish) or where an applied finish is required. Finishing top surfaces is given separately from that to formed surfaces. See Table 8.08 for details.

For work classed as "inserts" and "grouting beneath plates" see Table 8.08.

| *Specimen Item Descriptions for Finishing of Surfaces and Inserts* | Number | Item description | Unit |
|---|---|---|---|
| Item descriptions for applied finishing state the material and the thickness. See Item Code G814. | | CONCRETE ANCILLARIES.<br><br>Concrete Accessories.<br><br>Finishing of top surfaces. | |
| Item descriptions for inserts are deemed to include the supply of the inserts unless otherwise stated. Item Code G382.1 is an example. | G814 | Granolithic finish, thickness 50 mm; as Specification clause 16.07 including surface hardener as Specification clause 16.11, paved areas. | m2 |
| Item code G832.2 includes fixing and casting in but excludes the supply of the insert. | | Finishing of formed surfaces. | |
| Item Code G382.3 includes grouting in to preformed holes but excludes the supply and fixing of the inserts. In addition an item would be measured for formwork for the preformed hole. | G821 | Aggregate exposure using retarder; as Specification clause 16.17, surfaces of plinths, flood walls as Drawing 107/17. | m2 |
| | | Inserts. | |
| Inserts which need to be described with additional description as Rules G/M15 and G/A15 and 16 are shown in the diagram below | 832.1 | P.v.c.pipes, diameter 75 mm, through reinforced concrete walls, thickness 300 mm; weep holes. | nr |
| | | Inserts excluding the supply of the inserts | |
| —Any type in preformed openings | G832.2 | Set of four anchor bolts, projecting above top surface of concrete including supplying and fixing sleeves and grouting sleeves in cement mortar(1:2); as Drawing No. 107/33. | nr |
| —Within volume<br><br>←——Projecting two surfaces<br><br>←—Projecting one surface | | Inserts excluding the supply and fixing of the inserts. | |
| | G832.3 | Pipes, nominal bore 200 mm, and grouting in with cement mortar (1:2) to 250 mm diameter preformed opening in reinforced concrete suspended slabs, thickness 300 mm, projecting from both sides. | nr |

SECTION

Fig. G1. Inserts

Class H covers the manufacture, erection, joining and fixing of precast concrete units. The majority of the descriptive features in the Class relate to structural units. Among the specific exclusions from the Class are post-tensioned prestressing, pipework, manholes, piles, paving units, kerbs, traffic sign supports, tunnel linings, blockwork and fencing of precast concrete. This excluded work is measured as provided in other Classes of the CESMM. For work included in the Class and for exclusions from the Class refer to the "Includes" and "Excludes" at the head of the Class H classification table in the CESMM. Cross references are also made to work included in Class H in the "Excludes" at the head of the classification tables in CESMM Classes G, M, N and W.

Table 8.09 Precast Concrete

Generally - State specification of concrete (Rule H/A1). State position in the Works of units (Rule H/A1)  Units deemed to include reinforcement, formwork, joints and finishes (Rule H/C1)  Give particulars of tendons and prestressing for prestressed units (Rule H/A3)

Components cast in other than their final position are generally classed as precast (Rule H/D2). Class as in-situ concrete the site precasting of units where for reasons other than to obtain multiple use of formwork and where work is characteristic of in situ but involves movement into final position after casting and give movement operations as items in Temporary Works Class A (Rule H/D3)

| 1st Division - Units with different dimensions shall be given different mark or type numbers (Rule H/A2) | | | 2nd Division | 3rd Division |
|---|---|---|---|---|
| Beams | nr | State cross-section type and principal dimensions (Rule H/A4) | State length range as 2nd Division feature | State mass range of each unit as 3rd Division features. State actual mass where over 20 t (Rule H/D1) |
| Prestressed pre-tensioned beams | nr | | | |
| Prestressed post-tensioned beams | nr | State mark or type number (Rule H/A2) | | |
| Columns | nr | | | |
| Slabs | nr | State average thickness (Rule H/A5)  State mark or type number (Rule H/A2) | State area range as 2nd Division features | |
| Segmental units | nr | State cross-section type and principal dimensions (Rule H/A4) State mark or type number (Rule H/A2) | | |
| Units for subways, culverts and ducts | m | State cross-section type and principal dimensions (Rule H/A4) State mark or type number (Rule H/A2)  State mass per m (Rule H/A6) | The length measured shall be the total length of identical units (Rule H/M1) | |

Table 8.09 Precast Concrete (cont.

| 1st Division | | 2nd Division | 3rd Division |
|---|---|---|---|
| Copings, sills and wier blocks        m<br><br>The length measured shall be the total length of identical units (Rule H/M1) | State cross-section type and principal dimensions (Rule H/A4)<br><br>State mark or type number (Rule H/A2)<br><br>State mass per m (Rule H/A6) | State cross-sectional area range as 2nd Division features | |

COMMENTARY

Precast Concrete (Refer to Table 8.09)

Itemisation  in accordance with Class H of the CESMM provides items for each different  size  of each different type of precast concrete unit. The  units included  in  any one item must be identical. The quantities for  units  for subways,  culverts  and  ducts and also those for copings,  sills  and  wier blocks  are given in linear metres. Those for other classifications give the number of units. Table 8.09 sets out the First Division descriptive features and  notes the units of measurement and the details required to be stated in item descriptions.

*Specimen Item Descriptions for Precast Concrete Beams*

The specimen item descriptions for beams are given to comply with Class H of CESMM.  They state:-

the specification of the concrete,

the position in the Works of each unit,

the identity of the units,

cross-sectional type,

principal cross-sectional dimensions.

length,

mass of each unit,  and

particulars of prestressing and tendons (for prestressed units)

| Number | Item Description | Unit |
|---|---|---|
| | PRECAST CONCRETE.<br><br>Ordinary prescribed mix concrete, grade C40, Specification clause "X".<br><br>Moorlands Bridge Deck. | |
| H113 | Secondary beams, inverted tee, 180 x 420 mm, length 4.00 m, mass 500 kg - 1t, mark SB2. | nr |
| H368 | Prestressed post-tensioned main beams, I section, 800 x 1380 mm, length 22.50 m, mass 30t, mark B2, pre-stressing and tendons as Drawing No. "Y" and Specification clause "W". | nr |

Fig. H1. Precast concrete bridge beams.

MEASURED EXAMPLES

Three measured examples follow:

        Concrete Sea Wall              -  Example FE.1.

        Reinforced Concrete Structure  -  Example FE.2

        Circular Mass Concrete Reservoir  -  Example FE.3

Concrete Sea Wall - Example FE.1

   The  Example FE.1. sets out the dimensions for a concrete sea wall, as shown
on  Drawing  No. F/D/1. It illustrates the application of the CESMM  to  the
measurement of work carried out in a location where it is affected by a body
of  tidal water. (See Commentary on Paragraph 5.20 of the CESMM on page  26,
Chapter  2). The elements of the work and the order in which they have  been
taken  off  are  foundations,  wall  and  incidental  work.  The  balustrade,
pavement  and flood wall to the promenade above the wall are not measured in
the Example.

Reinforced Concrete Structure - Example FE.2.

   In  Example  FE.2. the dimensions are set out in the centre of the  page  to
allow  space  for diagrams on one side and commentary on the other. For  the
purpose  of the Example, the inclusion of the diagrams alongside the  taking
off  which  relates  to  them  is  considered  preferable  to  providing  an
arrangement  drawing  with  details on a separate page. It  serves  also  to
illustrate diagrametically the methodical approach to the measurement of the
structure  whereby  it is broken down into its several elements and each  is
taken off and completed separately.

      In  the  Example the lengths of the beams and columns have either  been
timesed  or  brought  to a total in waste. On large structures  it  is  more
convenient  to  prepare  schedules  and  collect  together  the  lengths  of
components  of  similar classification and cross-sectional  dimensions.  One
total  for  each  is  then  transferred  to  the  dimension  sheets  for
multiplication by its cross-sectional dimensions.

Circular Mass Concrete Reservoir - Example FE.3

   The  Example  FE.3 gives the complete taking off for the  Circular  Concrete
Reservoir shown  on Drawing F/D/3, with the exception of that for the joints
in  the  concrete and that for associated pipework. An example of  measuring
joints  in  concrete  is  given  in  Example  FE.1.  Measuring pipework  is
illustrated in Chapter 9.

      Before  commencing taking off, the methodical approach is to decide how
best  the  work  can first be broken down into sections or elements  for  the
purpose  of  measurement. When  this  has  been  done  the  taking  off  is
concentrated on one section or element until complete. Each is dealt with in
a  similar  manner  until  the  whole  of the taking off  is  complete.  The
elemental  break down used for the Example and the order of taking off is as
follows:-

   1. Bases and footings, 2. Blinding and formation, 3. Perimeter wall,
   4. Cross wall, 5. Earthworks, 6. Perimeter footpath, 7. Bank and seeding.

      The choice of commencing with the taking of dimensions for the concrete
work rather than commencing with the excavation and working through more or
less in the order of construction is a personal one.  The reason is that
when taking dimensions from drawings it is considered convenient to take off
and record the work which represents the dimensioned form of the work (in
this case the concrete) and later to generate from the dimensions taken
those which are appropriate to the excavation and other earthworks.  Others
may choose to adopt an order of take off different from that in the Example.

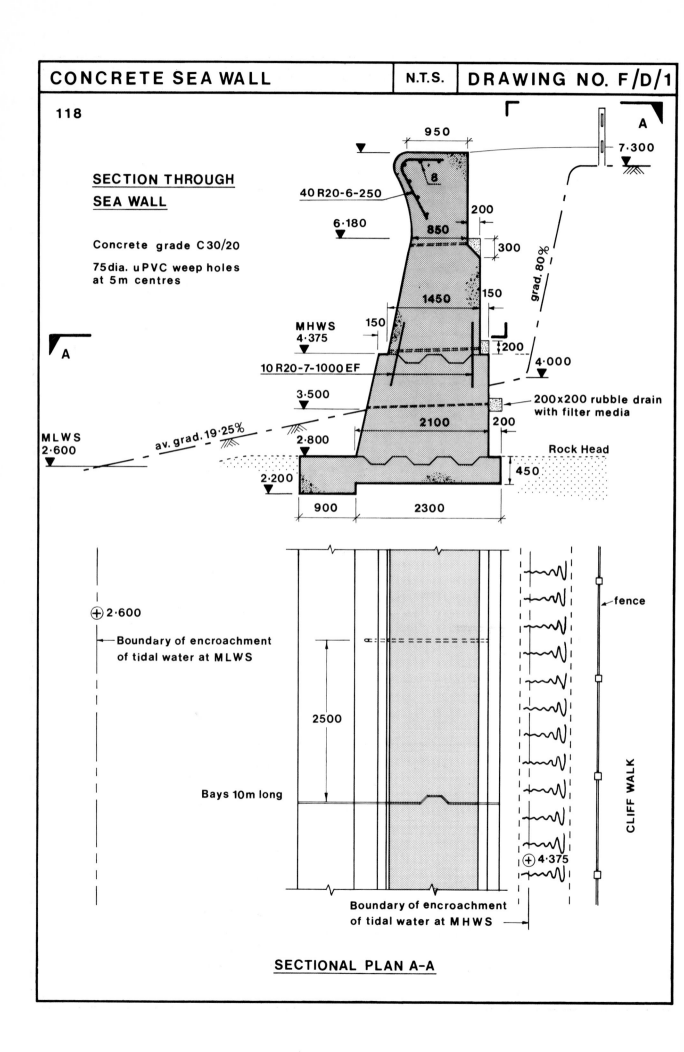

## CONCRETE SEA WALL   N.T.S.   DRAWING NO. F/D/1

### SECTION THROUGH SEA WALL

Concrete grade C30/20

75 dia. uPVC weep holes at 5m centres

950

7·300

40 R20-6-250

6·180

200

850

300

1450

150

150

MHWS
4·375

10 R20-7-1000 EF

200

grad. 80%

4·000

3·500

200×200 rubble drain
with filter media

2·800

2100

200

MLWS
2·600

av. grad. 19·25%

Rock Head

2·200

450

900   2300

⊕ 2·600

Boundary of encroachment
of tidal water at MLWS

2500

Bays 10m long

fence

⊕ 4·375

CLIFF WALK

Boundary of encroachment
of tidal water at MHWS

### SECTIONAL PLAN A-A

**WALL TOP DETAIL**

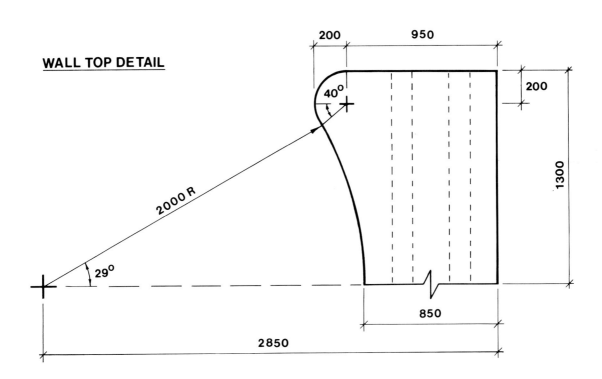

**VERTICAL JOINT DETAIL**

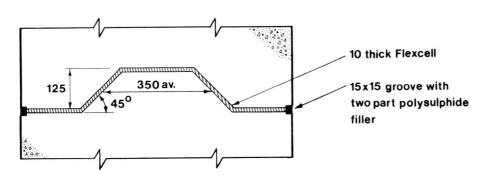

10 thick Flexcell

15 x 15 groove with two part polysulphide filler

| ABRIDGED BAR SCHEDULE | | | | |
|---|---|---|---|---|
| (Each 10 m length of wall) | | | | |
| MEMBER | BAR MARK | TYPE AND SIZE | TOTAL No. | LENGTH OF EACH BAR mm |
| SEA WALL | 6 | R20 | 40 | 1600 |
| on Dwg No. F/D/1 | 7 | R20 | 20 | 1000 |
|  | 8 | T16 | 6 | 10000 |

120

CONC. SEA WALL - DRG. No. F/D/1
EXAMPLE FE.1.

State in Preamble:-
The Site of the proposed Sea Wall is
below North Cliff on the beach of
Lyme Bay between Spray Point and the
Lido. The position of the Wall in
relation to the anticipated ranges of
fluctuation of tidal encroachment
and the anticipated range of fluctuation of water surface levels
are indicated on Drawing No F/D/1

NOTE: All conc. ord. prescribed mix
to BS.5328, ct. to BS 12, agg.
to BS 882 unless o/w stated

|  |  | Fdns |  |
|---|---|---|---|
|  |  | 2800 | 2800 |
|  |  | 2350 | 2200 |
|  |  | 450 | 600 |

| 10.00 | { Provn. of conc. Grade |
| 0.90 | { C30, 20mm agg. |
| 0.60 | |
| 10.00 | (F163 |
| 2.30 | |
| 0.45 | |

| 10.00 | Placg. of conc., mass |
| 0.90 | footgs. thickn. e.500mm, |
| 0.60 | against excavd. surf. |
|  | part below MLWS. |
|  | (F424 |

| 10.00 | Placg. of conc. all as last |
| 2.30 | item, but thickn. |
| 0.45 | 300-500mm |
|  | (F423 |

(1)

The Example gives the dimensions for a 10 m long section of the Sea Wall between vertical movement joints.

The statement at the start of the Example, for inclusion in Preamble, identifies the body of open water which exists on the Site. It gives details of the boundaries and water surface levels anticipated and makes reference to the Drawing on which these are shown. This is in compliance with Paragraph 5.20 of the CESMM. (See Commentary on that Paragraph in Chapter 2). The statement in Preamble does not guarantee that when the work is carried out the actual boundaries and water surface levels will be as anticipated.

The provision of concrete is classified in accordance with BS 5328. (See Table 8.02).

The concrete in the Example is all of one mix. The Note avoids repeating details in the several items.

Rule F/D6 of the CESMM. (See Table 8.03) does not apply to the placing of concrete in footings. Separate items are given in the Example for the different thickness ranges.

It is assumed there is an express requirement for the concrete in footings to be placed against the excavated surfaces to avoid having to excavate more rock than is necessary. It is stated in the item descriptions where concrete is to be placed against excavated surfaces. (See first panel of Table 8.03).

Where the concrete is placed below low water level, additional description is given in the items of the Example to bring this to notice. (See Paragraph 5.10 of the CESMM and the Commentary on that Paragraph in Chapter 2).

CONC. SEA WALL. DRG. NO F/D/1

Fdns. (cont

```
2300  650              450
 900  200  ½/3200=1600
3200  450             2050
            4000
      2050 × 19.25% = 395
```

Av Orig Surf. centre trench = 3605
Exc Surf higher level trench = 2350
Av depth trench to +2.300 m = 1255

(4000 - 2350) - (450 × 19.25%) = 1563

| | |
|---|---|
| 10.00 | Excavn for fdns max |
| 3.20 | depth 1-2 m, below |
| 1.26 | body of open water in |
| 10.00 | Lyme Bay      (E324 |
| 0.90 | |
| 0.15 | |
| | & |
| | Excavn ancills disposal |
| | of excavd matl. (E532 |
| | |
| 10.00 | Ddt Both last items |
| 3.20 | (E324 and E532 |
| 0.45 | |
| 10.00 | & |
| 0.90 | |
| 0.15 | Add Excavn for fdns, rock, |
| | max depth 1-2 m, below |
| | body of open water in |
| | Lyme Bay      (E334 |
| | |
| | & |
| | |
| | Add Excavn ancills |
| | disposal of excavd |
| | matl rock (E533 |

(2)

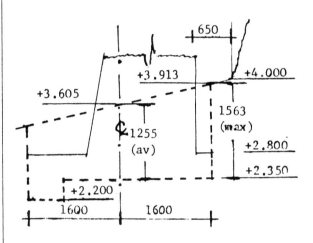

## CONC. SEA WALL - DRG. NO. F/D/1

**Fdns. (cont.**

| | |
|---|---|
| 10.00 | Excavn. ancills. prepn. |
| 3.20 | of excavd. surfs. rock. |
| | (E523.1 |

```
2800
2200
 600
```

| | |
|---|---|
| 2/ 10.00 | Excavn. ancills. prepn |
| 0.60 | of excavd. surf. rock; |
| | vertical.    (E523.2 |

**Backfill above footg**

```
1255        4000
 450        2800
 805        1206
      (50×19.25%=125
1075        1075
 700
2)1775      3500
 888        2800
             700
700 × 22.22% = 156
```

| | |
|---|---|
| 10.00 | Fillg. to strucs. sel |
| 3.20 | excavd matl. o/t. topsoil |
| 0.81 | or rock    (E614 |

&

Ddt. Excavn ancills disposal
of excavd. matl. (E532

| | |
|---|---|
| 10.00 | Ddt. Fillg to s.trucs a.b |
| 1.94 | (E614 |
| 0.89 | |
| ½/ 10.00 | |
| 0.16 | & |
| 0.70 | |

Add Excavn ancills. disposal
of excavd. matl (E532

(3)

Preparation of excavated surfaces is measured where the concrete is in contact with the excavated surface. (See note on Rule E/M11, 2nd Division panel of Table 7.02, page 79).

The volume occupied by the concrete footing has been measured in the preceding column of dimensions for excavation in rock and also the disposal of the rock. The volume of backfilling is first measured in the adjoining column as the whole volume of the excavation above the level of the footings. This is followed by an item reducing the disposal of excavated material by the volume required for filling. The penultimate and last items in the adjoining column adjust the filling and disposal of excavated material items, respectively, for the volume occupied by the lower part of the wall. (See diagram below).

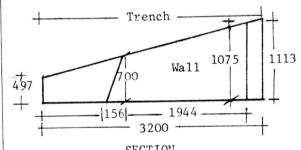

SECTION

The following are waste calculations relating to the dimensions set down for concrete in the next column of dimensions.

Heights

```
4375   6180   7480   200   1300
2800   4375   6180   129    329
1575   1805   1300   329    971
```

Widths

```
2100      1050      850
1750      1450     2000
2)3850   2)2500
1925      1250     2850
```

CONC SEA WALL - DRG NO. F/D/1

__Wall up to +4.375m__

| | |
|---|---|
| 10.00<br>1.93<br><u>1.58</u> | Provn of conc. Grade C30 20mm. agg.<br>(F163 |

&

Placg of conc., mass, walls, thickn e 500mm, below M.H.W.S., base battering sea wall.
(F444.2

__Wall +4.375 - 6.180 m__

| | |
|---|---|
| 10.00<br>1.25<br><u>1.81</u> | Provn. of conc. C30 a.b.<br>(F163 |

&

Placg of conc. mass walls thickn. e 500mm battering sea wall
(F444.1

| | |
|---|---|
| 10.00<br>0.20<br>0.20 | Ddt. Both last items<br>(F163 + F444.1 |

__Shaped wall above +6.180m__

| | |
|---|---|
| 10.00<br>2.85<br><u>0.97</u> | Add. Provn of conc C30 a.b. (F163 |
| 10.00<br>0.95<br>0.33 | |

&

| | | | |
|---|---|---|---|
| 130/<br>360/ | 22/<br>7/ | 10.00<br>0.20<br>0.20 | Placg of conc, rfcd. walls, thickn e 500mm sea wall shaped profile (F544 |
| ½/ | | 10.00<br>0.15<br>0.13 | |

| | | | | |
|---|---|---|---|---|
| | | | 31.33 | |
| 29/<br>360/ | 22/<br>7/ | 10.00<br>2.00<br>2.00 | | Ddt. Both last items (F163 + F544<br>( Want (a) |
| ½/ | | 10.00<br>1.75<br>0.97 | | ( Want (b) |

| | |
|---|---|
| 18.61 | |

(4)

123

COMMENTARY

Where walls are tapered or are of a sectional shape which would be difficult to classify according to thickness, consideration may be given to substituting features, in the item descriptions, identifying section shapes in place of the features of thickness ranges at 3rd Division level.

The wall in the Example is of special sectional shape, but is readily classified according to standard thickness ranges and does not call for special consideration in this respect. In the Example the standard feature "walls" is used at 2nd Division level in the item descriptions for placing the concrete. Additional description is included in the item descriptions for placing to distinguish different characteristics of the work in different parts of the wall and to distinguish the concrete to be placed in the sea wall from that placed in straightforward walls, such as flood walls, which may be billed in the same Part of the Bill of Quantities.

The cross-section dimensions used for the concrete and the placing in the shaped top of the wall are taken as those of the large rectangle, the small rectangle, the 200 mm radius sector and the small triangle. These are followed by dimensions for the deduction of want (a) (the 2000 mm radius sector) and want (b) (the large triangle) as shown on the dimensioned section diagram below.

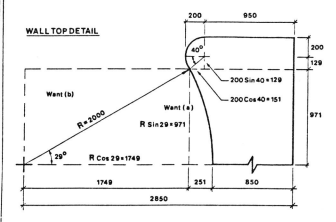

WALL TOP DETAIL

CONC. SEA WALL - DRG. NO. F/D/1

Wall (cont. Back

Fmw. rough fin.

| | | |
|---|---|---|
| 10.00 | Plane vert: below | |
| 1.58 | MHWS (G145.2 | |

$$\begin{array}{cc} & 1.81 \\ 3.11 & 0.97 \\ \text{less splay } 0.20 & 0.33 \\ \hline 2.91 & 3.11 \end{array}$$

| | | |
|---|---|---|
| 10.00 | Plane vert. (G145.1 | |
| 2.91 | | |

$$\sqrt{(200^2 + 200^2)} = \underline{283}$$

| | | |
|---|---|---|
| 10.00 | Plane slopg. width | |
| 0.28 | 0.2 – 0.4 m, to upper | |
| | surfs. (G143 | |

$$1575 \times 22.22\% = \underline{350}$$
$$\sqrt{(1575^2 + 350^2)} = \underline{1613}$$

Front

Fmw. fair fin

| | | |
|---|---|---|
| 10.00 | Plane slopg: below | |
| 1.61 | MHWS. (G225.2 | |

$$1805 \times 22.22\% = \underline{401}$$
$$\sqrt{(1805^2 + 401^2)} = \underline{1849}$$
$$\frac{130}{360} \left/ \frac{22}{7} \right/ 2 / 200 = \underline{454}$$
$$\frac{29}{360} \left/ \frac{22}{7} \right/ 2 / 2000 = \underline{1013}$$
$$\overline{3316}$$

| | | |
|---|---|---|
| 10.00 | For conc. compon. of | |
| | constant cross-sectn. to | |
| | shaped face of sea wall, | |
| | total girth of sectn 3316 | |
| | mm the sectn of convex | |
| | curve r. 200 mm (454 m gt) | |
| | concave curve r 2000 mm | |
| | (1013 mm gt) & plane slopg. | |
| | lower face 1849 mm gt. as | |
| | Drg No F/D/1 ((G283 | |

(5)

COMMENTARY

Except for the formwork to the sloping offset given in the third item of the adjoining column, the formwork to the back of the wall is in plane vertical areas exceeding 1.22 m wide (See note on Rule G/D2 in the first panel Table 8.04). That to the back of the base, being below high water level, will require to be installed between tides. It is here given as a separate item with additional description noting that it is below MHWS.

The level of the sand on the beach side of the wall base may not always be constant. It is practical to take fair finish formwork for the full height of the base, rather than separate and classify as rough finish that which is below the beach level shown on the Drawing.

The inclination to the vertical of the face of the wall works out at 1 in 4.5 (22.22%). This gives an angle of inclination to the vertical of approximately 12 degrees 32 minutes, which qualifies to be classified under Rule G/D1 of the CESMM as plane sloping. (See the lower panels of Table 8.04 on page 104).

Formwork to the shaped face of the wall above the base is here measured by length in one item and classified "For components of constant cross section". The item description gives the details required by Rules G/A5 and G/A6 of the CESMM. (See penultimate 3rd Division panel of Table 8.04).

The girth of the formwork given in the item is illustrated by the heavy line on the adjoining diagram of section.

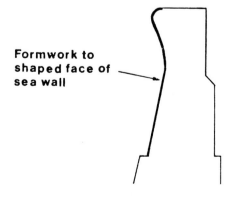

**Formwork to shaped face of sea wall**

CONC. SEA WALL — DRG. NO. F/D/1

Wall (cont.

Conc access.

| | |
|---|---|
| 10.00 | Fin. of top surf, steel |
| 0.95 | trowel (G812 |

$2/\frac{1}{2}/0.25 = 0.25$   $\underline{10.00}$   0.25)9.75
       $\underline{9.75}$     39+1.40

| | |
|---|---|
| 40/1.60 | Rfmt. |
| | M.s. bars BS4449 nom. |
| | si 20mm; shaped links |
| | × 2.466 Kg/m |
| | = _____ Kg (G516 |

| | |
|---|---|
| 6/10.00 | H.y. s. bars BS.4449 |
| | nom. si 16mm |
| | × 1.579 Kg/m |
| | _____ Kg (G525 |

Constr + Mvmt Jts

Joints open surf. plain

| | |
|---|---|
| 10.00 | Width 2.10 m; horiz. |
| 2.10 | 3 No 350×125 mm 2ce |
| | splyd grooves lengthwise; |
| | below MHWS (G613.2 |

| | |
|---|---|
| 10.00 | Width 1.45 m; horiz, |
| 1.45 | 2 No 350×125 mm 2ce |
| | splyd grooves lengthwise |
| | 2 No 20 mm dia. × 1 m |
| | long metal dowels @ |
| | 1m intervals in lgth |
| | G613.1 |

| | |
|---|---|
| 10/2 | Joints |
| | Dowels plain m.s. |
| | 20mm dia. × 1m long. |
| | (G681 |

(6)

COMMENTARY

Formwork is not necessary to the flat top surface of the wall. It is exposed and needs to be finished. It is here taken for steel trowel finish.

Dimensions for reinforcement are taken from the bar schedule on the Drawing. Items are taken to imply the inclusion of normal bending and hooking as required by the Specification and Drawing. Bending bars to the profile of the concrete component is considered to be something more than the normal and is noted in the item description.

Joints are measured only where they are expressly required. Unless it is otherwise stated, joints shown on the Engineer's drawings are taken as being expressly required. Open surface joints are defined as those which do not require support of the whole surface during casting. (See Table 8.06). The area items for joints are taken to include formwork and supplying and fitting filler material, if required. It is a requirement of Rule G/A11 of the CESMM that item descriptions shall give details of the components of the joints including composite components, such as dowel assemblies, dowel bars and their sizes and spacings as well as the thickness of filler material. The dowels, waterstops and the like are measured and described as provided in the Class G classification table (See Table 8.06) and are given in separate items from those of the joints.

CONC. SEA WALL - DRG. No. F/D/1

Wall (cont. C.M Jts

joints formd. surf wi
10mm thickn. "Flexcell"
fill; vert, wi 2ce
splyd vert. nib or
groove 350 x 125 mm
and 15 x 15 mm face
groove. Drg. F/D/2

| | |
|---|---|
| 2/½/ 1.93 | Width or depth. |
| 1.58 | 1.93 m; below MHWS |
| | (G643.2 |

| | |
|---|---|
| 2/½/ 1.25 | Width or depth |
| 1.81 | 1.25 m.    (G643.1 |

$$\frac{(31.33 - 18.61)}{10.00 \times 1.30} = 0.98$$

| | |
|---|---|
| 2/½/ 0.98 | Width or depth 0.5 |
| 1.30 | – 1m, between shaped |
| | sections of wall tops |
| | (G642 |

```
  1613
  1849
   150      454    4562
   950     1013    1467
  4562     1467    6029
```

Joints, seald. groove
2 part polysulpide
15 x 15 mm (G670

| | |
|---|---|
| 2/½/ 6.03 | |
| 2/½/ 5.03 | |

$$\frac{0.9 \times 0.6 + 2.3 \times 0.45}{3.20} = 0.49$$

Footing

Joints formd surf wi
10mm thickn "Flexcell"
filler; vert.

| | |
|---|---|
| 2/½/ 3.20 | Width or depth n.e |
| 0.49 | 0.5 m; below MHWS |
| | (G641 |

(7)

COMMENTARY

The joints previously measured are the horizontal construction joints shown on the Drawing which are taken as being expressly required. The items here measured are the vertical joints between the sections of the wall. The vertical joints will usually divide a wall of this description into sections of similar length with joints at equidistant intervals. The procedure often followed when taking off is to take the quantities for one section and times this up for the number of sections in the length and then make adjustment for ends and for differences in depths or heights. Adjustment for depths and heights will usually only affect the base below the constant sectional profile of the sea wall. The wall measured in the Example is assumed to be one intermediate section of the wall between vertical joints. Half a vertical joint is measured for each end of the wall.

The waste calculation to arrive at the average width of the shaped top section of the wall uses the volume of the concrete in that part of the wall (Squared out in Column (4)) and divides this volume by the length (10.00 m) and then by the height (1.30 m).

Joints are taken at their average width and the last waste calculations in the adjoining column are those to arrive at the average depth of the vertical joints at the end of the footing.

CONC. SEA WALL - DRG. F/D/1

Wall ( cont

Weep holes

Conc. access, inserts
75 mm diam. p.v.c
pipes as weep holes
thro. mass conc. walls

| | |
|---|---|
| 2 | Thickn. 1925 m; below MHWS. (G832.3 |
| 2 | Thickn. 1450 mm (G832.2 |
| 2 | Thickn. 900 mm (G832.1 |

( End of Conc access )

Cliff face + Backfill

$$7300$$
$$4000 \quad\quad 100 - 80 = 20\%$$
$$3300 \times 20\% = 660$$
$$\sqrt{(3300^2 + 660^2} = 3365$$
$$\frac{660}{3365} = 0.19614 = Tan\ 11°16'$$

| | |
|---|---|
| 10.00 3.37 0.10 | Gen excavn. weathd. s/soil and veg. matter, average thickn. of 100mm to cliff face inclined at an angle 45-90° to hor (E429 |

&

Excavn. ancills.
disposal of excavd.
matt. (E532

(8)

## COMMENTARY

Weep holes are classified as inserts. Item descriptions describe the inserts and items are deemed to include their supply, unless otherwise stated. Item descriptions need to state, by additional description, where inserts project from one or both surfaces of the concrete and also where they are wholly within the volume of concrete (See Table 8.08). The inserts in the Example are cast with ends flush with the concrete and no additional description as to their position in relation to the surface of the concrete is required.

The Rule requiring that a line be drawn across the description column to denote the end of the items to which a sub-heading relates, is applicable only to the Bill of Quantities and does not apply to the dimension sheets. Where sub-headings are used in taking off, they apply to the items listed under them. The end of the items to which the immediate preceding sub-heading applies is signified by a new sub-heading or a note indicating the end of the items to which the sub-heading applies. In the Example the items following the inserts revert to items to which the immediate sub-heading does not apply and the note "End of Conc. Access." is included to ensure this is understood.

Excavating an almost vertical surface of the cliff face is not specifically covered by a feature of classification in the Class E table of CESMM. It is considered appropriate to classify it as "General excavation" carried out in the appropriate material listed in CESMM at 2nd Division and to indicate the particular nature of the work in a non-standard special descriptive feature included at 3rd Division level.

CONC. SEA WALL - DRG. No. F/D/1

Wall (cont. Backfill.

½/650x19.25% = 62.5
                    3300
7300   av. d  3363      1500
4375   2/750= 1500       180
2925           660      1320
             2)2160
        av w  1080

| | |
|---|---|
| 10.00 | Fillg to strucs imported |
| 1.08 | quarry waste hardcore, |
| 3.36 | Spec. clause "X" |
| 10.00 | (E617 |
| 0.15 | |
| 2.93 | (offset |
| 10.00 | |
| 0.20 | ( " |
| 1.32 | |

Drains back of wall

2925
 200
----
2725

0.15 x 0.20 = 0.03
0.20 x 0.20 = 0.04

1420
 300
----
1120

Rubble drains and trenches, trenches for unpiped rubble drains, to back of Sea Wall

| | |
|---|---|
| 10.00 | Cross-sectn area 0.03m² Comm. Surf at an inter. surf. within a filled vol. 2.73 m below top of fillg. (K431.1 |
| 10.00 | Cross-sectn area 0.04m² Comm Surf at an inter surf. within a filld vol. 1.12 m below top of fillg. (K431.2 |

(9)

COMMENTARY

The filled volume measured is shown on the broken cross-section in the following diagram.

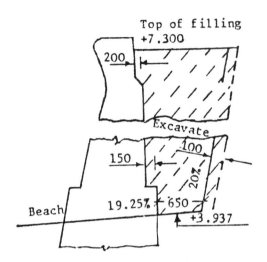

Wastes calculate the average depth of bulk filling by adding the vertical depth of 3300 mm at the front of the cliff (See wastes "General excavations" in Column 8) to the calculated 62.5 mm fall to the centre of the 650 mm space between wall and cliff at beach level. In calculating the average width (excluding the increase width because of offsets on the back of the wall) the backslope of 660 mm (See wastes "General excavation" in Column 8) is added to twice the width at the bottom of the filling i.e. 2/750 mm (650 + 100 mm excavation) and dividing by two.

It is assumed that the filter media in the drains to the back of the wall will be small gauge and will need to be placed in a sinking in the bulk filling to support it. A suitable way to achieve this is to bring the level of the bulk filling up to the level of the top of each drain and to excavate the sinking in the bulk filling. The items in the Example are based on this method. It is considered reasonable to classify these sinkings as "Rubble drains", giving the actual size of the trenches because they are small, and describing and stating the Commencing Surface. A sinking will not be required for the drain behind the footing, this can be filled in, in place of backfilling.

CONC. SEA WALL — DRG. NO. F/D/1

Drains back of wall
/cont.

Rubble drains and
trenches /cont.

| | | | |
|---|---|---|---|
| 10.00 | | | {Fillg. rubble drains wi |
| 0.20 | | | filter media as Spec. |
| 0.20 | | | clause "X" (K410 |
| 10.00 | | | |
| 0.15 | | | |
| 0.20 | | | |
| 10.00 | | | |
| 0.20 | | | |
| 0.20 | | | |

(End of "Rubble drains")

| | | | |
|---|---|---|---|
| 10.00 | | | {Extra to excavn and |
| 0.15 | | | backfill to pipe trench |
| 0.20 | | | excavn, compacted |
| 10.00 | | | hardcore (L114 |
| 0.20 | | | |
| 0.20 | | | |

| | | | |
|---|---|---|---|
| 10.00 | | | {Ddt. Fillg to strucs. |
| 0.15 | | | imported quarry |
| 0.20 | | | waste hardcore a.b. |
| 10.00 | | | |
| 0.20 | | | (E617 |
| 0.20 | | | |

| | | | |
|---|---|---|---|
| 10.00 | | | Ddt. Fillg to strucs. |
| 0.20 | | | sel. excavd. matl o/t. |
| 0.20 | | | topsoil or rock (E614 |

&

Add. Excavn. ancills.
disposal of excavd.
matl. (E532

END OF CONC. SEA WALL

(10)

## COMMENTARY

No distinction is made in the Example between the rubble drain filling in the drain trenches and that filled in as a drain in place of the backfilling behind the footing of the wall. It is considered to be work of similar character. It is measured in the first set of dimensions in the adjoining column.

The drain trench items previously measured include for excavation in soft material. An item for the extra to that excavation is here given for excavating in compacted hardcore.

The first Ddt. item in the adjoining column, deducts bulk hardcore filling behind the wall, to the extent that its volume is replaced by the volume of filter media in trenches, measured in the last two sets of dimensions in the item at the head of this column.

The Ddt. and Add items at the foot of the adjoining column adjust by reduction the volume of the backfilling around the footing (measured in Column 3), and thereby increase the volume of disposal of excavated material, to take account of the volume of backfilling replaced by the volume of filter media.

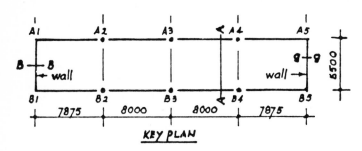

**KEY PLAN**

NOTES: All cols.    500 x 500
Edge beams. 1000 x 500
Walls.    250 thick
Slab.    350 thick

Key plan dimensions are to the
centre lines of cols and walls

| Component | Dimensions | Commentary |
|---|---|---|

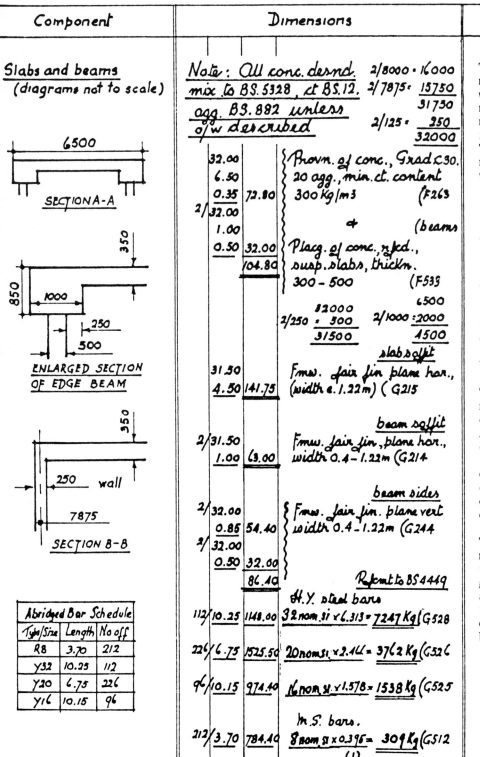

**Slabs and beams**
(diagrams not to scale)

Note: All conc. desnd.
mix to BS.5328, ct BS.12.
agg. BS.882 unless
o/w described

2/8000 · 16000
2/7875 · 15750
  31750
2/125 ·  250
  32000

SECTION A-A

6500

|  |  |  |
|---|---|---|
| 32.00 |  | Provn. of conc., Grad C30. |
| 6.50 |  | 20 agg., min. ct. content |
| 0.35 | 72.80 | 300 kg/m3 (F263 |
| 2/32.00 |  |  |
| 1.00 |  | & (beams |
| 0.50 | 32.00 | Placg. of conc., rfcd., |
|  | 104.80 | susp. slabs, thickn. |

300 - 500 (F533

ENLARGED SECTION
OF EDGE BEAM

850
350
1000
250
500

32000    6500
2/250 · 500   2/1000 : 2000
  31500   1500
  slab soffit

| 31.50 |  | Fmw. fair fin plane hor., |
| 4.50 | 141.75 | (width c. 1.22m) ( G215 |

beam soffit

| 2/31.50 |  | Fmw. fair fin., plane hor., |
| 1.00 | 69.00 | width 0.4 - 1.22m (G214 |

beam sides

| 2/32.00 |  | Fmw. fair fin. plane vert |
| 0.85 | 54.40 | width 0.4 - 1.22m (G244 |
| 2/32.00 |  |  |
| 0.50 | 32.00 |  |
|  | 86.40 |  |

250  wall
7875

SECTION B-B

Rfcmt to BS4449
H.Y. steel bars

| 112/10.25 | 1148.00 | 32 nom si x 6.313 = 7247 Kg (G528 |
| 226/6.75 | 1525.50 | 20 nom si x 2.44 = 3762 Kg (G526 |
| 96/10.15 | 974.40 | 16 nom si x 1.578 = 1538 Kg (G525 |

M.S. bars.

| 212/3.70 | 784.40 | 8 nom si x 0.395 = 309 Kg (G512 |

(1)

**Abridged Bar Schedule**

| Type/Size | Length | No off |
|---|---|---|
| R8 | 3.70 | 212 |
| Y32 | 10.25 | 112 |
| Y20 | 6.75 | 226 |
| Y16 | 10.15 | 96 |

The slab and beams are measured over the end walls, the walls when measured will need to be measured to the underside of these components. They could have been measured inside the walls. The walls would then be measured to the top of the slab.

It is assumed that the beams are not expressly required to be cast separately. The placing of concrete in the beams is measured as part of the suspended slab. The classification thickness of the slab excludes the thickness of integral beams. See Table 8.03.

The mass of reinforcement is here calculated on the dimension sheets. A simpler method is to calculate the mass on the bar schedule and to enter the totals so calculated with their descriptions on the dimension sheets.

The mass of reinforcement is here calculated to the nearest kilogramme. When collected and cast in the abstract, it would be reduced to tonnes for billing. See Table 8.05.

| Component | Dimensions | Commentary |
|---|---|---|

**Component**

Columns 6 off
(diagrams not to scale

beam

5000

ground level

1000

base

ELEVATION.

500

500

PLAN

| Abridged Bar Schedule | | | |
|---|---|---|---|
| Type + Size | Length | No per col. | No off cols |
| Y32 | 5725 | 6 | 6 |
| R8 | 2000 | 17 | 6 |

**Dimensions**

_Cals_

2/3/ 0.50
     0.50
     5.00   7.50    Provn. of conc, Grad.C.30 20 agg.; min.ct content 300 kg/m3  (F.263

&

Plac. of conc., rfcd. cols. c.s.a. 0.1-0.25m2; cols. A2-A4 and B2-B4  (F553

2/3/ 5.00   30.00   Fmw. fair fin., for conc. components of constant c.s. columns 500x500mm, cols A2-A4 and B2-B4  (G282

$$\frac{\begin{array}{r}1000\\ 75\end{array}}{925}$$

2/3/ 0.93   5.58   Ddt. Fmw. as last item.  (G282

&

Add Fmw rough fin, for conc. components of constant c.s. columns 500x500mm, cols A2-A4 and B2-B4 below ground  (G182

6/6/ 5.73   H.y. steel bars nom.si.32mm,
206.28 × 6.313 = 1302 Kg  (vert  (G528

6/17/ 2.00   Ms.bars.nom si.8mm
204.00 × 0.395 = 81 Kg  (Links  (G512

(2)

**Commentary**

It is important to state location of members in the Works where special characteristics may affect the method or rate of placing concrete. If this particular Example was billed as a separate Part of the Bill of Quantities, with a heading giving the title of the work, it is considered that members would be sufficiently located by the standard features which name the members, i.e. columns, suspended slabs, etc. Precise location has been added to item F553 merely as an example of how the Note at the foot of page 38 of the CESMM would be implimented where it is wished to direct attention to a particular location which would not be clear without added description.

All columns being of constant cross-section the formwork is measured as a linear item according to the option provided in the Note at the foot of page 41 of the CESMM. Location details are added to the description as required by the Note.

Formwork fair finish would not be required below ground. The "Ddt" and "Add" items substitute formwork rough finish for that part of the column which is below ground. Formwork fair finish is taken to the exposed surfaces of the columns and extended to 75 mm below ground level.

| Component | Dimensions | | | Commentary |
|---|---|---|---|---|

**Walls 2 off**
(diagrams not to scale)

6500

ELEVATION

250

5850

SECTION A-A

| Abridged Bar Schedule | | |
|---|---|---|
| Type/Size | Length | No. off |
| Y8 | 6.30 | 50 |
| Y12 | 5.80 | 44 |

**Dimensions column:**

_walls_

2/ 6.50
0.25
5.00    16.25
2/ 4.50
0.25
0.50    1.13
        17.38

Prov. of conc., Grad. 30, 20 agg; min ct content 300 kg/m3    (F263
&
Place of conc., rfcd., walls, thickn 150 - 300 mm    (F542

2/ 6.50
5.85    76.05
2/ 6.50
5.00    65.00
2/ 4.50
0.50    4.50
        145.55

Fmw. fair fin. plane vert. (width ≥ 1.22m) (G245
(inner face
( "    "

_wall ends_

2/2/ 0.25
5.00    5.00

Fmw. fair fin. plane vert. width 0.2 - 0.4m
(G243

_rfcmt_

H.Y. steel bars

50/ 6.30 315.00   8 nom. si × 0.395 = 124 Kg (G522

44/ 5.80 255.20   12 nom. si × 0.888 = 227 Kg (G524

**Commentary column:**

The wall is measured to the underside of the slab and beams. See Commentary to the first column of dimensions in this Example. The formwork to the outer face of the wall is taken up to the top of this slab.

In the description for the formwork to the faces of the wall, "width exceeding 1.22 m" is noted merely as an aid to coding, which, in practice, may not be carried out at the same time as the dimensions are taken. The item description would read "Formwork fair finish plane vertical" in the Bill of Quantities. See Rule G/D2 of the CESMM.

The whole of the formwork to the wall has been measured as fair finish. The formwork to the part of the wall below ground level (not shown) could be rough finish. if so, it should be given separately. Where the depth below ground is shallow, it may be considered reasonable to take the fair finish formwork down to the top of the foundation rather than give separately a narrow width of formwork rough finish.

(3)

| Component | Dimensions | Commentary |
|---|---|---|

**Component column:**

Foundations
(diagrams not to scale

Column bases 2/3. 6 off

2000

11y32-1

2000

500

11y32-1

PLAN

6y32-2

2R8-3

A-A

Bars ref. 2 = 1700 girth
"    "    3 = 2000 girth

Wall foundations 2 off

1000

250 wall

4y12-1

B        B

2 x 21y12-2

PLAN

B-B

Bars ref. 2 = 1700 girth.
Cover to bars 50

**Dimensions column:**

Blindg.

2/3/ 2.00
2.00
0.08  1.92
2/ 6.75
1.00
0.08  1.08
   3.00

Provn. of conc., Grad. C10.
40 agg; min ct. content
250 kg/m3     (F214  (bases
         &       (footgs
Placg. of conc. mass blindg.,
thickn n.e. 150 mm
         (F411

Bases + footgs

2/3/ 2.00
2.00
0.60  14.40
2/ 6.75
1.00
0.60  8.10
   22.50

Provn. of conc., Grad. C30.
20 agg; min ct content
300 kg/m3    (F263  (bases
         &       (footgs
Placg. of conc. rfcd. bases
and footgs., thickn e.500mm
         (F524

2/7250 =  14500
2/1000 =   2000
          16500

2/3/4/ 2.00
0.60  28.80
2/ 16.50
0.60  19.80
   48.60

Fmw. rough fin., plane vert.,
width 0.40 - 1.22m
         (G144        (footgs

2/3/2/11/ 1.90  250.80
2/3/6/   1.70  61.20
       312.00 x 6.313 = 1970 Kg  (G528

H.y. steel bars nom. si. 32mm
         (bases

2/3/2/ 2.00
   24.00 x0.395 = 9 Kg  (G512 (bases

M.s. bars nom. si 8 mm

2/4/ 7.20  57.60
2/21/2/ 1.70  142.80
   200.40 x 0.888 = 178 Kg

H.y. steel bars nom si.12 mm
         (G524  (footgs

(4)

**Commentary column:**

The dimensions in the adjoining column are for the concrete and concrete ancillaries. Related earthwork items are not measured.

Formwork is measured to the vertical side surfaces of the column bases and the wall foundations, it being assumed that the Specification does not expressly require that concrete be cast against excavated surfaces.

Formwork is not required to be measured to the edges of the blinding concrete not exceeding 0.2 m wide. See first panel Table 8.04.

A bar schedule is not provided and the dimensions for the bar reinforcement have been taken from the details given in the diagrams.

Bar reinforcement of 32 mm nominal size and greater would be grouped together in one item in the Bill. When taking dimensions the precise diameters are given to enable the mass to be calculated.

134

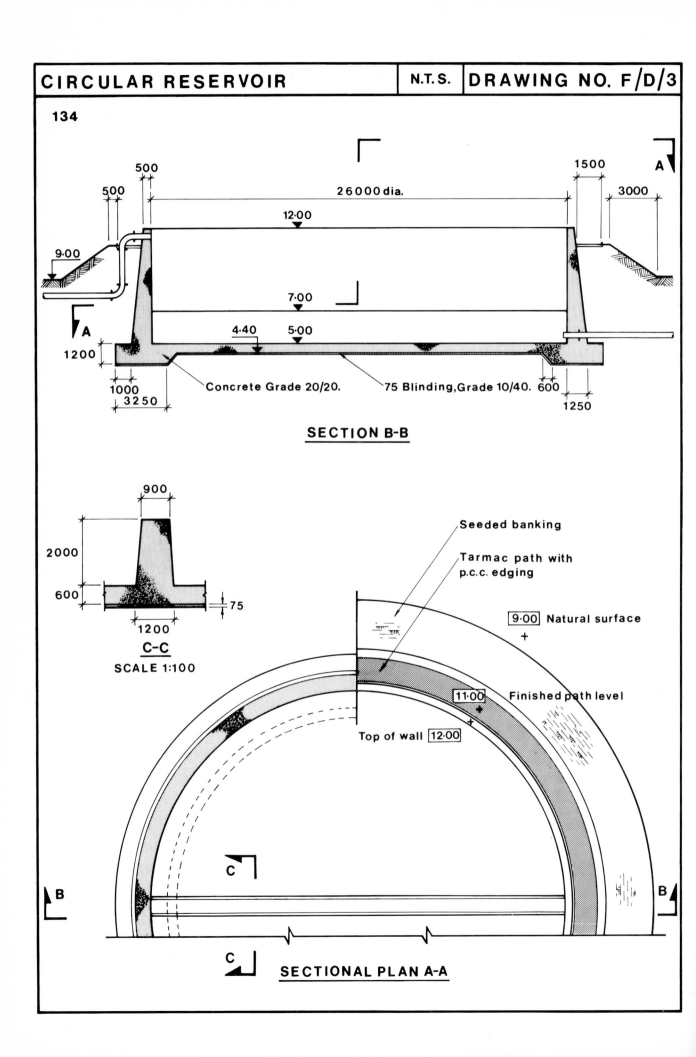

500
500
500
26000 dia.
1500
3000
9·00
12·00
7·00
4·40
5·00
1200
1000
3250
Concrete Grade 20/20.
75 Blinding, Grade 10/40.
600
1250
A

**SECTION B-B**

900
2000
600
75
1200
**C-C**
SCALE 1:100

Seeded banking

Tarmac path with
p.c.c. edging

9·00  Natural surface
+

11·00  Finished path level

Top of wall  12·00

B

**SECTIONAL PLAN A-A**

CIRC. CONC. RESERVOIR    DRG.No.F/D/3

EXAMPLE FE.3

<u>Note</u> : <u>All in situ conc. to be</u>
<u>desnd. mix BS. 5328, ct</u>
<u>to BS.12, min. ct content</u>
<u>310 Kg/m³, agg to BS. 882,</u>
<u>unless o/w described.</u>

<u>Bases & Footgs.</u>

|  |  | 26000 |
|---|---|---|
| 2/ | 1250 = | 2500 |
| 2/ | 1000 = | 2000 |
| diam. base | | 30500 |

| | | 26000 |
|---|---|---|
| 2/ | 1000 = | 2000 |
| | | 24000 |
| | | 30500 |
| | 2) | 54500 |
| footgs. | | 27250 |

| | | 24000 |
|---|---|---|
| 2/⅓/ | 600 = | 400 |
| | | 23600 |

| 2/ | 1000 = | 2000 |
|---|---|---|
| | | 1250 |
| | | 3250 |

| | 2) | 30500 |
|---|---|---|
| radius | | 15250 |

| 22/7/ | 15.25 | Provn. of conc. Grad. C20 |
| | 15.25 | 20 agg. (F243  ( g. slab. |
| | 0.60 | |
| 22/7/ | 27.25 | |
| | 3.25 | |
| ½/22/7/ | 0.60 | & | (footgs. |
| | 23.60 | |
| | 0.60 | (splay. |
| | 0.60 | |

Placg. of conc., mass
footgs & g. slab, thickn.
e.500 mm
(F424

(1)

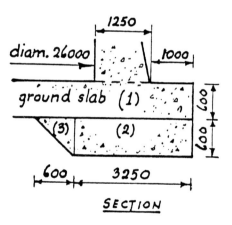

CIRC. CONC. RESERVOIR    DRG. No. F/D/3

Bases + Footgs (cont.

| | | |
|---|---|---|
| 22/7 | 13.00 | Conc. access.. fin of |
| | 13.00 | top surfs.; spade fin. |
| | | (G819 |

| | | |
|---|---|---|
| | 26.00 | Ddt. last item    (G813 |
| | 1.20 | (cross wall. |

| | | |
|---|---|---|
| 22/7 | 30.50 | Fmw. rough fin., curvd. |
| | 1.20 | one radius in one plane, |
| | | width 0.4 – 1.22 m.; radius |
| | | 15.25 m, perim of base |
| | | (G154.1 |

Blindg + Formation

600 × 1.414 = 848

| | | |
|---|---|---|
| 22/7 | 15.25 | Provn. of conc., ord. |
| | 15.25 | prescbd. mix to BS 5328, |
| | 0.08 | Grad. 10, ct. BS 12, 40mm |
| 22/7 | 23.40 | agg., min. ct. content |
| | 0.85 | 150 kg/m3    (F114 |
| | 0.08 | (slope |

+

| | | |
|---|---|---|
| | | Placg. of conc., mass |
| | | blindg.. thickn. n.e. 150 |
| | | mm    (F411 |

2/½/600 = 
$$\begin{array}{r} 24000 \\ \underline{600} \\ 23400 \end{array}$$

| | | |
|---|---|---|
| 22/7 | 23.40 | Ddt both last items |
| | 0.60 | (hor. replaced |
| | 0.08 | (by slope. |

(2)

COMMENTARY

The first item in the adjoining column is for the surface finish to the top of the base which is assumed to be spade finish. The second item deducts the surface finish for the area occupied by the base of the cross wall. If preferred the deduction could be made when dealing with the cross wall.

The formwork is for the side surfaces of the base, it being assumed that the Specification does not expressly require that the concrete shall be cast against the excavated surface. It is helpful to indicate the location of curved formwork in item descriptions. The width of the formwork is that of the thickness of the mass base at the edges. Formwork to the edges of the blinding is not measurable. Width classification is applicable to formwork curved to one radius.

The multiplier 1.414 is the Secant of 45 degrees and is used to calculate the slope length of the splayed inner edge of the thicknessing to the perimeter of the base.

The first set of dimensions for blinding cover the plan area of the base, the second set covers the sloping blinding. The work is, therefore, overmeasured to the extent of the flat area replaced by the slope. The Deduct item adjusts this. Distinction has not been made between placing horizontal blinding and placing that to slope, it being considered the cost difference is insufficient to merit separate itemisation.

Although in practical terms the underside of the sloping blinding does not require support during casting, it is advisable for the Specification to expressly require that the blinding be cast against the excavated surfaces. There is then no question of measuring formwork between the blinding and the excavated surface in consequence of Rule G/M2(e) of CESMM.

CIRC. CONC. RESERVOIR  DRG. No F/D/3

| | | |
|---|---|---|
| | | Blindg & Formation (cont. |
| | | 24000 |
| | | 22800 |
| | 2 | 46800 |
| | | 23400 |
| $\frac{22}{7}$ | 23.40<br>0.85 | Fmw. rough fin., curvd.<br>varying radius (conical)<br>max. radius 12.00 m,<br>min radius 11.40 m;<br>upper surfs of s.labg.<br>blindg.    (G160.1 |
| | | Formation. |
| $\frac{22}{7}$ | 15.25<br>15.25 | Excavn. ancills. prepn.<br>of excavd. surfs.<br>(E522.1 |
| $\frac{22}{7}$ | 23.40<br>0.60 | Ddt. last item. |
| $\frac{22}{7}$ | 23.40<br>0.85 | Excavn. ancills. prepn.<br>of excavd. surfs.,<br>curvd. and slobg. 10-<br>45° to horiz. (E 522.2 |
| | | Walls. perim<br>26000<br>2/500 = 1000<br>2 ) 27000<br>radius top 13500<br>26000<br>2/1250 = 2500<br>2 ) 28500<br>radius base 14250<br>14.25² = 203.06<br>13.50² = 182.25<br>14.25 × 13.50 = 192.38<br>577.69 |

(3)

## COMMENTARY

The upper surface of the blinding concrete is inclined at an angle exceeding 15 degrees to the horizontal and formwork is measured to the surface in accordance with Rule G/M3 of the CESMM. The item description states it is to upper surfaces and that it is to blinding concrete, as required by Rules G/A2 and G/A3, respectively, of the CESMM.

Preparation of excavated surfaces is deemed to be carried out on material other than topsoil, rock or artificial hard material unless otherwise stated, Rule E/D5 of the CESMM. Item descriptions identify preparation carried out on inclined surfaces as required by Rule E/A7 of the CESMM.

The reservoir above the ground slab if imagined to be filled solid represents the frustum of a cone. The method chosen to measure the volume of the concrete in the perimeter walls is to first measure the volume of this frustum and deduct from it the cylindrical void. See sketch in the Commentary to the next column of dimensions. In the waste at the foot of the adjoining column, the top and bottom radii are first established. The formula for the frustum of a cone =

$$\frac{22}{7} \times \frac{1}{3} \text{ height } (R^2 + r^2 + Rr)$$

where R is the large radius and r the small. Calculations which represent the part of the formula in brackets are carried out in the waste column. The resultant is carried to the dimension column and the application of the remainder of the formula is carried out in the dimension and timesing columns. See first item in the next column of dimensions.

| | | | |
|---|---|---|---|

CIRC. CONC. RESERVOIR    DRG.No.F/D/3

Walls. perim (cont

$\frac{22}{7}\Big/\frac{1}{3}\Big/$ 577.69
        7.00
        1.00

Provn of conc. Grad.c20
20 agg.    (F243

&

Placg. of conc., mass
walls, thickn. e.500 mm
        (F444

$\frac{22}{7}\Big/$ 13.00
      13.00
      7.00

Ddt. both last items
            (core

$\frac{22}{7}\Big/$ 26.00
      7.00

Fmw. fair fin., curvd.
to one radius in one
plane, radius 13.00m,
intl. face of perim wall
            (G255

```
            900
           1200
       2) 2100
           1050
```

$\frac{2}{}\Big/$ 1.05
      2.00

Ddt. last item. (G255
        (ends of cross wall

Exposed extl. face of perim
wall.        1250
              500
              750

$\frac{750}{7000}$ = 0.107 = 6° 10'

        batter = 10.71%

below fin. level   1000
                    150
                   1150

2/1150 × 10.71% =   27000
                     246
  max. diam         27246
  min. diam         27000
              2) 54246
  mean diam = 27123

1150 × 1.006 = 1157 (slope lgth
Note: 1.006 = Secant of 6° 10'

(4)

## COMMENTARY

The first set of dimensions in the adjoining column represent the volume of the frustum of a cone (See Commentary to preceding column of dimensions). The dimensions entered against the Deduct are those for the volume of the cylindrical void. See sketch below. The third dimension of 1.00 in the first set of dimensions is entered merely to indicate cubic dimensions.

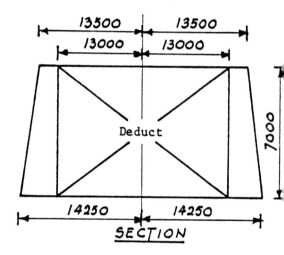

Location of the curved formwork is given as additional description. Where the ends of the internal dividing walls abut the inside of the perimeter wall, the formwork to the latter is deducted. See Deduct item. Code G255.

For the purpose of measuring the formwork to the external face of the perimeter wall, the area which is above finished path level and that which is below needs to be separated. It being assumed that exposed external surfaces will have fair finish formwork. The waste at the foot of the adjoining column are the preliminary calculations to establish the dimensions of the formwork for the external exposed face of the perimeter wall. The calculations allow for the fair finish formwork extending to 150 mm below the finished path level. This is a practical allowance; it is not governed by a rule of CESMM.

| | | | | CIRC. CONC. RESERVOIR   DRG. NO. F/D/3 |
|---|---|---|---|---|

Walls, perim (cont.

Extl. face

27246 ÷ 2 = 13623

27000 ÷ 2 = 13500

| $\frac{22}{7}$ / | 27.12 |
|---|---|
| | 1.16 |

Fmw. fair fin., curvd. varying radius (conical) max. radius 13.62 m min. radius 13.50 m, extl. face of perim wall
(G260

```
    7000
    1150
    5850
```

```
          27000
2/750 =   1500
          28500
          27246
       2)55746
          27873
```

5850 × 1.006 = 5885

| $\frac{22}{7}$ / | 27.88 |
|---|---|
| | 5.89 |

Fmw. rough fin., curvd. varying radius (conical) max. radius 14.25 m min. radius 13.62 m, extl. face perim wall below ground (G160.2

```
    27000
    26000
  2)53000
    26500
```

Top perim wall

| $\frac{22}{7}$ / | 26.50 |
|---|---|
| | 0.50 |

Conc. access, fin of top surf., steel trow fin.        (G812

(5)

The formwork to the outer face of the perimeter wall comes within the classification "other curved". It is described as provided in Rule G/A4(c) of the CESMM and item descriptions state maximum and minimum radii. The first item is for the formwork above path level. The second item is for that below the level of the path. See sketch below.

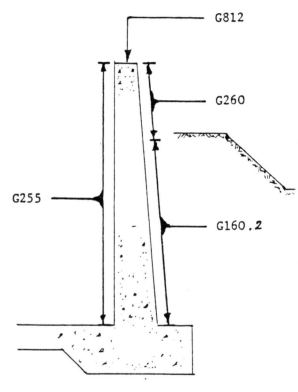

G812

G260

G255

G160.2

SECTION

An item is given for finishing the top surface of the wall on the assumption that it is specified to be steel trowelled finish. The dimensions represent the mean circumference of the top of the wall multiplied by the width.

CIRC. CONC. RESERVOIR    DRG. No F/D/3

<u>Walls. - Intl. cross wall</u>

$$\begin{array}{r} 900 \\ 1200 \\ \hline 2\overline{)2100} \\ \hline 1050 \end{array}$$

| | |
|---|---|
| 26.00<br>1.05<br>2.00 | Provn. of conc., Grade 20<br>20 agg.    (F243 |

&

Placg. of conc., mass
walls, thickn. e 500 mm
(F444

$$\begin{array}{r} 1200 \\ 900 \\ \hline 2\overline{)300} \\ \hline 150 \end{array}$$

$$\frac{150}{2000} = 0.075 = 4°20'$$

$$2000 \times 1.003 = \underline{2006}$$

| | |
|---|---|
| 2/ 26.00<br>2.01 | Fmw. fair fin., battd.<br>(G235 |

<u>Top of cross wall</u>

| | |
|---|---|
| 26.00<br>0.90 | Conc. access., fin of<br>top surfs., steel trow.<br>fin.    (G812 |

(6)

COMMENTARY

The section of the internal cross wall is as shown in the following diagram.

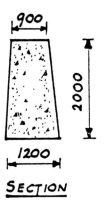

SECTION

The length of the internal wall is taken on its centre line. The slight reduction both as regards concrete and formwork due to the curved abutments is neglected.

The whole of the concrete in the wall exceeds 500 mm in thickness and is classified accordingly. Width for calculating volume is taken as the average width. See waste calculation.

The faces of the wall each have a batter of 150 mm in a height of 2.00 m. From these dimensions it is found that the angle of inclination is approximately 4 degrees, 20 seconds to the vertical. The formwork being to a surface inclined at an angle within the range 0 - 10 degrees to the vertical is classified as "battered". The slope length of the formwork is calculated by multiplying the height of the wall by the Secant of 4 degrees, 20 seconds.

It is assumed that the top of the wall is required to be steel trowelled finish and an item is measured for this.

CIRC. CONC. RESERVOIR. DRG. No. F/D/3

Earthworks for struc
Strip top soil.

$$
\begin{array}{r}
26000 \\
2/500 \quad = 1000 \\
2/1000 \times 10.71\% = 214 \\
2/2000 \quad = 4000 \\
2/3000 \quad = 6000 \\
2\,)\overline{37214} \\
\overline{18607}
\end{array}
$$

$\dfrac{22}{7}$ | 18.61
      18.61
      0.15

Gen. excavn. topsoil,
max. depth n.e. 0.25 m;
Excavd. Surf. underside
topsoil.    (E 411

&

Excavn. ancills.
disposal of excavd. matl.
topsoil.    (E 531

Bulk dig.

$$
\begin{array}{rr}
600 & 5000 \\
75 & 675 \\
\overline{675} \; \text{formn.} & \overline{4325}
\end{array}
$$

$$
\begin{array}{lr}
\text{topsoil} & 9000 \\
 & 150 \\
\text{Radius } 15.25 \rceil & 8850 \\
\text{as Col (1)} & 4325 \\
\text{Depth} & \overline{4525}
\end{array}
$$

$\dfrac{22}{7}$ | 15.25
      15.25
      4.53

Gen. excavn., max depth
2 – 5 m; Comm. Surf.
underside topsoil,
Excavd. Surf. 0.6 m
above Fin. Surf (E 425

&

Excavn. ancills.
disposal of excavd. matl
          (E 532

(7)

COMMENTARY

The first item measured for excavation assumes there is a specified requirement for top soil to be excavated and kept separate from the other excavated material. A separate stage is thereby created (See Rule E/M5 of CESMM). The first item in the adjoining column of dimensions gives the excavation of the top soil as a separate stage of the general excavation and the description identifies the Excavated Surface and states the maximum depth of the stage. The diameter of the area of top soil is built up in waste and is divided by 2 to give radius. It is assumed soil is to be removed from beneath the perimeter banking. The extent is illustrated by dotted lines in the sketch given below.

General excavation below the top soil is given in the item under the heading "Bulk dig". It is measured over the spread of the foundation as provided in Rule E/M6 of the CESMM. The depth (as calculated in waste) is measured to the level of the predominant formation. This excavation is indicated by cross hatching in the sketch below. As the Commencing Surface and the Excavated Surface for the work in the item are not the Original Surface and the Final Surface, respectively, each are identified in the item description.

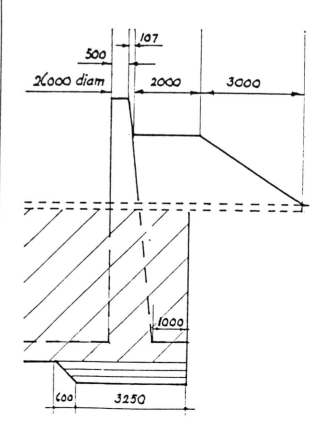

142

## CIRC. CONC. RESERVOIR DRG. No. F/D/3

Perim. fdn.

75 × 1.414 = 106

2/31= 23600 ........ 75
........ 62 ........ 31
23538
2/½/31 = ........ 24000
........ 31
23969

| 22/7 | 27.25 | Excavn. for fdns, max. depth 0.5-1m; Comm.Surf. 0.60m above Final Surf., sink below g. slab. (E323 |
| | 3.25 | |
| | 0.60 | |
| ½/22/7 | 23.54 | |
| | 0.60 | |
| | 0.60 | |
| 22/7 | 23.97 | |
| | 0.03 | |
| | 0.60 | |

&

Excavn ancills. disposal of excavd matl (E532

Fill around perim. wall
........ 30500
2/½/ 1000 = ........ 1000
........ 29500
3850 × 10.71% = 412
........ 29500
2/½/1000 = 1000
2/⅓/412 = 275 ........ 1275
........ 28225

| 22/7 | 29.50 | Fillg. to strucs, sel. excavd. matl. other than topsoil or rock. (E614 |
| | 1.00 | |
| | 3.85 | |
| ½/22/7 | 28.23 | |
| | 0.41 | |
| | 3.85 | |

&

Ddt. Excavn ancills. disposal of excavd. matl. (E532

(8)

Excavation indicated by horizontal hatching in the sketch in the preceding column of Commentary is classified "Excavation for foundations". In accordance with paragraph 5.21 of the CESMM, the description states the Commencing Surface. The first set of dimensions attached to the description is taken the same as that for the rectangular section of the concrete footing from Column (1) of this Example. The second set represents the triangular section of the excavation. The third set provide for the volume of the strip additional to the rectangular section as shown in section at (a) in the following sketch.

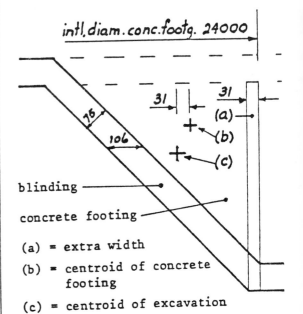

intl. diam. conc. footg. 24000

blinding

concrete footing

(a) = extra width

(b) = centroid of concrete footing

(c) = centroid of excavation

## SECTION

The filling here measured fills the excavated void between the battered external face of the wall and the vertical excavated surface up to the underside of the top soil. For measurement convention, see Rule E/M6 of the CESMM.

The volume of disposal of excavated material, previously taken for the whole of the excavated material resulting from the general excavation and the excavation for foundations, is reduced by the "Ddt" item.

| | |
|---|---|
| | CIRC. CONC. RESERVOIR.  DRG.NO.F/D/3 |

Perim. Footpath.

```
                          27000
        2/1000 x 10.71% =  214
                          27214
        2/1500 = 3000
                          30214
                          27214
                    2 ) 57428
                          28714
```

22/7 /28.71
1.50

Li. duty pavements, bit. macadam, to BS.1621 Table 4, 6 mm. agg. depth 50mm.  (R752

of

Li. duty pavements, granular base DTp Spec. clause 803, depth 100mm
  (R713

```
                          30214
              2/51 =  102
              2/75 =  150
                          30466
   1500                  27214
     51              2 ) 57680
     75                  28840
   1626
```

22/7 /28.84
1.63

Fillg. ancills., prepn. of filld. surfs.
  (E722

```
                          30214
      2/½/51 =              51
                          30265
```

22/7 /30.27

Edgings, p.c.conc., to BS.340, Fig.11, 51 x 152mm, curvd. to radius 0.12 m. bedd. and haunchd. with conc. grad. 20, as detail Drg. No.8.  (R441

(9)

## COMMENTARY

The surfacing and base of the footpath is measured as provided in Class R of the CESMM. Class R is examined in Chapter 13.

The following diagram indicates the width dimensions of the footpath. The height of the wall above the footpath (1000) is multiplied by the rate of batter (10.71%) to calculate the dimension 107 mm.

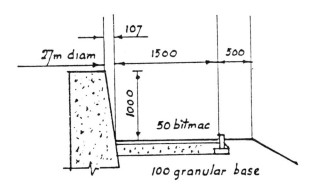

SECTION - PERIMETER PATH

The first set of waste calculations in the adjoining column of dimensions determines the diameter of the centre line of the footpath. The dimensions of the surfacing and the base are the mean girth of the footpath multiplied by the width. Measurements are taken at the top surface. See Rule R/M1 of the CESMM.

Preparation of filled surfaces is measured beneath the base and the foundation to the edging.

The item description for edging makes reference to the detailed drawing reproduced below.

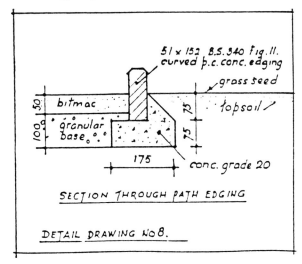

SECTION THROUGH PATH EDGING

DETAIL DRAWING NO 8.

CIRC. CONC. RESERVOIR    DRG. No. F/D/3

Soil + seed banks to path

| | |
|---|---|
| path level | 11000 |
| nat. g. level | 9000 |
| | 2000 |

$$\frac{2000}{3000} = 0.666 = Tan$$

$$= 33° 40'$$

$$3000 \times 1.202 = 3605$$

$$
\begin{array}{r}
30214 \\
2/500 \cdot \underline{1000} \\
31214 \\
2/225 \cdot \underline{450} \\
30764 \\
\\
31214 \\
\underline{37214} \\
2\overline{)68428} \\
34214
\end{array}
$$

<u>Hor top</u>

$\frac{22}{7}$ / 30.76
0.45

Fillg. thickn. 150 mm
excavd. topsoil
(E641.1

$\frac{22}{7}$ / 34.21
3.61

Fillg thickn. 150 mm
excavd. topsoil, surfs.
10 - 45 degrees to hor.
(E641.2

$\frac{22}{7}$ / 30.76
0.45
0.15
$\frac{22}{7}$ / 34.21
3.61
0.15

Ddt. Excavn ancills.,
disposal of excavd.
matl. topsoil
(E531

(10)

The dimensions for the banking to the path are shown on the following diagram.

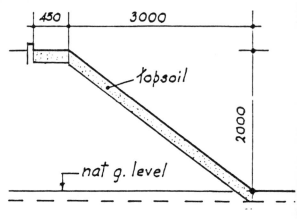

SECTION

Wastes first calculate height and then slope length. The angle at the toe of the bank is found either by calculator or by reference to Trig. Tables after the Tan. of the angle has been calculated by dividing height by the spread of the bank. The slope length is found by multiplying the spread by the Secant of the angle.

The uniform layer of top soil is classified "Filling to stated thickness". That upon surfaces (a) inclined at 10 - 45 degrees to the horizontal (b) inclined at 45 - 90 degrees to the horizontal (c) vertical are each given separately from those which are horizontal.

Excavated top soil has previously been measured for disposal. The volume required for the top soil filling is deducted from the disposal item.

The surfaces of the bulk filling are to receive the Permanent Works of a uniform layer of top soil. The surface of the uniform layer of top soil are to receive the Permanent Works of grass seed. In accordance with Rule E/M22 the trimming of these surfaces are not measureable.

| | | | | CIRC. CONC. RESERVOIR | DRG No F/D/3 |
|---|---|---|---|---|---|

_Soil & seed banks (cont_

_Hor._

$\frac{22}{7}$ / 30.76
0.45

Landscapg., grass seedg.,
surfs.n.e. 10 degrees.,
Spec. clause "X" (E830.1

_Slope_

$\frac{22}{7}$ / 34.21
9.61

Landscapg., grass seedg
surfs ov. 10 degrees,
S.pec. clause "X" (E830.2

_Bulk fillg. bankg._

$150 \times 1.202 = 180 - 150 = 30\,mm$
$30 \times 1.501 = \underline{45\,mm}$

diam. soil strip 37214
2/45 = $\underline{\quad 90}$
       37124
2/3000 = $\underline{6000}$
       31124

       27000
$2/1150 \times 10.71\%$ = $\underline{\quad 246}$
       27246
$2/2000 \times 10.71\%$ $\underline{\quad 428}$
       27674

       27674
       31124
2 ) 58798
diam centroid (a) $\underline{29399}$

       31124
$2/\frac{1}{3}/3000$ = $\underline{2000}$
diam centroid (b) 33124

       27246
$\frac{2}{3}/428$ = $\underline{\quad 285}$
diam centroid (c) $\underline{27531}$

       2000
$150 \times 10.71\%$ = $\underline{\quad 16}$
       1984
       $\underline{\quad 45}$
       1939
$2000 \times 10.71\%$ = $\underline{\quad 214}$
width (a) $\underline{1725}$

(11)

The dimensions for the grass seeding are a repeat of those in the preceding column for the topsoil filling.

The first waste calculation under the heading "Bulk fillg." uses trigonometry to find the differences between the overall width of the bank and that of the bulk filling.

1.202 = Secant of 33 degrees 40

1.501 = Cotan. of 33 degrees 40

The following diagram shows the difference.

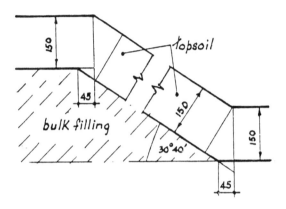

For the purpose of measurement, the cross-section of the bulk filling is divided into a rectangle and two triangles. See diagram below.

Further wastes are used to calculate the minimum and maximum diameters of the bulk filling. They are also used to calculate the centroids, as illustrated in the following diagram.

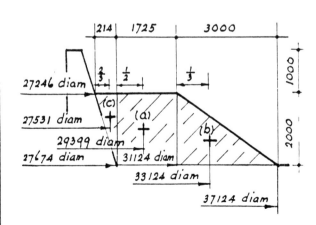

CIRC. CONC. RESERVOIR    DRG.F/D/3

| | | | |
|---|---|---|---|
| | | Bulk fillg. bankg. (cont. | |
| | | | |
| | | Fillg. to strucs. sel. | |
| $\frac{22}{7}$/ | 29.40 | excavd. matl. oth. than | |
| | 1.73 | tapsoil or rack (E614 | |
| | 2.00 | (a | |
| $\frac{22}{7}$/$\frac{1}{2}$/ | 33.12 | | |
| | 3.00 | | |
| | 2.00 | & (b | |
| $\frac{22}{7}$/$\frac{1}{2}$/ | 27.53 | | |
| | 0.21 | (c | |
| | 2.00 | | |
| | | Ddt. Excavn. ancills. | |
| | | disposal of excavd. | |
| | | matl.        (E532 | |

NOTE: Pipework is not
here measured. The
foll conc. ancills is
reqd in connection
with pipework.

| | | | |
|---|---|---|---|
| | 1 | Conc. ancills., inserts, | |
| | | (excludg supply and | |
| | | fixg. of inserts); pipes | |
| | | nom bore 200 mm and | |
| | | groutg. w.i.t. mor(1:2) | |
| | | to 250 dia. preformed | |
| | | opg in 550 mm (av) thick | |
| | | mass conc. wall and proj. | |
| | | one surf. conc. (G832 | |
| | | & | |
| | | Conc. ancills., fmw. rough | |
| | | fin., for voids, small | |
| | | circ., depth 0.5 - 1 m | |
| | | (G172 | |

(12)

## COMMENTARY

The dimensions entered against the items in the adjoining column represent the circumference of the circles at the centroids multiplied by the cross-section for each of the sections (a), (b) and (c), respectively.

Notice that the filling to the banking is classified as "to structures".

A volume, equal to that of the filling, is deducted from the volume of excavated material previously measured for disposal.

The entry of the pipe through the concrete wall is classified as inserts. Since the pipe is supplied and fixed elsewhere, the item for the insert is qualified to this effect.

It is assumed that the pipes will not be cast in but will enter through a preformed holed in the wall and an item for formwork is measured for forming the hole.

# 9 Pipework - CESMM Classes: I-L

Each of the four Classes I - L of the CESMM are sub-divisions of the overall classification "Pipework". All four Classes are considered in this Chapter. Sewer renovation, other than the work measurable under Class K and Class L is included in Class Y (See Rule Y/M2, Table 18.01, Chapter 18).

Class I covers the provision, laying and jointing of pipes. Where the items describe the pipes as "in trenches" they include the laying of the pipes in the trenches and excavating and backfilling the pipe trenches.

The measurement of pipelines will usually start with the measurement of the pipes in accordance with Class I. The Class I items need to be complemented by items for the work covered by the other three Classes to the extent that such work is required in the pipelines. For example, fittings and valves in the run of pipes are measured under Class J. Manholes and other chambers, gullies, crossings, reinstatement and sundry ancillaries as listed in the table of classification, if required, are measured under Class K. Items measured under Classes I, J and K and also items other than "Extras to excavation and backfilling" in Class L, which include excavation and backfilling, are deemed to include excavation in material other than rock or artificial hard material and backfilling with the material excavated. Any excavation in rock or artifical hard material and any backfilling with material other than that excavated, is given as items of extras to the previously included excavation and backfilling in accordance with Class L. Beds, haunches, surrounds and other supports required for the pipes together with any required wrapping of the pipes are measured under Class L. Items for the laying of pipes in headings, or by thrust boring or pipe jacking, where expressly required, are given under Class L; these items are given in addition to the items for the provision laying and jointing of pipes "not in trenches" given under Class I.

The rules in Class I apply to ducts and metal culverts, included in Class K, except that items are deemed to include cutting and fittings and the lengths measured for those not in trenches include the lengths occupied by fittings. Class K provides also features of classification for ditches and rubble drains and for the work additional to the pipes in trenches when French drains are required to be constructed.

For work included in Class I to L and for exclusions from the Classes, refer to the "Includes" and "Excludes" given at the head of the classification tables (for these Classes in the CESMM). References to work included in the Classes are also made in the "Excludes" for other Classes at the head of the classification tables in the CESMM as follows:-

References to work included in Classes I, J, K, L, and Y :-

Class E - Excavation for pipes and sewers, manholes, etc.

References to work included in Classes I, J, K and L :-

Class M - Metalwork in pipework

Class N - Pipework

Class R - Drainage

Class T - Pipe laying in headings, tunnels and shafts.

References to work included in Classes I and J :-

Class H - Precast concrete pipework

References to work included in Classes I, J and K:-

       Class W  -  Waterproofed joints

References to work included in Class K:-

       Class H  -  Precast concrete manholes, catchpits and gullies

References to work included in Classes K and L:-

       Class F -  In-situ concrete for drainage and pipework

       Class G -  Formwork and reinforcement; drainage and pipework

References to work included in Class L:-

       Class Y  -  Extras to excavation and backfilling etc.

References to work in Classes K and Y:-

       Class U  -  Brickwork to manholes, pipework and sewer renovation

Where a contract includes more than one type of pipeline, the work in each is grouped under a descriptive title. For example, Drainage, Water Mains, etc. Each may form a Part of the Bill of Quantities or a sub-division of a Part. Each sub-division may be further divided. For example, Drainage may be divided to group separately Sewers and Drains, French and Rubble Drains, etc. The appropriate items from all Classes being grouped in the Part or sub-division to which they relate.

*PIPEWORK - PIPES - CESMM CLASS I*

Item descriptions state the location or type of pipework so that pipe runs can be identified by reference to the Drawings. In addition, for work which is adjudged to comprise sections of differing characteristics, the Bill may group the work into sections giving separately the items for each section of work of particular characteristic. For example, items for work in open ground will be given separately from those for work in confined situations.

Table 9.01    Pipes

Generally - Items deemed to include the supply of all materials by Contractor, unless otherwise stated, and for pipe cutting (Rule I/C1)

| 1st Division | | | 2nd Division |
|---|---|---|---|
| Clay pipes | m | State materials, joint types, lining requirements, BS reference and specified quality (Rule I/A2) | State nominal bore of pipe (Rule I/A2) |
| Presetressed concrete pipes | m | | |
| Other concrete pipes | m | State location or type of pipework in each item or group of items so that runs can be identified by reference to Drawings (Rule I/A1) | |
| Cast or spun iron pipes | m | | |
| Steel pipes | m | Exclude pipes and fittings in backdrops to manholes and include in items for backdrop manholes in Class K (Rule I/M5) | |
| Plastic pipes | m | | |
| Asbestos cement pipes | m | | |
| Pitch fibre pipes | m | | |

Table 9.01    Pipes (cont.

| 3rd Division | |
|---|---|
| Not in trenches | Applies where pipes are expressly required not to be laid in trenches (Rule I/D2) |
| | Applies to pipes suspended or supported above ground or other surface, to pipes in headings, tunnels and shafts, to pipes installed by thrust boring and pipe jacking and pipes laid within separately measured excavated volumes (Rule I/D1). Give separate items for and state each such category (Rule I/A3) |
| | Measure lengths along centre line of pipes excluding lengths of fittings and valves. Measure to inside surface of manholes and other chambers where built in, but exclude lengths of pipes and fittings in backdrops of manholes (Rules I/M3 and I/M5) |
| | Give additional items in Classes K and L for work in connection with pipes not in trenches other than the provision, laying and jointing of pipes (Rule I/M4) |
| In trenches | State depth range as 3rd Division features. State trench depths exceeding 4 m to next higher multiple of 0.5 m (Rule I/A6) |
| | Measure depths from Commencing Surface to invert (Rule I/D3). State Commencing Surface when it is not Original Surface (Rule I/A4). Measure completed work from Commencing Surface used when preparing Bill of Quantities (Rule I/M1) |
| | Measure lengths along centre line of pipes over fittings and valves to inside surface of manholes and other chambers but exclude lengths of pipes and fittings in backdrops to manholes (Rules I/M3 and I/M5) |
| | Deemed to include excavation, preparation of surfaces, disposal of excavated material, upholding sides, backfilling and removal of existing services, except to the extent such work is included in Classes J, K and L (Rule I/C2) |
| | State where more than one pipe is expressly required to be run in one trench and identify pipe run. State where pipes are laid in French or rubble drains (Rule I/A5) |
| | Backfilling trenches is not measured except as set out in Class K for French and rubble drains and except where backfilled, as Class L, with other than the material excavated (Rule I/M2) |

COMMENTARY

Pipes (refer to Table 9.01)

Items for pipes include the supply of all materials by the Contractor, unless the item descriptions state otherwise. They include also for pipe cutting, but see "straight specials" under Class J.

COMMENTARY

Pipes (cont.

The 1st Division descriptive features for pipes in Class I of the CESMM require to be amplified so that item descriptions state the materials, the joint types, the lining requirements and any applicable BS reference and specified quality. The 2nd Division features are overriden by Rule I/A2 which requires item descriptions to state the actual nominal bores of the pipes. 3rd Division features distinguish pipes laid in trenches from those which are not.

Pipes are measured linearly, in metres, along their centre lines. The lengths entering manholes and other chambers are measured to the inside face of the manhole or chamber, except that pipes and fittings in backdrops to manholes are measured in the items for manholes in Class K.

*Pipes Not in Trenches*

Pipes are classified "not in trenches" where it is expressly required that they shall not be laid in trenches. The categories of pipework to which the classification applies are given in Rule I/A3. See first panel of Table 9.01 under 3rd Division on Page 149. Each category is given separately and each is identified in the item descriptions when measuring the pipe items under Class I. Items additional to those in Class I are given under Classes K and L for work in connection with pipes not in trenches. See Tables given later for Classes K and L and subsequent Commentary.

The lengths measured for pipes "not in trenches" exclude the lengths occupied by fittings and valves.

*Pipes in Trenches*

Items for pipes "in trenches" include the excavation of trenches and for backfilling the trenches with the materials excavated and are deemed to include upholding sides and other work stated in Rule I/C2. See Table 9.01.

The lengths measured for pipes "in trenches" include the lengths occupied by fittings and valves. (This measurement convention is different from that applicable to pipes "not in trenches"). Where pipe bores change at fittings it is usual to measure the pipe of largest bore over the fitting. This convention is noted in Preamble so that the estimator knows the pipe cost he may offset against that of the fitting.

The appropriate 3rd Division depth range within which pipes are laid is measured from the Commencing Surface to the pipe invert. The Commencing Surface is identified in the item descriptions when it is not the Original Surface. The Commencing Surface adopted when preparing the Bill of Quantities is adopted when measuring the completed work.

Separate items are given for each pipe when it is expressly required that more than one pipe is laid in one trench. The depth classification is that of the particular pipe. A statement giving the location of the pipe run combined with the phrase "in shared trench" in the item description of each pipe will usually identify pipes in these situations as required by Rule I/A5. See last panel of Table 9.01. This Rule also requires that item description shall state where pipes are laid in French or rubble drains.

Items in addition to those in Class I are measured under Class L when hard material is to be excavated and when backfilling is required to be in material other than that excavated. Additional items are also given under Class K when pipes cross obstructions etc., when there is work to surfaces and reinstatement and when supports to sides of excavation are expressly required to be left in.

Table 9.02  Fittings and Valves for Pipework

Generally - Items deemed to include the supply of materials by the
           Contractor unless otherwise stated (Rule J/C1)

           Items deemed to include for excavation, preparation of surfaces,
           disposal of excavated material, upholding sides of excavation,
           backfilling and removal of existing services except to the extent
           that such work is included in Classes I, K and L (Rule J/C2)

           Pipe fittings comprising backdrops to manholes shall be included
           in items for manholes in Class K (Rule J/M1)

           State when fittings are to pipework not in trenches (Rule J/A4)

| 1st Division | | State materials, joint types, lining requirements, BS reference and specified qualities (Rule J/A1) |
|---|---|---|
| Clay pipe fittings | nr | |
| Prestressed concrete pipe fittings | nr | |
| Other concrete pipe fittings | nr | |
| Cast or spun iron pipe fittings     nr | State principal dimensions of fittings when nominal bore exceeds 300 mm (Rule J/A2) | |
| Steel pipe fittings     nr | State principal dimensions (Rule J/A2) | |
| Plastic pipe fittings     nr | | |
| Asbestos cement pipe fittings   nr | | |

| 2nd Division | | 3rd Division |
|---|---|---|
| Bends | Give separately vertical bends exceeding 300 mm nominal bore and so describe (Rule J/A3) | State nominal bore (Rule J/A1) |
| Junctions and branches | | Classify pipe fittings of different bores according to nominal bore of largest pipe (Rule J/D1) |
| Tapers | | |
| Double collars | | |
| Adaptors | | |
| Glands | | State if with puddle flange (Rule J/A1) |
| Bellmouths | | |
| Straight specials<br><br>Deemed to include cutting (Rule J/C3) | Measure only when non-standard lengths of straight pipes expressly required (Rule J/M2)<br><br>Use classification for non-standard lengths of straight pipe (Rule J/D2) | |

Table 9.02  Fittings and Valves for Pipework (cont.

| 1st Division | | | 2nd Division | 3rd Division |
|---|---|---|---|---|
| Valves and penstocks | nr | State materials and additional requirements such as joints, drain cocks, extension spindles and brackets, BS reference and specified quality (Rule J/A5) | State type of valve or penstock as 2nd Division features | State nominal bore (Rule J/A5) |

COMMENTARY

Fittings and Valves (refer to Table 9.02)

Fittings and valves are described and an item giving quantity by number is given in the Bill of Quantities for each type. For details to be stated in the item descriptions see Table 9.02. Actual nominal bores of valves and fittings are stated in the descriptions in place of the 3rd Division range. Fittings are classified according to their largest bore. Fittings comprising backdrops to manholes are part of the manhole and are not measured under Class J. The tumbling bay junction, although it occurs on the horizontal run of pipes which are measured to the inside face of the manhole, is considered to be a fitting comprising the backdrop.

*PIPEWORK - MANHOLES AND PIPEWORK ANCILLARIES -CESMM CLASS K*

Items in Class K are deemed to include excavation, preparation of surfaces, disposal of excavated material, upholding sides of excavation, backfilling and removal of existing services to the extent that this work is not included in Classes I, J and K. They are deemed also to include concrete, reinforcement, formwork, joints and finishes (See Rules K/C1 and K/C2). These two Coverage Rules are not repeated but apply to all Tables here given in Class K.

Table 9.03 Manholes, Other Chambers and Gullies

| 1st Division | | 2nd Division | | 3rd Division |
|---|---|---|---|---|
| Manholes<br><br>Other stated chambers | State type or mark numbers of manholes or other chambers details of which are given elsewhere in the Contract (Rule K/A1)<br><br>Deemed to include different arrangements of inlets and outlets, access shafts of different heights, metalwork and connection pipes (Rule K/C3)<br><br>Manholes with backdrops are demed to include pipe fittings in backdrops (Rule K/C4)<br><br>State types and loading duties of covers (Rule K/A2)<br><br>Class drawpits as other stated chambers (Rule K/D3) | Brick<br><br>*Brick with backdrop<br><br>In situ concrete<br><br>*In situ concrete with backdrop<br><br>Precast concrete<br><br>*Precast concrete with backdrop<br><br>*Note: Descriptive features marked thus * above, do not apply to other stated chambers | nr<br><br><br>nr<br><br>nr<br><br><br>nr<br><br>nr<br><br><br>nr | Measure depths from tops of covers to channel inverts or tops of base slabs whichever is the lower (Rule K/D2)<br><br>State depth range as 3rd Division features<br><br>State actual depth where exceeding 4 m |

Table 9.03  Manholes, Other Chambers and Gullies (cont.

| 1st Division | | 2nd Division | 3rd Division |
|---|---|---|---|
| Gullies | State type or mark number as for manholes (Rule K/A1)<br><br>Deemed to include different arrangements of inlets, etc., as for manholes (Rule K/C3)<br><br>State types and loading duties of covers (Rule K/A2) | Classify as 2nd Division descriptive features    nr | |

NOTE:  Manholes and other chambers may be measured in detail as set out in other Classes of the CESMM (Note at foot of Page 51 of CESMM).

COMMENTARY

Manholes and Other Chambers (refer to Table 9.03)

Manholes  and other chambers are enumerated and are given by depth range, or depth  where exceeding 4 m deep. Separate items distinguish different  forms of  manholes  and  chambers.  Items  are deemed  to  include  for  different arrangements  of  inlets or for access shafts of different heights etc.,  as Rule  K/C3. See Table 9.03. Items for manholes with backdrops are deemed  to include  the  pipes  and fittings in the backdrops. The  loading  duties  of manhole  covers  are  stated  in  item  descriptions.  Apart  from  extra  for excavating  any  hard material and for any backfilling with  material  other than that excavated (both of which are measured, if required, under Class L) the  items represent the complete construction of the manholes and  chambers as  detailed in the Contract. Concrete or similar surrounds are detailed and made part of the manhole or chamber and are not classed as backfilling.

Depths  of  manholes  and other chambers are measured from the tops  of  the covers to the channel inverts or the tops of the base slabs whichever is the lower.  Where the benchings, channels and bases of manholes are  monolithic, it is necessary to state in preamble the convention adopted in measuring the depths.  Unless  otherwise  stated, it will be assumed that  the  Commencing Surface  for the excavation is approximately that of the cover and that  the Commencing Surface is the Original Surface.

Manholes  and  other chambers may be measured in detail as set  out  in other  Classes of the CESMM. Specimen item descriptions typical for the work in a precast concrete manhole, measured in detail, are given in Fig. K1.

Where  it is thought advisable, when measuring manholes in detail,  the descriptions  use  features which identify the items of work more  precisely than would  be  the  case if standard descriptive features were  used.  When coding  these items the work described in the particular feature may be suf- ficiently analogous to that described in the standard descriptive feature to make it  reasonable to use the standard code for it. Where a feature is con- sidered  special and the digit 9 is used to denote the non-standard  feature it may  be advisable to bill items out of the usual order of ascending  code number  to achieve a logical Bill order. See Item Code E925 in Fig. K1. (The 9 is introduced  into  this  code to illustrate billing out of  order,  Some practitioners may consider the work sufficiently analogous to foundations to code it E325).

Where  manholes measured in detail are of precast concrete rings, there would  appear  to be the options of casting the in situ  concrete  surrounds against the excavated surface or using formwork. In this situation there are many practical  reasons  against casting the concrete against the  excavated surface.  It  is considered practical to measure formwork to  support  the outer face.

| Number | Item description | Unit | COMMENTARY |
|--------|------------------|------|------------|
| | **"X" NR. MANHOLES, PRECAST CONCRETE.** | | |
| | <u>EARTHWORKS.</u> | | |
| E925 | Excavation for manholes, maximum depth 2 - 5 m. | m3 | |
| | <u>Excavation ancillaries.</u> | | |
| E522.1 | Preparation of excavated surfaces. | m2 | |
| E522.2 | Preparation of excavated surfaces; vertical curved. | m2 | |
| E532 | Disposal of excavated material. | m3 | |
| E613 | Filling around tops manhole shafts. | m3 | |
| | <u>IN SITU CONCRETE.</u> | | |
| F143 | Provision of concrete, ordinary prescribed mix to BS 5328, grade C20, cement to BS 12, 20 mm aggregate to BS 882. | m3 | |
| | <u>Placing of concrete.</u> | | |
| F422 | Mass bases, thickness 150 - 300 mm; cast against excavated surfaces. | m3 | |
| F441 | Curved walls, thickness not exceeding 150 mm; surround to precast units. | m3 | |
| F480 | Mass benchings, diameter 1630 mm, thickness 675 mm. | m3 | |
| | **CONCRETE ANCILLARIES.** | | |
| | <u>Formwork rough finish, curved to one radius in one plane.</u> | | |
| G154 | Radius 815 mm, width 0.4 - 1.22 mm; vertical edges of benchings. | m2 | |
| G155 | Radius 815 mm; vertical surrounds to chamber sections. | m2 | |

**COMMENTARY**

The specimen item descriptions are typical for the work shown on the following details of a manhole in precast concrete construction. (Assumed 1200 mm internal diameter).

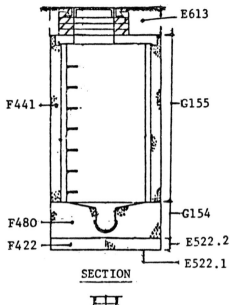

**SECTION**

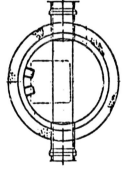

**PLAN**

The volume of excavation, Item Code E925 would be calculated:-

$D^2$ x 0.7854 x H, where D = external diameter and H = height from underside of base to top of cover.

The Items assume formwork to the outer face of concrete above the top of the base.

Fig. K1.   Specimen item descriptions for precast concrete  manholes measured in detail in  accordance  with the option afforded by the  Note at the foot of page 51 of the CESMM.

| Number | Item description | Unit |
|---|---|---|
| | "X" NR. MANHOLES PRECAST CONCRETE (cont. | |
| | CONCRETE ANCILLARIES (cont. | |
| | Formwork fair finish. | |
| G244 | Plane vertical width 0.4 - 1.22 m. | m2 |
| G284 | For components of constant cross-section; upper surfaces of half round straight main channel, diameter 300 mm. | m |
| | Concrete accessories. | |
| G812 | Finishing of top surfaces, steel trowel; to slope | m2 |
| G832 | Inserts; ends of 300 mm diameter pipes cast into concrete for a length of 215 mm, projecting from two surfaces, excluding supply of pipe. | nr |
| | PRECAST CONCRETE. | |
| H599 | Heavy duty manhole chamber cover slabs to BS 5911, diameter 1500 mm, thickness 150 mm, with perforation for manhole cover. | nr |
| H999 | Manhole chamber sections to BS 5911, diameter 1200 mm, with step irons BS 1247 cast in at 300 mm vertical intervals. | m |
| | BRICKWORK. | |
| | Engineering brickwork, class B bricks, jointing and flush pointing in Class M mortar, English bond. | |
| U321 | Thickness 215 mm, vertical straight walls; tops of shafts. | m2 |
| U378 | Surface features, fair facing. | m2 |
| | MISCELLANEOUS METALWORK. | |
| N999 | Cast iron coated manhole cover and frame to BS 497 (reference MA-60), bedded and flaunched in grade M1 mortar. | nr |

COMMENTARY

The finish to the benching is assumed to be by steel trowel and the formed surface of the channel is taken as being left fair from fair finish formwork. The formwork to form the channel is taken as two items, the half-round lower part would be of constant cross-section and the formwork to it is so described. Above the channel, the formwork to the edge of the benching is given as plain vertical it would be slightly tapered in its length to allow for the fall in the channel.

It is assumed that the Specification makes clear the jointing and pointing requirements for the precast concrete units.

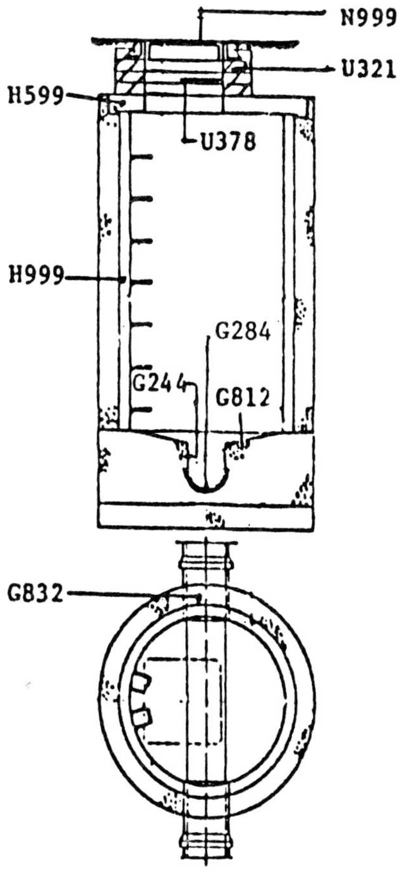


Fig. K1. Continuation of specimen item descriptions for precast concrete manholes measured in detail.

Table 9.04   French and Rubble Drains, Ditches and Trenches

| 1st Division | 2nd Division | | 3rd Division |
|---|---|---|---|
| French drains, rubble drains, ditches and trenches. | Filling French and rubble drains with graded material    m3 | State nature of filling material (Rule K/A3) | |
| | Filling French and rubble drains with rubble    m3 | Excavation and pipe laying shall be measured in Class I (Rule K/M1) | |
| Measure centre line for multiple pipes equi-distant between in-side faces of outer pipe walls (Rule K/D1) | Trenches for unpiped rubble drains    m | | Measure the cross-section-al area to the Excavated Sur-face (Rule K/M2) |
| | Rectangular section    unlined    m ditches:                 lined    m | State lining mate-rials and dimens-ions in descrip-tions for lined ditches (Rule K/A4) | State cross-sectional area range as 3rd Division range |
| | Vee section    unlined    m ditches:                 lined    m | | State actual cross-section-al area where exceeding 3 m2 |
| | Trenches for pipes or cables not to be laid by the Contractor | | |

| Number | Item description | Unit |
|---|---|---|
| | PIPEWORK - PIPES.  Clay land drain pipes as Specifica-tion clause 2.23, in French drains. | |
| I112 | Nominal bore 150 mm, in trenches, depth not exceeding 1.5 m; Commenc-ing Surface carriageway formation. | m |
| | PIPEWORK - MANHOLES AND PIPEWORK ANCILLARIES.  French drains. | |
| K410 | Filling French drains with graded material; Specification clause 2.03. | m3 |
| | PIPEWORK - SUPPORTS AND PROTECTION, ANCILLARIES TO LAYING AND EXCAVATION.  Imported granular material as Speci-fication clause 2.35. | |
| L331 | Beds depth 100 mm, nominal bore not exceeding 200 mm; Drawing No. PD/L. | m |

Fig.K2. Specimen Item Descriptions for French Drain.

FRENCH DRAIN - DRAWING PD/1
(not to scale)

Carriageway formation

K410

1000

150

100

L331

650

SECTION

COMMENTARY

French and Rubble Drains and Ditches (refer to Table 9.04

Pipes and excavation for piped French and rubble drains are measured as provided in Class I of the CESMM. Trenches for unpiped rubble drains are measured under Class K, as indicated in Table 9.04. The filling of French and rubble drains is measured by volume and is given separately.

Lined and unlined ditches and also trenches for unpiped rubble drains are each classified, in the 3rd Division, according to cross-sectional area. The cross-section is measured from the Excavated Surfaces. Trenches and ditches which taper and extend into more than one cross-sectional area range are divided into separate items for each standard cross-sectional area range. Item descriptions for lined ditches state the materials and dimensions of the lining and, in cases where the whole of the Excavated Surfaces are not lined, they define the extent of the lining.

Table 9.05   Ducts and Metal Culverts

Generally - The Rules in Class I for pipes apply to ducts and metal culverts, except as otherwise stated in 2nd Division (Rules K/M3, K/D5 and K/A5)

| 1st Division | 2nd Division | 3rd Division |
|---|---|---|
| Ducts and metal culverts    m<br><br>Measure centre line for multiple ducts etc., as Rule K/D1  See Table 9.04 | Use the 2nd Division descriptive features.<br><br>State materials, joint types, sizes etc., as for pipes in Class I.<br><br>Include lengths of fittings in lengths measured for ducts etc., not in trenches otherwise measure lengths as for pipes in Class I. (Rule K/M3).<br><br>State maximum nominal internal cross-sectional dimensions for non circular metal ducts (Rule K/D4).<br><br>Items deemed to include cutting and fittings (Rule K/C5) | Classify in accordance with the 3rd Division features as either:-<br><br>Not in trenches, or<br><br>In trenches, stating 3rd Division depth range, or state depth to next higher multiple of 0.5 m when exceeding 4 m deep. |

COMMENTARY

Ducts and Metal Culverts (Refer to Table 9.05)

Ducts and metal culverts are measured in linear metres and are covered by descriptive features in Class K. See Table 9.05. The Rules in Class I, which refer to pipes apply to ducts and metal culverts except as otherwise stated in Table 9.05. Items measurable under Classes K & L in addition to the pipes in Class I would, where appropriate, be measurable for ducts and metal culverts. In item descriptions for non-circular metal ducts, the maximum nominal internal cross-sectional dimensions are substituted for the nominal internal diameter in the 2nd Division.

Table 9.06 Crossings, Reinstatement and Other Pipework Ancillaries

Generally - Items, etc., set out in this Table are measured for pipes, ducts and culverts (Rules K/M4 and K/M6)

| 1st Division | 2nd Division | | 3rd Division |
|---|---|---|---|
| Crossings    nr<br><br>Deemed to include reinstate- ment unless otherwise stated (Rule K/C6) | River, stream or canal | State width range as 2nd Division, or State actual width where exceeding 10 m.<br>Measure width along centre line of pipe, duct or culvert when water surface is at level (or higher level of fluctuation  if applic- able) shown on the drawing to which reference is given in Pre- amble in accordance with Para- graph 5.20 of CESMM. (Rule K/D6)<br>Measure crossings of streams only where width exceed 1 m (Rule K/M5)<br>State type of linings where to be broken through and reinstated. (Rule K/A6) | State bore range as 3rd Division features, or State actual bore when it exceeds 1800 mm<br><br>To classify bore use maxi- mum nominal distance bet- ween inside faces of out- er walls of pipe, duct or culvert (Rule K/D7) |
| | Hedge: Wall: Fence;          Give each separately | | |
| | Sewer or drain | | |
| | Other underground services - State service | | |
| Reinstate- ment      m<br><br>Measure lengths along centre lines of pipes and include lengths of manholes (Rule K/M7)<br><br>Additional reinstate- ment deemed to be includ- ed with manholes (Rule K/C7) | Breaking up and temporary rein- statement of:- | State type and depths of surfac- ing including base and sub-base courses (Rule K/A7) | |
| | roads | Items deemed to include the re- moval and reinstatement of kerbs and channels (Rule K/C8) | |
| | footpaths | | |
| | Breaking up and temporary and permanent rein- statement | Class crossings of roads and paths as breaking up and rein- stating of roads and paths (Rule K/D8) | |
| | roads | | |
| | footpaths | | |
| | Reinstatement of land | | State whether grassland, gardens, sports fields or cultivated land (Rule K/A9) |
| | Strip topsoil from easement and reinstate<br><br>Deemed to in- clude storing topsoil (Rule K/C9) | Measure only when top- soil expressly required to be stripped and rein- stated for a width great- er than nominal width given in Rule L/D1 (Rule K/M8)<br><br>State any limitation on width to be stripped and reinstated (Rule K/A8) | |

Table 9.06  Crossings, Reinstatement and Other Pipework Ancillaries (cont.

| 1st Division | 2nd Division | | 3rd Division |
|---|---|---|---|
| Other Pipework ancillaries<br><br>Measure for pipes, ducts and metal culverts (Rule K/M9) | Reinstatement of field drains   m | Measure lengths as nominal trench, width given in Rule L/D1 (Rule K/M10)<br><br>Deemed to include connections to existing field drains (Rule K/C10) | |
| | Marker posts   nr | State size and type (Rule K/A10) | |
| | Timber supports left in excavations   m2<br><br>Metal supports left in excavations   m2 | Measure undeveloped area in contact with surface for which supports are expressly required to be left in (Rule K/M11) | |
| | Connection to existing:-<br><br>manholes and chambers   nr<br><br>pipes, ducts and culverts   nr | State nature of existing service and extent of work to be included (Rule K/A11) | State bore range. Classify bore, all as given for "Reinstatement" previously (Rule K/D7) |

COMMENTARY

Crossings, Reinstatement and Other Pipework Ancillaries (Refer to Table 9.06)

The Commentary on crossings, reinstatement and other pipework ancillaries which follows is applicable to pipes, ducts and metal culverts.

*Crossings*

A numbered item for a crossing is given in addition to the pipes and other work when a pipeline crosses a feature of the kind indicated in the 2nd Division of "Crossings" in Table 9.06. The location of the numbered items for the crossings of rivers, streams, canals, etc., and also the pipes measured in Class I for the crossing and any other work related to the pipelines in the crossings are identified by reference in the item descriptions to the particular body of water identified in the Preamble. See paragraph 5.20 of the CESMM. An alternative to identifying location in item descriptions is to give all the work in the pipeline of the crossing under a heading which refers to the Preamble which identifies the body of water to be crossed.

The width of crossings, which cross water, is measured at the water surface level in accordance with the conventions and as noted in the 2nd Division panel against the feature "Crossings" in Table 9.06. Other measurement conventions and details to be given in item descriptions for crossings are given against the feature in Table 9.06.

Crossings, Reinstatement and Other Pipework Ancillaries (cont.

*Reinstatement and Other Pipework Ancillaries*

Reinstatement of surfaces excavated or broken through for pipelines and also the stripping of topsoil and reinstating of an easement are measured in linear metres. The descriptive feature, together with measurement conventions and the details to be given in item descriptions are set out against the feature "Reinstatement" in Table 9.06. Stripping and reinstating an easement is measured only where the stripping and reinstatement of a width greater than the nominal trench width is expressly required.

Other pipework ancillaries as noted against the feature in Table 9.06 require to be measured where they occur in the work. Timber and metal supports left in excavation are measured only where it is expressly required they are left in.

Separate items are given for each type of connection between pipework and existing work, each giving the number of connections. Item descriptions are required to state the nature of the existing services and may give locational or other identifying information. They also state or identify associated work (such as the alteration of existing manholes and benchings or pipework and maintaining the flow of the existing during the making of the connections) intended to be included in the items. Where connections are made between new and existing pipes with fittings, such as junctions or saddles, the pipes, fittings, beds, etc., may be measured in the runs of the new pipework as provided in Classes I, J and L. The items for the connections would then state that pipes, fittings, etc., are measured separately.

*PIPEWORK - SUPPORTS AND PROTECTION, ANCILLARIES
TO LAYING AND EXCAVATION - CESMM CLASS L*

---

Table 9.07  Class L, Generally

---

Generally - Give items in this Class in addition to the items for:-

    (i) the provision, laying and jointing of pipes, ducts and
         culverts and for the excavation and backfilling of trenches in
         Classes I and K (Rule L/M1)

    (ii) manholes and other chambers in Classes K and Y (Rule L/M1)

    Measure work in this Class associated with ducts and metal
    culverts as set out for work associated with pipes. Use the
    maximum nominal distance between the inside faces of the outer
    duct or culvert walls as the dimension for the 3rd Division
    classification of bore, where appropriate (Rule L/M2)

    Items in this Class are deemed to include:-

    (a) excavation, preparation of surfaces, disposal of excavated
         material, upholding sides of excavation, backfilling and
         removal of existing services except to the extent such work is
         included in Classes I, J and K or in the items for extras to
         excavation and backfilling in this Class (Rule L/C1)

    (b) concrete reinforcement, formwork, joints and finishes (Rule
         L/C2)

    Measure breaking up and reinstatement of roads and pavings
    under Class K (Rule L/M3)

---

COMMENTARY

Class L Generally (Refer to Table 9.07)

Items in addition to those measured under Class I for the pipes are measured under Class L where pipes are expressly required to be laid by special methods and also where pipes are required to be protected or supported. Any excavation in rock or hard material and any backfilling expressly required to be in material other than that excavated are measured under Class L as extra over the trench, manhole or other excavation measured under Classes I, J, K and Y. Subsequent Tables and Commentary are given for the individual classifications included in Class L.

Table 9.08   Extras to Excavation and Backfilling

Generally - See "Generally" Table 9.07

1st Division   Extras to excavation and backfilling   m3

| 2nd Division | | 3rd Division | |
|---|---|---|---|
| In pipe trenches | Calculate volumes as Rules L/M4 and L/D1. See subsequent Commentary | Excavation of rock <br><br> Excavation of mass concrete <br><br> Excavation of reinforced concrete <br><br> Excavation of other artificial hard material (State material) | Ignore isolated volume unless it exceeds 0.25 m3 (Rule L/M8) |
| In manholes and other chambers | Calculate volumes as Rule L/M5. See subsequent Commentary | | |
| In headings <br><br> In thrust boring <br><br> In pipe jacking | Calculate volumes by multiplying internal cross-sectional area of pipe by length excavated or backfilled. Packing to headings is not measured (Rule L/M6) | | |
| | | Backfilling above Final Surface:- <br><br> with concrete <br><br> with material other than concrete (State material) | Measure only when it is expressly required that material excavated is not used for backfilling (Rule L/M7) |
| | | Excavation of natural material below Final Surface and backfilling:- <br><br> with concrete <br><br> with material other than concrete | Measure only when expressly required (Rule L/M7) <br><br> State nature of material other than concrete |

COMMENTARY

Extras to Excavation and Backfilling (refer to Table 9.08)

Excavation in rock or other artificial hard material and backfilling, where the backfilling is expressly required to be carried out with material other than that excavated, are each classified, under Class L, as extras to the excavation and backfilling included in the items in Classes I, J, K and Y. Items for the work give the quantities by volume in m3 and state the materials. (See Table 9.08). The volume of the work in trenches is determined using the average depth and length of the material removed or backfilled and the notional width of trench. The notional width of trench is that which is stated in the Contract. Where no such width is stated, the width is taken as the maximum distance between the inside faces of the outer pipe walls, plus 500 mm where this maximum distance does not exceed one metre, or plus 750 mm where this maximum distance exceeds one metre.

The volume of extra for excavation of rock or artificial hard material in manholes and other chambers is calculated from the maximum plan areas of the manholes or chambers and the average depth of the material removed.

Extras to backfilling to manholes or other chambers, where it is expressly required to be carried out with material other than that excavated, is measured the nett volume of the fill required outside the manholes or other chambers, subject to no volume of filling being measured outside the maximum plan area of the manholes or other chambers.

Extras to excavation for excavating in rock or other hard material and for backfilling with material other than that excavated is measured under Class L where it is required to manholes measured under Class K and also to new manholes measured under Class Y.

Table 9.09 Special Pipe Laying Methods

Generally - See "Generally" Table 9.07

1st Division

| Special pipe laying methods   m | Measure only where expressly required (Rule L/M9)

Identify run of pipe (Rule L/A1)

Deemed to include crossings, provision and removal of access pits, shafts and jacking blocks, unless otherwise stated and other work associated with special pipe laying methods not included in the items for pipes in Class I (Rule L/C3)

Where expressly stated in Contract to be executed by the Contractor and where the nature and extent of access pits, shafts and jacking blocks are expressly stated in the Contract, give them as Specified Requirements in Class A (Rule L/M10) |

| 2nd Division | | 3rd Division |
|---|---|---|
| In headings | State type of packing materials (Rule L/A1) | State nominal bore range or state actual nominal bore where exceeding 1800 mm. |
| Thrust boring | | |
| Pipe jacking | | |

COMMENTARY

Special Pipe Laying Methods (refer to Table 9.09)

The rules governing the measurement of pipes expressly required to be laid in headings or by thrust boring or by pipe jacking are straightforward. First items for the pipes are measured in linear metres under Class I. They are classed "not in trenches". Item descriptions state the location of the pipe runs and the special method by which the pipes are to be laid. They state also the actual nominal bore of the pipes and the further details required to be stated for Class I items as noted in Table 9.01.

Following items in Class I, items in Class L are measured. They give the length and state the particular special method by which the pipes are to be laid. They state also the location of the run of the pipes. These items cover the complete installation of pipes laid by special methods, except that should hard material be encountered installing the pipes or should special backfilling be required items of extra to excavation or backfilling are given by volume. Rule L/M6 provides that the volume shall be calculated by multiplying the internal cross-sectional area of the pipes by the length of the excavation or backfilling as appropriate.

Items for special pipe laying methods are deemed to include all work associated with the special pipe laying methods. See Table 9.09. Should, however, the Contract expressly require that the Contractor shall carry out access pits, shafts and jacking blocks the nature of which is expressly stated in the Contract, these items would be given as Specified Requirements under Class A.

Specimen item descriptions for pipework in headings are given below.

| Number | Item Description | Unit | |
|--------|-----------------|------|---|
| I121 | PIPEWORK IN HEADING UNDER YATTON ROAD, MH19-MH20, DRAWING NO. 29/8.<br><br>PIPEWORK - PIPES.<br><br>Vitrified clay pipes to BS 65/540 Part 1, with mechanical flexible joints to BS 65/540:Part 2, not in trenches.<br><br>Nominal Bore 300 mm; in headings. | m | The descriptions assume the heading is in soft material. For hard material see Commentary above.<br><br>The requirements of Rule I/A1, I/A3 and L/A1 of the CESMM (See Tables 9.01 and 9.09) are complied with by grouping the items for pipework and laying by special methods under an identifying heading. |
| L212 | PIPEWORK - SUPPORTS AND PROTECTION, ANCILLARIES TO LAYING AND EXCAVATION.<br><br>Special pipe laying methods.<br><br>In headings, nominal bore 200 - 300 mm; and packing with grade C10 concrete to completely fill headings. | m | The grouped items would appear to be best positioned in Bill following the items in Class L. |

Fig. L1. Pipework in headings

---

Table 9.10 Supports and Protection

---

Generally - See "Generally" Table 9.07

Measure lengths of beds, haunches and surrounds and wrapping and lagging along pipe centre lines over fittings and valves but not including lengths occupied by manholes and chambers through which support or protection is not continued Rules (L/M11 and L/M12)

| 1st Division | 2nd Division | | 3rd Division |
|---|---|---|---|
| Beds          m<br><br>Haunches      m<br><br>Surrounds     m | Sand<br><br>Selected granular material<br><br>Imported granular material<br><br>Mass concrete<br><br>Reinforced concrete | State materials used, and state depth of beds (Rule L/A2)<br><br>Items for surrounds includes beds. Items for haunches includes beds. (Rule L/D2)<br><br>Describe where to multiple pipes and state number of pipes and maximum nominal distance between inside faces of outer pipe walls (Rule L/A3) | State nominal bore range as 3rd Division features, or, State actual nominal bore where it exceeds 1800 mm.<br><br>For multiple pipes use nominal distance between inside faces of outer pipe walls as dimension for classification (Rule L/D3) |
| Wrapping and Lagging      m | State materials used (Rule L/A4)<br><br>Deemed to include for wrapping and lagging fittings, valves and joints (Rule L/C4) | | |
| Concrete stools and thrust blocks      nr | State specification of concrete and whether reinforced (Rule L/A5)<br><br>State volume range as 2nd Division features, or State actual volume where it exceeds 6 m3. Exclude volume occupied by pipe (Rule L/D4)<br><br>Deemed to include pipe fixings (Rule L/C5) | | |
| Other isolated pipe supports      nr | State principal dimensions. State materials used (Rule L/A6)<br><br>State height range as 2nd Division features. State actual height where over 6 m.<br><br>Measure height from ground or other supporting surface to invert of highest pipe where supported from below and to lowest pipe where pipes are supported from above. Where two pipes or more are carried by a support classify in 3rd Division by aggregate bore of pipes supported (Rules L/D5 and L/D6) | | |

COMMENTARY

## Supports and protection (refer to Table 9.10)

### Beds, Haunches and Surrounds

Beds, haunches and surrounds to pipework are measured and given in linear metres. (See "Generally" in Table 9.10). Items for haunches and items for surrounds each include the related beds.

Item descriptions state the materials used and the depths of the beds. They identify the cross-sectional profiles of the beds, haunches or surrounds (usually by drawing reference). Notwithstanding that the 3rd Division features provide for items to group nominal bores within ranges, separate items using the same nominal bore range, or stating a single nominal bore, may require to be given to distinguish cross-sectional profiles of differing cost characteristics.

The items for beds, haunches and surrounds cover their complete construction including materials, concrete etc., and the excavation work in normal soft ground. See "Generally" Table 9.07. Where hard materials require to be excavated, items for extras to excavation for excavating the hard materials are measured and are given by volume in m3.

Items include the additional excavation (beyond that included in the Class I items) to the extent that it is material other than rock or artificial hard material. Any rock or artificial hard material within the additional excavation which is to be removed is given by volume in accordance with the items in this Class for extras to excavation and backfilling.

### Wrapping and Lagging

Wrapping and lagging pipes are measured and given in linear metres. The convention for determining lengths is given in Rule L/M12. See "Generally" Table 9.10. Separate items are not given for wrapping or lagging fittings and valves. The 3rd Division features provide for the nominal bore of the pipes wrapped or lagged to be grouped in ranges. The assessed cost difference between work to pipes within a range may be considered such as to make it advisable to give items for each nominal bore in place of the nominal bore range.

### Concrete Stools and Thrust Blocks

Item quantities give the number of concrete stools and thrust blocks. Item descriptions state the specification of the concrete and are required to state the volume range within which each stool or block falls and the nominal bore range of the related pipework. The items include excavation, formwork and reinforcement, if required, and item descriptions identify requirements in respect of these and any other requirements. The cost difference between the lower and higher volumes in the standard volume ranges could, in some cases, be substantial. Further itemisation is sometimes introduced to distinguish cost difference.

Enumerated items as here discussed are not appropriate for concrete stools of substantial construction. They would be dealt with as structures and measured and itemised in detail as provided in other Classes appropriate to the work.

COMMENTARY

Supports and Protection (cont.

*Isolated Pipe Supports*

Isolated pipe supports are enumerated, they include metal hangers as well as other forms of support. Item descriptions state the materials used and the principal dimensions of the supports. They state also the heights of the supports and also the nominal bore of the pipes supported within stated ranges. See Table 9.10. It is not appropriate to give substantial structure type pipe supports as enumerated items. They are measured and itemised in detail in accordance with other Classes appropriate to the work.

EXAMPLES

Two examples follow:

Measured Example - IE.1

The Measured Example IE.1, covers the taking of the dimensions for the pipeline work from MH.1 to MH.3 shown on Drawing No.I/D/1. This is considered to be a pipe run of particular cost characteristic. The dimensions for other pipe runs would be recorded in a similar way. In the Example a schedule is used in combination with a conventional dimension sheet for the taking off. The work on the schedule being totalled for billing direct. The work on the dimension sheet being that which would be collected on to an abstract with that related to other pipe runs.

Specimen Bill of Quantities, Example - IE.2

The specimen Bill at Example IE.2 is for the Work Items (excluding the General Items) for the Surface Water Sewers, excluding the Pumping Station and Rising Main, shown on Drawing No. I/D/1. In keeping with Rule A1 of Class I of the CESMM, the Bill indicates the location of the runs of pipes and groups together those considered to involve similar cost characteristics.

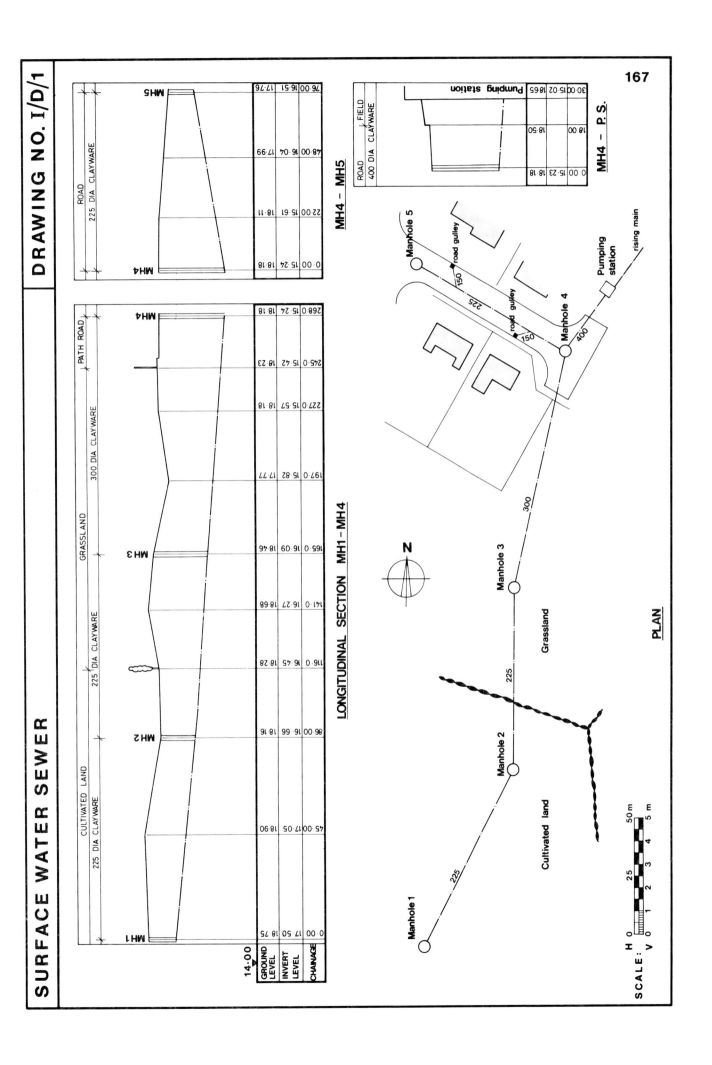

# SURFACE WATER SEWER

# DRAWING NO. I/D/1

**167**

## LONGITUDINAL SECTION MH1 – MH4

| | MH1 | | | | MH2 | | | | MH3 | | | | MH4 |
|---|---|---|---|---|---|---|---|---|---|---|---|---|---|
| GROUND LEVEL | 18.75 | | 18.90 | | 18.16 | | 18.28 | 18.68 | 18.46 | | 17.77 | 18.18 | 18.23 | 18.24 |
| INVERT LEVEL | 17.50 | | 17.05 | | 16.66 | | 16.45 | 16.27 | 16.09 | | 15.82 | 15.57 | 15.42 | 15.24 |
| CHAINAGE | 0.00 | | 45.00 | | 96.00 | | 116.0 | 141.0 | 165.0 | | 197.0 | 227.0 | 245.0 | 268.0 |

CULTIVATED LAND | GRASSLAND | PATH ROAD

225 DIA CLAYWARE | 225 DIA CLAYWARE | 300 DIA CLAYWARE

## MH4 – MH5

| | MH4 | | | | | MH5 |
|---|---|---|---|---|---|---|
| | 18.24 | | 18.11 | | 17.99 | 17.51 |
| | 15.24 | | 15.61 | | 16.04 | 16.51 |
| | 0.00 | | 22.00 | | 48.00 | 76.00 |

ROAD
225 DIA CLAYWARE

## MH4 – P.S.

| | | | Pumping station |
|---|---|---|---|
| 18.18 | 18.00 | 18.50 | 18.65 |
| 15.23 | | | 15.02 |
| 0.00 | | | 30.00 |

ROAD | FIELD
400 DIA CLAYWARE

## PLAN

Manhole 1
Manhole 2
Manhole 3
Manhole 4
Manhole 5

225
225
300
225
225
400
150
150

road gulley
road gulley
road gulley

Pumping station

rising main

Cultivated land
Grassland

N

SCALE: H 0   25   50 m
       V 0   1 2 3 4 5   5 m

14.00

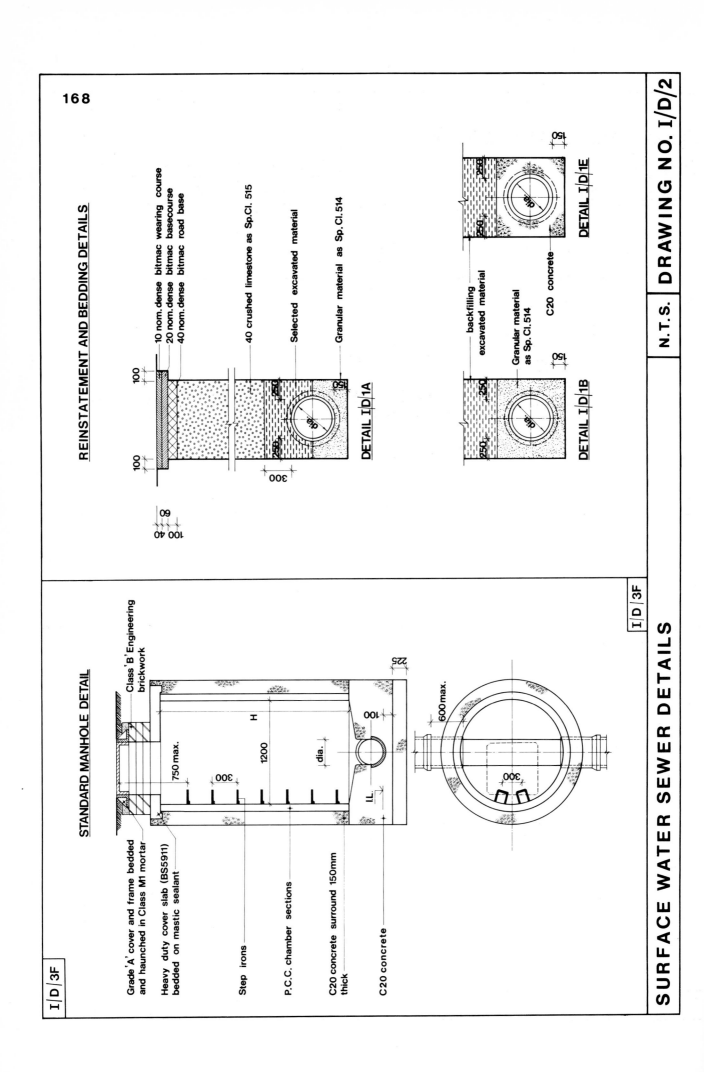

## REINSTATEMENT AND BEDDING DETAILS

10 nom. dense bitmac wearing course
20 nom. dense bitmac basecourse
40 nom. dense bitmac road base

40 crushed limestone as Sp. Cl. 515

Selected excavated material

Granular material as Sp. Cl. 514

**DETAIL I/D/1A**

backfilling excavated material

Granular material as Sp. Cl. 514

C20 concrete

**DETAIL I/D/1B**

**DETAIL I/D/1E**

## STANDARD MANHOLE DETAIL

Class 'B' Engineering brickwork

Grade 'A' cover and frame bedded and haunched in Class M1 mortar

Heavy duty cover slab (BS5911) bedded on mastic sealant

Step irons

P.C.C. chamber sections

C20 concrete surround 150mm thick

C20 concrete

I/D/3F

# SURFACE WATER SEWER DETAILS

| N.T.S. | DRAWING NO. I/D/2 |

| | | PIPES | | | |
|---|---|---|---|---|---|
| SURFACE WATER SEWER - DRG No I/1 | | 225 ∅ Vit. Clay Pipes flex. Jts. in Trenches | | | |
| SCHEDULE No 1, | | | | | |
| MH 1 - MH2 - MH3 | | n.e.1.5 | 1.5-2 | 2-2.5 | |
| MH 1 - Chain 45 (45.00) | 45.00 | | | | |
| GL    Inv    Depth | 18.75 | | | | |
| MH1    18.75 - 17.50 = 1.25 \| 1.50 | 26.25 | | 26.25 | | |
| Ch.45    18.90 - 17.05 = 1.85 \| 1.25 | | | | | |
| Diff    0.60 \| 0.25 | 18.75 | | | | |
| $\frac{0.25 \times 45.00}{0.60}$   18.75    Less ½/MH 1 | 0.60 | | | | |
| | 18.15 | 18.15 | | | |
| Chain 45 - MH 2 (86 - 45 = 41.00) | 41.00 | | | | |
| GL    Inv    Depth    Less ½/MH 2 | 0.60 | | | | |
| Ch.45    1.85 | 40.40 | | 40.40 | | |
| MH.2    18.16 - 16.66 = 1.50 | | | | | |
| MH 2 - Chain 116 (116 - 86 = 30.00) | 30.00 | | | | |
| GL    Inv    Depth    Less ½/MH 2 | 0.60 | | | | |
| MH 2    1.50 | 29.40 | | 29.40 | | |
| Ch 116    18.28 - 16.45 = 1.83 | | | | | |
| Chain 116 - 141 (141 - 116 = 25.00) | 25.00 | | | | |
| GL    Inv    Depth | 7.33 | | 7.33 | | |
| Ch.116    1.83 \| 2.00 | 17.67 | | | 17.67 | |
| Ch 141    18.68 - 16.27 = 2.41 \| 1.83 | | | | | |
| Diff.    0.58 \| 0.17 | | | | | |
| $\frac{0.17 \times 25.00}{0.58} = 7.33$ | | | | | |
| Chain 141 - MH 3 (165 - 141 = 24.00) | 24.00 | | | | |
| GL    Inv    Depth    Less ½/MH 3 | 0.60 | | | | |
| Ch.141    2.41 | 23.40 | | | 23.40 | |
| MH 3    18.46 - 16.09    2.37 | | | | | |
| | | 18.15 | 103.38 | 41.07 | |

SURFACE WATER SEWER DRG.No.I/D/1

EXAMPLE IE.1

PIPES. MH 1-2-3

NOTE

Bill direct from Schedule No.1. pipes in trenches MH 1-2-3

PIPEWORK ANCILLS.

1

Crossgs. hedge, pipe bore n.e. 300mm
(K641

½/MH.1. =
116.00
0.83
116.83

Reinstatement

116.83

Reinstatement of land. pipe bore n.e 300mm cult. land (K751.2

165.00
116.00
49.00

49.00

Reinstatement of land. pipe bore n.e 300mm, grassland (K751.1

165.00
Less.MH's ²/1.65 = 3.30
161.70

SUPPORTS, ETC

Surrounds w beds depth 150mm importd. gran matl. Spec cl. 514

161.70

Pipe nom bore 200 - 300 m m
Drawing No I/D/1B
(L532

---

86.00
2/½/1.65 = 1.65
84.35

116.00
86.00
30.00
½/ 1.65 = 0.83
MH2-Ch116 = 29.17

225   0.60   0.20
500   0.20   0.00
725  2)0.80   0.20
       0.40   0.10

ANCILLS to LAYING

Extras to excavn and backfill

84.35
0.73
0.40

29.17
0.73
0.10

In pipe trenches, excavn of rock
(L111

---

COMMENTARY

The calculations on the left hand side of Schedule No. 1, determine by interpolation the points of division between the different depth ranges of the pipe trenches.

The linear dimension for reinstatement includes the lengths occupied by manholes. See Table 9.06.

The linear dimension for granular beds, haunches and surrounds, excludes the lengths occupied by manholes. See Table 9.10.

Rock contours are not shown on the Drawing. The Example assumes that rock will be encountered at 600 mm above the base of the granular bed at Manhole No. 1 and will run out to zero at Chainage 116. The width entered for excavation of rock is determined as provided in Rules L/M4 and L/D1 of CESMM. See Commentary following Table 9.08.

| Number | Item description | Unit | Quantity | Rate | Amount | |
|--------|------------------|------|----------|------|--------|---|
| | | | | | £ | p |
| | PIPEWORK - PIPES. | | | | | |
| | Vitrified clay pipes to BS 65, normal type with flexible mechanical joints. | | | | | |
| | Between manholes 1 - 2 and 2 - 3 Drawing No. I/D/I. | | | | | |
| I122.1 | Nominal bore 225 mm, in trenches, depth not exceeding 1.5 m. | m | 18 | | | |
| I123.1 | Nominal bore 225 mm, in trenches, depth 1.5 - 2 m. | m | 103 | | | |
| I124.1 | Nominal bore 225 mm, in trenches, depth 2 - 2.5 m. | m | 41 | | | |
| | Between manholes 3 - 4 and 4 - Pumping Station, Drawing No. I/D/1. | | | | | |
| I123.2 | Nominal bore 300 mm, in trenches, depth 1.5 - 2 m. | m | 6 | | | |
| I124.2 | Nominal bore 300 mm, in trenches, depth 2 - 2.5 m. | m | 55 | | | |
| I125.1 | Nominal bore 300 mm, in trenches, depth 2.5 - 3 m. | m | 40 | | | |
| I135 | Nominal bore 400 mm, in trenches, depth 2.5 - 3 m. | m | 3 | | | |
| I136 | Nominal bore 400 mm, in trenches, depth 3 - 3.5 m. | m | 21 | | | |
| I137 | Nominal bore 400 mm, in trenches, depth 3.5 - 4 m. | m | 6 | | | |
| | Between manholes 4 and 5, Drawing No. I/D/1. | | | | | |
| I122.2 | Nominal bore 225 mm, in trenches, depth not exceeding 1.5 m. | m | 9 | | | |
| I123.3 | Nominal bore 225 mm, in trenches, depth 1.5 - 2 m. | m | 20 | | | |
| I124.3 | Nominal bore 225 mm, in trenches, depth 2 - 2.5 m. | m | 24 | | | |
| I125.2 | Nominal bore 225 mm, in trenches, depth 2.5 - 3 m. | m | 21 | | | |
| | (1)          To Part 3 Summary          Page total | | | | | |

| Number | Item description | Unit | Quantity | Rate | Amount £ | p |
|--------|-----------------|------|----------|------|----------|---|
| | PIPEWORK - PIPES (cont. | | | | | |
| | Vitrified clay pipes to BS 65 normal type with flexible mechanical joints (cont. | | | | | |
| | Road Gulley branches | | | | | |
| I112 | Nominal bore 150 mm, in trenches, depth not exceeding 1.5 m. | m | 17 | | | |
| I113 | Nominal bore 150 mm, in trenches, depth 1.5 - 2 m. | m | 3 | | | |
| | PIPEWORK - FITTINGS AND VALVES. | | | | | |
| | Vitrified clay pipe fittings to BS 65, normal type flexible mechanical joints | | | | | |
| J111 | Bends, nominal bore 150 mm. | nr | 4 | | | |
| J122 | Junction, single "Y", nominal bore 225 mm. | nr | 2 | | | |
| | PIPEWORK - MANHOLES AND PIPEWORK ANCILLARIES | | | | | |
| | Manholes as Drawing No. I/D/3F the chamber sections surrounded with concrete as Specification clause 503, with Grade A heavy duty coated cast iron covers and frames, 600 mm square clear opening, as BS 497. | | | | | |
| K151 | Precast concrete, depth not exceeding 1.5 m. | nr | 2 | | | |
| K152 | Precast concrete, depth 1.5 - 2 m. | nr | 1 | | | |
| K153 | Precast concrete, depth 2 - 2.5 m. | nr | 1 | | | |
| K155 | Precast concrete, depth 3 - 3.5 m. | nr | 1 | | | |

| Number | Item description | Unit | Quantity | Rate | Amount £ | p |
|--------|-----------------|------|----------|------|----------|---|
| | PIPEWORK - MANHOLES AND PIPEWORK ANCILLARIES (cont. | | | | | |
| | Vitrified clay gullies and bedding and surrounding with concrete as Specification clause 508. | | | | | |
| K310 | 400 mm Diameter road gully, 750 mm deep, with rodding eye, stopper and 150 mm outlet and coupling joint and with 450 mm nominal width cast iron coated hinged grating, as BS. 497 reference GA2-450 on two courses of one brick thick Class B engineering brickwork raised off gully surround. | nr | 2 | | | |
| | Crossings. | | | | | |
| K641 | Hedge, pipe bore not exceeding 300 mm. | nr | 1 | | | |
| K661 | Fence, pipe bore not exceeding 300 mm. | nr | 1 | | | |
| | Reinstatement. | | | | | |
| K731 | Breaking up and temporary and permanent reinstatement of roads, pipe bore not exceeding 300 mm; detail Drawing No. I/D/1A. | m | 118 | | | |
| K732 | Breaking up and temporary and permanent reinstatement of roads, pipe bore 300 - 900 mm; detail Drawing No. I/D/1A. | m | 16 | | | |
| K741 | Breaking up and temporary and permanent reinstatement of footpaths, pipe bore not exceeding 300 mm; detail Drawing No. I/D/1A. | m | 2 | | | |
| K742 | Breaking up and temporary and permanent reinstatement of footpaths, pipe bore 300 - 900 mm; detail Drawing I/D/1A. | m | 2 | | | |
| K751.1 | Reinstatement of land, pipe bore not exceeding 300 mm; grassland. | m | 129 | | | |
| K751.2 | Reinstatement of land, pipe bore not exceeding 300 mm; cultivated land. | m | 117 | | | |
| K752 | Reinstatement of land, pipe bore 300 - 900 mm; grassland. | m | 12 | | | |

(3)     To Part 3 Summary     Page total

| Number | Item description | Unit | Quantity | Rate | Amount | |
|--------|------------------|------|----------|------|--------|---|
| | | | | | £ | p |
| | PIPEWORK - SUPPORTS AND PROTECTION, ANCILLARIES TO LAYING AND EXCAVATION. | | | | | |
| | Extras to excavation and backfilling. | | | | | |
| L111 | In pipe trenches, excavation of rock. | m3 | 27 | | | |
| L116 | In pipe trenches, backfilling above the Final Surface with 40 mm nominal maximum size broken limestone, Specification clause 515; in roads and footpaths. | m3 | 117 | | | |
| L121 | In manholes, excavation of rock. | m3 | 2 | | | |
| | Haunches, with beds depth 150 mm, imported granular material, Specification clause 514. | | | | | |
| L431 | Pipe nominal bore not exceeding 200 mm, Drawing No. I/D/1A. | m | 6 | | | |
| L432 | Pipe nominal bore 200 - 300 mm, Drawing No. I/D/1A. | m | 96 | | | |
| L433 | Pipe nominal bore 300 - 600 mm, Drawing No. I/D/1A. | m | 17 | | | |
| | Surrounds, with beds depth 150 mm, imported granular material, Specification clause 514. | | | | | |
| L532 | Pipe nominal bore 200 - 300 mm, Drawing No. I/D/1B. | m | 241 | | | |
| L533 | Pipe nominal bore 300 - 600 mm, Drawing No. I/D/1B. | m | 12 | | | |
| | Surrounds with beds depth 150 mm, mass concrete Specification clause 503, detail Drawing No. I/D/1E. | | | | | |
| L541 | Pipe nominal bore not exceeding 200 mm. | m | 14 | | | |

|            (4)        To Part 3 Summary        Page total | | |

# 10 Structural Metalwork and Miscellaneous Metalwork – CESMM Classes: M and N

The CESMM provides two main classifications for metalwork and designates them Classes M and N. Class M features components of structural metalwork and sets the rules for their measurement. Class N is appropriate for the measurement of metalwork components, not included in Class M, which are associated with metalwork for structures and also for various other metalwork components which may be encountered in civil engineering work. The application of each Class is subject to the specific exclusions given in the "Excludes" preceding the classification table for each Class in the CESMM. References to work included in Classes M or N are made in the "Excludes" above the classification tables in Classes P, Q and S.

*STRUCTURAL METALWORK - CESMM CLASS M*

The method of measurement set out in the CESMM relies on drawings to provide some of the information which tenderers require. For structural metalwork it is usual to provide tenderers with dimensioned drawings showing lay out, sections and sizes of the members and details of any connections and other fittings.

---

Table 10.01   Structural Metalwork

---

Generally - The mass of members shall be that of the plates, rolled sections, shear connectors, stiffeners, cleats, packs, splice plates and other fittings (Rule M/M3). Exclude mass of weld fillets, bolts, nuts, washers, rivets and protective coatings (Rule M/M4)

Calculate the mass of members, other than plates and flats, from the overall length of the members with no deduction for splay cut or mitred ends (Rule M/M2). Make no deduction from the mass for notches and holes each not exceeding 0.1 m2 in area measured in plane (Rule M/M5). Make no allowance for rolling margin or other permissible deviations (Rule M/M4)

Take mass of mild steel to BS 4360 grades 43A1 and 43A as 785 kg/m2 per 100 mm thickness (7.85 t/m3). Take mass of other metals as stated in the Specification or the suppliers catalogue (Rule M/M6)

Classify under Class N other metal components not included in this Class but associated with metal structures (Rule M/M1)

---

COMMENTARY

Structural Metalwork (refer to Table 10.01)

Table 10.01 outlines the Rules in Class M of the CESMM which apply to structural metalwork generally. Quantities attached to the members give their calculated mass. The mass of members, other than "plates or flats" is calculated from the overall lengths with no deduction for splay cut or mitred ends. The mass of attached fittings is included in the mass of a member. Fabrication of structural metalwork is given separately from erection, see subsequent Tables and Commentary. The Rules for calculating mass apply to both fabrication and erection.

Quantities are given in tonnes. They may be entered in the Bill to the nearest one tenth of a tonne. See Paragraph 5.18 of the CESMM.

Table 10.02  Fabrication and Erection

Fabrication - Deemed to include delivery of fabricated metalwork to site (Rule M/C1)

| 1st Division | | 2nd Division | 3rd Division |
|---|---|---|---|
| Fabrication of main members for bridges　　t | State materials and grades of materials (Rule M/A1)　　Identify tapered and castellated members (Rule M/A2)　　Identify cranked members except those in portal frame (Rule M/A3) | Rolled sections　　Plates and flats　　Built-up box or hollow sections | Straight on plan　　Curved on plan　　Straigth on plan and cambered　　Curved on plan and cambered |
| Fabrication of subsidiary members for bridges　　t | | Deck panels | |
| | | Bracings | |
| | | External diaphragms | |
| Fabrication of members for frames　　Fabrication of other members | State materials and grades of materials (Rule M/A1)　　Identify tapered and castellated members (Rule M/A2)　　Identify cranked members except those in portal frames (Rule M/A3) | Columns　　t　　Beams　　t　　Portal frames　　t | Straight on plan　　Curved on plan　　Straigth on plan and cambered　　Curved on plan and cambered |
| | | Trestles, towers and built-up columns　t　State details of members comprising boom and infill construction (Rule M/A4)　　Trusses and built-up girders　t | |
| | | Bracings, purlins and cladding rails t | |
| | | Grillages　　t | |
| | | Anchorages and holding down bolt assemblies　nr　Measure by number of complete assemblies (Rule M/M7)　　State particulars of type (Rule M/A5) | |

Table 10.02 Fabrication and Erection (cont.

Erection - Deemed to include work carried out after delivery of fabricated metalwork to Site (Rule M/C2)

| 1st Division | | 2nd Division | | 3rd Division |
|---|---|---|---|---|
| Erection of members for bridges<br><br>Erection of members for frames<br><br>Erection of other members | Identify and locate separate bridges and structural frames and where appropriate, parts of bridges or frames (Rule M/A6) | Trial erection   t<br><br>Permanent erection   t | State where fixing clips and resilient pads are used to secure overhead crane rails (Rule M/A7) | |
| | | Site bolts   nr<br><br>Deemed to include supply and delivery to site (Rule M/C3) | State type and enumerate as 2nd Division features | State diameter range as 3rd Division features |

COMMENTARY

Structural Metalwork (cont.

Metalwork components associated with metal structures but not listed in the Class M classification table are measured and classified under Class N.

Fabrication and Erection (refer to Table 10.02)

*Fabrication*

For the purpose of measurement, the fabrication of structural metalwork is divided into three main classifications, i.e. for bridges, for frames and for other members. Within each of the main classifications members are classified and described in accordance with 2nd Division features which identify the members. The identified members are further classified according to their shape as set out in 3rd Division features. Item descriptions identify members which are tapered or which are castellated. Cranked members, other than those in portal frames, and/or other unusual members are similarly identified.

The quantities for fabrication of structural metalwork give the mass in tonnes for each classification, calculated as outlined in Table 10.01. See also preceding Commentary "Structual Metalwork".

Rule M/A4 of the CESMM requires item descriptions for trestles, towers and built-up columns and for trusses and built-up girders to state details of the members which comprise the boom and infill construction.

Separate items are given for anchorage and holding down bolt assemblies. Items are given to cover the complete assemblies. Each type is described or identified and quantities give the number of each. Bridge bearings are measured and classified as provided in Class N. The casting in to concrete or mortices in concrete for these items is given as "Inserts" and measured under Class G.

COMMENTARY

Fabrication and Erection (cont.

*Erection*

Items for the erection of structural metalwork group together the mass of the members in one item for each bridge or structural frame (or where appropriate each part of a bridge or structural frame) which is identified and located in the item description. Quantities give the mass in tonnes for each bridge, frame or part as the case may be. Separate items are given for site bolts, see Table 10.02. Trial erection is given separately where this is specifically required. It is appropriate for different parts of bridges and structural frames to be given as separate items, rather than as one item for the whole, where for identification purposes it would be helpful to do so, or to separate parts considered to have different cost characteristics.

Table 10.03   Surface Treatment

| 1st Division | | 2nd Division | | 3rd Division |
|---|---|---|---|---|
| Off Site surface treatment  m2 | Applies to treatment carried out before delivery to Site<br><br>Class surface treatment on Site as painting and measure under Class V (Rule M/M8) | Blast cleaning<br><br>Pickling<br><br>Flame cleaning<br><br>Wire brushing | | |
| | | Metal spraying<br><br>Galvanising<br><br>Painting | State materials and number of applications (Rule M/A8) | |

Surface Treatment (refer to Table 10.03)

The surface area of structural metalwork required to be treated before delivery to the site is measured in m2 and separate items are given for each type of treatment.

*MISCELLANEOUS METALWORK - CESMM CLASS N*

Table 10.04   Miscellaneous Metalwork

Generally - Items are deemed to include fixing to other work, supply of fixing components and drilling or cutting other work (Rule N/C1)

The masses calculated for miscellaneous metalwork assemblies shall include the mass of all metal components and attached pieces (Rule N/M2)

No deduction from masses or areas for openings and holes each not exceeding 0.5 m2 in area (Rule N/M3)

Measure painting carried out on Site under Class V (Rule N/M1)

Table 10.04 Miscellaneous Metalwork (cont.

| 1st Division | Note: No descriptive features are given for 1st Division - Code 1 or 2 as shown in CESMM | | |
|---|---|---|---|

| 2nd Division | | | 3rd Division |
|---|---|---|---|
| Stairways and landings | t | State specification and thickness of metal used. State off site surface treatment. State principal dimensions (Rule N/A1)  As an alternative to the additional descriptions to be given as required by Rule N/A1 (See above) item descriptions may identify assemblies by mark number in accordance with Paragraph 5.12 of CESMM (Note at foot of page 61 of CESMM) | Refer to the classification table for 3rd Division features which are noted below |
| Walkways and platforms | t | | |
| Ladders | m | State when items include safety loops, rest platforms or returned stringers (Rule N/A2) Measure length along stringers (Rule N/M4) | |
| Handrails | m | Measure along top member (Rule N/M4) | |
| Bridge parapets | m | | |
| Miscellaneous framing | m | Measure along external perimeter (Rule N/M5) | State section for miscellaneous framing |
| Plate flooring | m2 | Deemed to include supporting metalwork unless otherwise stated (Rule N/C2) | |
| Open grid flooring | m2 | | |
| Cladding | m2 | | |
| Welded mesh panelling | m2 | Deemed to include supporting metalwork unless otherwise stated (Rule N/C3) | |
| Duct covers | m2 | | |
| Tie rods | nr | Deemed to include concrete, reinforcement and joints (Rule N/C4) | |
| Walings | m | | |
| Bridge bearings | nr | | State type of Bridge bearing |
| Uncovered tanks | nr | | State volume range of tanks, or volume over 1000 m3 |
| Covered tanks | nr | | |

COMMENTARY

## Miscellaneous Metalwork (refer to Table 10.04)

The 1st Division of Class N lists no descriptive features. It provides numbers which serve as a coding device. The 2nd Division lists features for some of the various components of miscellaneous metalwork which may be required outside those classified as structural metalwork in a civil engineering contract. Items for miscellaneous metalwork combine the provision of the components, their erection or fixing and the fixings themselves.

The information to be given in the descriptions for miscellaneous metalwork items is set out in Rule N/A1 of the CESMM. (See Table 10.04 on page 179). It is considered preferable to use the alternative permitted by the Note at the foot of Page 61 and for brief identifying descriptions to make reference to drawings and the specification from which can be obtained the details which otherwise must be stated in the item descriptions.

The units of measurement and measurement conventions for the components are given in Table 10.04. Where item quantities are given by mass they include the mass of all components and attached pieces. It will be noted from the Table that items for flooring, weld mesh, panelling and duct covers are deemed to include supporting metalwork and that tie rods are deemed to include concrete, reinforcement and joints.

| *Specimen Item Descriptions for Miscellaneous Metalwork* | Number | Item description | Unit |
|---|---|---|---|
| Items in addition to those here would be measurable under Class G for "Inserts" for | | MISCELLANEOUS METALWORK.  Galvanised Mild Steel. | |
| (a) casting in to concrete, excluding supply of the anchorage cages for the parapets | N150 | Bridge parapets; Group P2, 48 km/h traffic speed, to concrete kerb with cage type anchorage, as Drawing 38/24. | m |
| (b) casting in only the tie rods into the anchorages | | Mild Steel. | |
| Binding the tie rods with protective tape should be measured as protective layers under Class W. | N240 | Tie rods; diameter 38 mm, length 7 m, with reinforced concrete anchorages, as Drawing 23/22. | nr |
| On site painting of parapets and protective painting of tie rods and waling, if required, should be measured under Class V | N250 | Walings; pair of channels, each 152 x 89 mm x 23.84 kg/m, back to back with distance pieces, as Drawing 23/24. | m |

EXAMPLE ME 1

Measured Example

The Measured Example is for part of the work for a steel bridge over a cutting. Excavation, foundations, abutments and other work which forms part of the bridge are not measured in the Example. The dimensions are for the structural metalwork and related incidental items only.

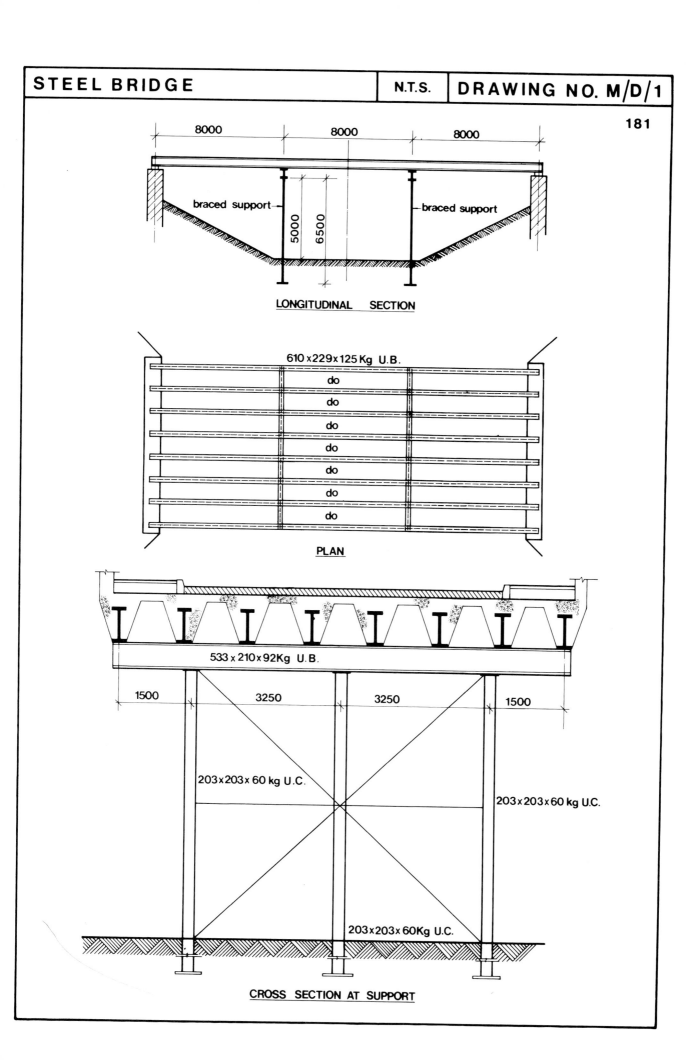

LONGITUDINAL SECTION

PLAN

CROSS SECTION AT SUPPORT

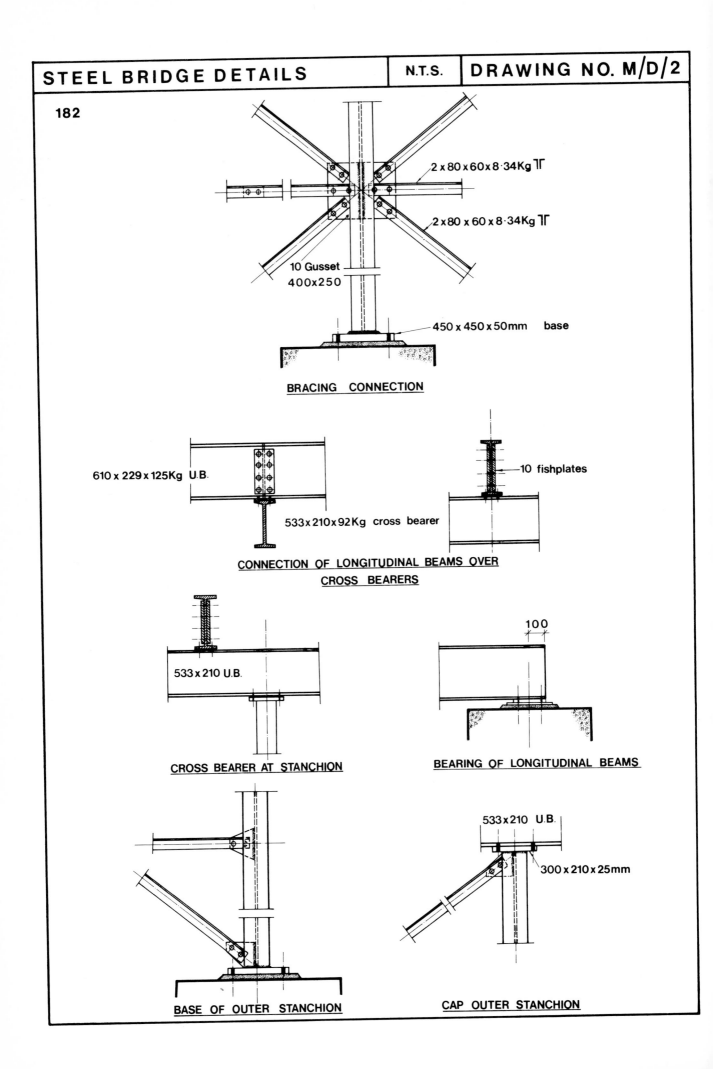

182

2 x 80 x 60 x 8·34Kg ⊤⊤

2 x 80 x 60 x 8·34Kg ⊤⊤

10 Gusset
400x250

450 x 450 x 50mm    base

BRACING   CONNECTION

610 x 229 x 125Kg U.B.

10 fishplates

533x210x92Kg  cross bearer

CONNECTION OF LONGITUDINAL BEAMS OVER
CROSS BEARERS

533 x 210 U.B.

100

CROSS BEARER AT STANCHION

BEARING OF LONGITUDINAL BEAMS

533 x 210  U.B.

300 x 210 x 25mm

BASE OF OUTER STANCHION

CAP  OUTER STANCHION

STEEL BRIDGE OVER CUTTING DRGS M/D/1+2

All steel Grade 43 A unless
o/w described

EXAMPLE ME 1

Deck beams

| | |
|---|---|
| 3/ 8000 = | 24000 |
| 2/ 100 = | 200 |
| | 24200 |

8/ 24.20 Kg
×
8/2/ 125.00
8/2/2/ 0.55
×
15.70

{ Fabricn. of main membs.
{ for bridges, rolld. sectns
{ xtra on plan (M 111

(610 × 229 U.B

(200 × 10 fish plates
+

{ Erectn of membs. for
{ bridges, perm. erectn.
(M 520

8/2/ 8
8/2/ 4

{ Erectn of membs. for
{ bridges, site bolts black
{ diam 20 - 24 mm (M 533

8/2/ 1

Bridge beargs., slide.
inc. plates + anchor
bolts. Drg. M/D/2
(N 262

+

Conc. access. inserts.
set 4 anch bolts. proj.
above surf conc. excludg.
supply of inserts
(G 832.1

+

Groutg. und. plates, area
n e 0.1 m2, ct. mor.
(1:2)      (G 841

(1)

COMMENTARY

Items for the fabrication of members include the provision of the structural metalwork components. They are given separately from the items for erection. See Table 10.02 and Commentary given previously. The dimensions for the fabrication and erection items are set down in the Example in a manner which allows the mass in kg. to be calculated on the dimension sheets. The first dimension of each set of two is the length of the member or attachment in metres, the second is its mass in kg. per metre.

When billing the structural metalwork, appropriate items can be listed under the sub headings "Fabrication of members.........." and "Erection of members ........" to avoid having to repeat these phrases in various item descriptions.

The code attached to the item for site bolts indicates that it relates to the erection of members for bridges. The item description given in the Bill for the bolts must state or otherwise indicate that the bolts relate to the erection of members for bridges. The site bolts here measured are those for the fishplate connections and those to attach the bridge beams to the trestle cross members.

Additional description is given in the items of bridge bearings to make clear the extent of the work intended to be included in the items.

Items for inserts identify the position of the inserts in relation to the surface of the concrete in accordance with Rule A15 in Class G of the CESMM.

STEEL BRIDGE OVER CUTTING. DRG. M/D/1~2

Deck Beams (cont

| | | |
|---|---|---|
| 8/ | 24.20 | Off Site surf. treatmt. blast cleang. Spec. clause "X" (M810 |
| | 2.08 | |
| 8/2/2/ | 1.20 | |
| | 0.42 | |

&

Off Site surf. treatmt. 2c. calcium. plumb. primer (M870

Trestles

Fabricn. of membs for frames, trestles stra on plan comprising 203  203 x 60 Kg/m U.C. legs 533 x 210 x 92 Kg/m U.B. cross membs. 80 x 60 x 8.34 Kg/m angle bracgs and 10 mm plates   (M341

| | Kg | |
|---|---|---|
| 2/3/ | 6.50 x 60.00 | (203 x 203 U.C. (legs. |
| 2/3/ | 0.45 x 177.00 | (450 x 50 plate (base |
| 2/3/ | 0.21 x 58.90 | (300 x 25 plate (cap |
| 2/2/ | 0.40 x 19.60 | (250 x 10 plate (gussets |
| 2/2/3/ | 0.20 x 19.60 | ( "  "  " ( " |
| 2/ | 9.73 x 92.00 | (533 x 210 U.B. (cross (membs |
| 2/2/2/ | 3.25 x 8.34 | (80 x 60 L (horiz |
| 2/4/2/ | 4.60 x 8.34 | (80 x 60 L (braces |
| 2/6/ | 0.15 x 6.28 | (80 x 10 plate (packers |

&

Erectn. of membs for frames, perm. erectn.   M620

(2)

COMMENTARY

Surface treatment measured under CESM Class M is that required to be carried out before the structural metalwork is delivered to the Site. On Site surface treatment before or after erection is classed as painting under CESMM Class V.

The second dimension of each set of two here given for surface treatment is the surface area in m2 per linear metre of the member. It is taken from a Steel Sections handbook.

Details of the members are stated in the item descriptions for trestles as provided in CESMM Rule M/A4.

When taking dimensions for structural metalwork, it is convenient to follow the dimensions of a main member with those for the plates and fittings attached to it before proceeding to set down the dimensions of another main member.

Trestles (cont.

| | | |
|---|---|---|
| 2/2/3/ | 2 | {Erectn of membs for |
| 2/ | 12 | {fras. site bolts, black, |
| 2/6/ | 2 | {diam.20-24mm (M633 |
| 2/3/ | 4 | |

COMMENTARY

The site bolts here measured are those for attaching the bracing to the gusset plates and also those for attaching the cross members of the trestles to the cap plates of the legs.

| 2/ | 3 | Fabricn of membs for fras., anchorage & h.d. bolt assemb. w. plate washrs. Drg.M/D/2 (M380 |
|---|---|---|

+

Conc. access. inserts set of 4 h.d. bolts, proj. above surf. conc. excludg. supply of inserts (G832.2

+

Groutg. und. plates, area 0.1 - 0.5 m2 a.b. (G842

Fixing holding down bolt assemblies are classed as "inserts" under CESMM Class G. A suffix number is added to the Code number to avoid different items having the same Code number (See last item in Column (1) of these dimensions).

For the purpose of the Example, it is assumed that the Detail Drawing referred to in the item description for anchorage assemblies, provides details and sizes of the holding down bolts, washers and plate washers.

Surface treatment items in Class M are confined to off-site work. The 1st Division descriptive feature makes this clear.

| | | |
|---|---|---|
| 2/3/ | 6.50 | {Off Site surf. treatmt. |
| | 1.20 | {blast cleang. a.b. (M810 |
| 2/3/ | 0.55 | |
| | 0.55 | + |
| 2/2/3/ | 0.24 | |
| | 0.33 | |
| 2/2/2/ | 0.41 | Off. Site surf treatmt |
| 2/2/2/3/ | 0.26 | 2ᶜ primer a.b. (M870 |
| | 0.21 | |
| | 0.26 | |
| 2/ | 9.73 | |
| | 1.84 | |
| 2/2/2/ | 3.25 | |
| | 0.28 | |
| 2/4/2/ | 4.60 | |
| | 0.28 | |
| 2/2/6/ | 0.16 | |
| | 0.09 | |

(3)

# 11 Timber - CESMM Class: O

Class O includes timber components and fittings, timber decking and fittings and fastenings for timber components and decking.

Provision for the classification of formwork, timber piles, timber sleepers, timber supports in tunnels and timber fencing is made in other Classes of the CESMM, and these are specifically excluded from Class O. See the "Excludes" at the head of the classification table of Class O in the CESMM. Class O applies only to timber in civil engineering construction work. It is not intended to apply to Building carpentry and joinery.

Cross reference is made to work included in Class O in the "Excludes" at the head of the classification table in Class N of the CESMM.

Table 11.01   Timber Components, Timber Decking and Fittings and Fastenings

Generally   Items are deemed to include for fixing, boring, cutting and jointing (Rule 0/C1)

| 1st Division | | | 2nd Division | 3rd Division |
|---|---|---|---|---|
| Hardwood components | m | Measure overall length with no allowance for joints (Rule 0/M1) | State nominal gross cross-sectional dimensions and thickness (Rule 0/A1) | State length range as 3rd Division features. State actual length where exceeding 20 m. |
| Softwood components | m | State structural use and location of components longer than 3 m (Rule 0/A2) | | |
| | | State grade or species (Rule 0/A1) | Use nominal gross cross-sectional area for classification (Rule 0/D1) | |
| | | State any impregnation requirement (Rule 0/A1) | | |
| | | State any special surface finish (Rule 0/A1) | | |
| Hardwood decking | m2 | State species (Rule 0/A3) | State nominal gross cross-sectional dimensions and thicknesses (Rule 0/A3) | |
| Softwood decking | m2 | State any impregnation requirement (Rule 0/A3) | | |
| | | State any special surface finish (Rule 0/A3) | Use nominal gross thickness for classification (Rule 0/D2) | |
| | | No deduction for openings and holes each not exceeding 0.5 m2 in area (Rule 0/M2) | | |
| Fittings and fastenings | nr | State materials, types and sizes (Rule 0/A4) | Straps | |
| | | | Spikes | |
| | | | Coach screws | |
| | | | Bolts | |
| | | | Plates | |

COMMENTARY

## Class 0 (refer to Table 11.01)

Item descriptions for timber components and timber decking state the timber grades or species. They state also any impregnation requirements and any special surface finish.

Items are deemed to include for fixing timber components and decking, and for any boring, cutting or jointing of the timber necessary for their fabrication and fixing. Item descriptions for otherwise similar components or decking distinguish different methods of fixing where the methods are adjudged to have cost differences. Fittings and fastenings for timber components and decking are given as numbered items.

*Timber Components*

Timber components are measured by length in metres. Rule 0/M1 of the CESMM requires that "the length of timber components measured shall be their overall lengths with no allowance for scarfed or other joints". This Rule is a Measurement Rule and governs the measurements to be taken to compute the quantities (See Paragraph 3.6 of the CESMM). It is not a Definition Rule governing the measurement of length for 3rd Division classification purposes. The application of Rule 0/M1 is illustrated in Fig. 01. The lengths as (A) are the lengths measured overall for the longitudinal members. They take no account of the extra lengths of timber in the lapped joints in the running lengths of the components and estimators must allow for this. The lengths as (B) are the lengths measured overall for the transverse members. They automatically include the extra length of timber in jointing the ends of components to other components. This may be considered inconsistent but it is the way Rule 0/M1 is applied in practice.

Item descriptions for timber components longer than 3 m state the location and structural use of the components.

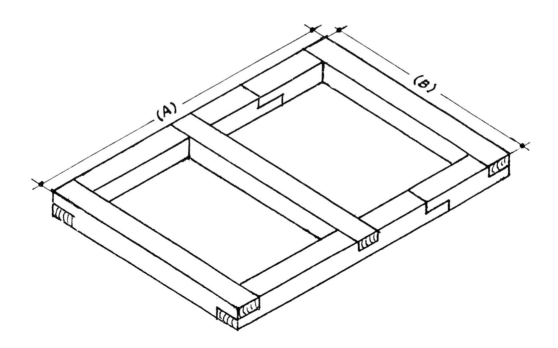

Fig. 01. Application of Rule 0/M1 of CESMM to measurement of timber components for computing quantities (See Fig.02. for length classification).

COMMENTARY

Class O (cont.

*Timber Components (cont.*

At 1st Division level timber components are classified either as "Hardwood" or "Softwood" as appropriate. The grade and specie being stated as additional description. Item descriptions also state the cross-sectional dimensions of the timber components before reduction by any surface finish (i.e. the nominal gross cross-sectional dimensions). The nominal gross cross-sectional dimensions are used to calculate the nominal gross cross-sectional areas for classification at 2nd Division level. The CESMM gives no Definition Rule governing how the lengths for classification at 3rd Division are to be measured. The bill compiler needs to use his own discretion and define in Preamble how 3rd Division classification lengths have been measured. Since structural joints are positioned by the Engineer to meet his structural design requirements it seems reasonable for length classification purpose to take the overall designed lengths of the pieces of timber as fabricated in the finished work (See Fig. O2.). Where lengths are left to the discretion of the contractor, the 3rd Division length classification (unless otherwise required) should be given as the minimum lengths of timber acceptable for the particular components.

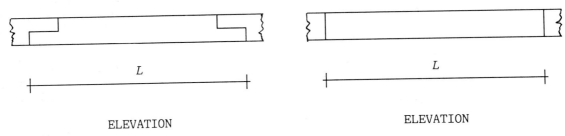

ELEVATION                              ELEVATION

*L* = Length used for 3rd Division classification of timber components

Fig. O2. Length classification of timber components.

*Timber decking*

Timber decking is measured by area and is given in m2. The area measured includes the areas of any openings individually not exceeding 0.5 m2.

The spaces between the boards or planks in open spaced decking is deducted where the area of individual spaces exceed 0.5 m2. Where individual spaces do not exceed 0.5 m2 in area the work is measured overall the spaces. It is usual for item descriptions for open spaced decking to state whether or not the spaces have been deducted.

The nominal gross thickness of decking is stated in item descriptions. The Second Division thickness range is overridden by Rule O/D2. The widths of the boards or planks used for the decking are stated or otherwise identified in item descriptions.

*Fittings and Fastenings*

Fittings and fastenings, of the type noted in the 2nd Division of this feature in Table 11.01, which are used to connect together or secure timber components or decking are given as separate items. The quantities give the number of each type. Fittings and fastenings other than those listed, such as timber connectors, etc., qualify also to be measured as separate items.

<u>Class O (cont.</u>

*Fittings and Fastenings (cont.)*

Item descriptions state or otherwise identify the materials, types, sizes and ancillary components, such as nuts, washers, etc., which are intended to be included in the items.

Items for fittings and fastenings include for any cutting or boring of the timber necessary for their fixing.

| Number | Item description | Unit |
|--------|-----------------|------|
| | <u>SUPERSTRUCTURE OF QUAY IN HARBOUR, FABRICATED TO PILES (MEASURED SEPAR-ATELY). REFER TO DRAWING NO. 20/38.</u> | |
| | <u>TIMBER.</u> | |
| | <u>Hardwood components, Greenheart, to BS 5756, grade HS.</u> | |
| | <u>Cross-sectional area 0.04 - 0.1 m2.</u> | |
| 0142.1 | 200 x 300 mm, length 1.5 - 3 m. | m |
| 0142.2 | 300 x 300 mm, length 1.5 - 3 m. | m |
| 0143 | 300 x 325 mm, length 3 - 5 m; diagonal braces between piles. | m |
| 0144 | 300 x 300 mm, length 5 - 8 m; horizontal deck bearers between piles | m |
| | <u>Cross-sectional area 0.1 - 0.2 m2.</u> | |
| 0154 | 300 x 400 mm, length 5 - 8 m; supports to braces between piles. | m |
| | <u>Hardwood decking, Jarrah, wrought finish.</u> | |
| | <u>Thickness 50 - 75 mm.</u> | |
| 0330.1 | 150 x 75 mm. | m2 |
| 0330.2 | 150 x 75 mm; with 19 mm spaces between planks (no deduction for spaces). | m2 |
| | <u>Fittings and fastenings.</u> | |
| | <u>Mild steel.</u> | |
| 0540 | Bolts; diameter 32 mm, length 600 mm, with plate washers both ends, counter-sunk flush, as Drawing No.3/27. | nr |

The Drawing given in the sub-heading is that which indicates the boundaries and surface levels of the water in the harbour. See Paragraph 5.20 of the CESMM.

The Rules of the CESMM require that the grade or specie be st-ated in item descrip-tions for components and the specie only be stated in the item de-scriptions for decking. See Rules O/A1 and Rules O/A3 in the CESMM. Notwithstanding these rules both grade and specie will normally be stated in item descrip-tions for components and decking. Otherwise, in the absence of a Specification require-ment, it is left open for the Contractor to use his discretion to provide a suitable grade of a specie if the grade is not stated or a suitable specie of the grade if a specie is not stated.

Fig. O3. Specimen item descriptions for timber and fittings for quay.

# 12 Piles and Piling Ancillaries – CESMM Classes: P and Q

Two Classes of the Work Classification are allocated in the CESMM to piling. Class P applies to the piles and to the driving or boring. Work to the piles other than that covered by Class P and work associated with piling is measured, to the extent provided, under Class Q. Boring for site investigation (included in Class B), ground anchors (included in Class C) and walings and tie rods (included in Class N) are listed in the CESMM as specific exclusions from Classes P and Q.

## *PILES - CESMM CLASS P*

Items for temporary works and plant are not given in the Bill of Quantities unless specific requirements are specified for them. Features of classification for piling plant (Items, Codes A337 and A338) and for temporary works (Item, Code 363) are listed in Class A of the CESMM. They serve to remind that tenderers may insert items for these, if they so choose, as Method-Related Charges.

Class P requires a set of items to be given for each group of piles. A group of piles being regarded as all piles of the same material, the same type and the same cross-sectional characteristics, installed from the same Commencing Surface in one location to support a single identified structure.

---

Table 12.01  Piles Generally

---

State materials of which piles are composed (Rule P/A1)

Identify preliminary piles (Rule P/A2)

Identify raking piles and state inclination ratios (Rule P/A2)

Identify structure to be supported and identify the Commencing Surface for the piles (Rule P/A3)

The Commencing Surface given in the Bill as the surface at which boring or driving is expected to begin shall be adopted when measuring the completed work (Rule P/M1)

---

COMMENTARY

Piles Generally (Refer to Table 12.01)

Item descriptions identify the structure to be supported by the piles and state the materials of which the piles are composed. They state also the actual section characteristics of the piles as provided in Rules P/A4, P/A6, P/A9 and P/A10 of the CESMM. These Rules override the Second Division ranges given in the classification table of Class P of the CESMM.

*Commencing Surfaces*

For piling on land the Commencing Surface may be the Original Surface or a surface below or above the Original Surface. For work in water the Original Surface is the natural bed of the river, sea, etc., the Commencing Surface may be the Original Surface or another surface. For example, the bed left after dredging. In all cases, item descriptions for driving and boring must identify the Commencing Surface. The same Commencing Surface adopted when preparing the Bill of Quantities is adopted when the work is admeasured.

Table 12.02 Cast in Place Piles

Generally - See Table 12.01

| 1st Division | | 2nd Division |
|---|---|---|
| Bored cast in place concrete piles | Identify contiguous bored piles (Rule P/A5) | State diameter (Rule P/A4) |
| Driven cast in place concrete piles | Use this classification for piles comprising driven permanent steel casings filled with concrete where piles are designed to carry the load on the concrete (Rule P/D2) | |

3rd Division

The following separate items, each indicated by a bracketed letter below, are measured for each group of piles

| (a) | Number of piles | nr | Give item for the number of piles in the group (Rule P/M2) |
|---|---|---|---|
| (b) | Concreted length | m | Give item for total concreted length of the piles in the group (Rule P/M2). Measure lengths from cut off levels expressly required to toe levels expressly required (Rule P/M3) |
| (c) | Depth bored or driven | m | Give items for total depth bored or driven for the group of piles (Rule P/M2)). State maximum depth, i.e. the depth which is not exceeded by any pile included in the item (Rule P/D1)

Measure along axes of the piles from the Commencing Surface to the toe levels of bored piles and to the bottom of the casing for driven cast in place piles (Rule P/M1) |

COMMENTARY

Cast in Place Piles (Refer to Table 12.02)

A set of several different items are given for each group of cast in place piles. In the Bill of Quantities an item giving the number of piles in a group is followed by separate items for the concreted length of piles and for the depth bored or driven for the group. The latter giving total depth and stating the maximum depth as noted against feature (c) in Table 12.02. A set of items following the same format is given for each group. (See Table 12.02 which sets out the descriptive features and notes also measurement conventions and units of measurement).

*Piles Concreted Temporarily Above Cut-off Level*

The concreted length of cast in place piles is measured as indicated in Table 12.02, with no allowance for cut off tolerances. Where for the temporary protection of the heads, it is expressly required that they are concreted to a higher level than cut off level, for subsequent removal, the additional lengths and their subsequent removal is given as a specified requirement in Class A.

## Table 12.03   Preformed Concrete, Timber and Isolated Steel Piles

Generally - See Table 12.01

| 1st Division | 2nd Division |
|---|---|
| Preformed concrete piles | State cross-section type and cross-sectional dimensions or diameter (Rule P/A6) |
| Preformed prestressed concrete piles | |
| Preformed concrete sheet piles | Classify in accordance with 2nd Division cross-sectional area ranges |
| Timber piles | |
| Isolated steel piles<br><br>   Use this classification for piles of concrete filled permanent steel cas-casings where the load is carried on the steel casing. Measure concrete filling as provided in Class Q(53\*) (Rule P/D5) | State mass per metre and cross-sectional dimensions (Rule P/A9)<br><br>Classify in accordance with 2nd Division mass ranges |

**3rd Division**

The following separate items, each indicated by a bracketed letter below, are measured for each group of piles

| | | | |
|---|---|---|---|
| (a) | Number of piles of stated length | nr | Give one or more items for the number of piles in the group (Rule P/M4) and (Rule P/M5)<br><br>State details of any treatments or coatings (Rule P/A7)<br><br>State lengths expressly required to be supplied excluding extension but in the case of preformed concrete and timber piles including the heads and shoes (Rule P/D3) and (Rule P/D4)<br><br>State details of driving heads and of shoes (Rule P/A8) |
| (b) | Depth driven | m | Give item for total depth driven (Rule P/M4) and (P/M5)<br><br>Measure driven depths along axes of piles from Commencing Surface to the bottom of the toes of the piles (Rule P/M1) |

COMMENTARY

Preformed Concrete, Timber and Isolated Steel Piles (Refer to Table 12.03)

The several separate items and details which require to be given for each group of preformed piles are noted in Table 12.03 which gives also the units of measurement.

Items for the number of preformed concrete, timber or isolated steel piles state the lengths expressly required. This is an exception to the general rule that quantities are given nett. The lengths of the piles admeasured are those ordered whatever the finished length in the work may be. Items for cutting off surplus lengths are measured under Class Q. Items for the depths driven give the total of the actual driven depths of the piles in linear metres.

COMMENTARY

Isolated Piles part in Tidal Water

Specimen item descriptions are
given below for the isolated
steel piles, part in tidal
water, for the jetty shown in
cross-section in the adjoining
diagram.  Piles assumed to be
of the section and size stated
in specimen items.  Length of
piles assumed for
the purpose of
specimen items.

Original Surface
and  Commencing Surface

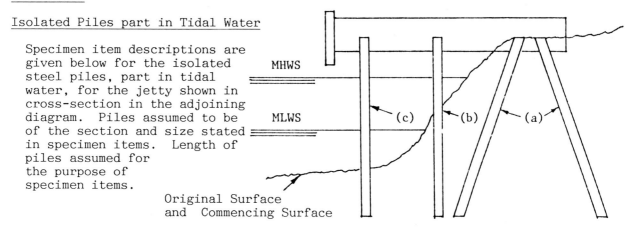

| Number | Item description | Unit |
|--------|-----------------|------|
|  | PILING TO JETTY IN TEIGNMOUTH HARBOUR (LOCATION DRAWING NO. 27/20). |  |
|  | PILES. |  |
|  | Isolated steel piles, steel to BS 4360, grade 50, "H" section, 305 x 305 mm, mass 137 kg/m. |  |
|  | Commencing Surface Original Surface of harbour embankment. |  |
| P751.1 | Number of piles, length 10.5 m; raking 1 in 2.85 from vertical. | nr |
| P752.1 | Depth driven. | m |
|  | Commencing Surface Original Surface of harbour embankment between high and low water levels. |  |
| P751.2 | Number of piles, length  10.0 m. | nr |
| P752.2 | Depth driven. | m |
|  | Commencing Surface Original Surface of harbour bed below low water level. |  |
| P751.3 | Number of piles, length 10.0 m. | nr |
| P752.3 | Depth driven. | m |

COMMENTARY

The location drawing stated
in the sub-heading of the
specimen descriptions is
that given in the Preamble
in accordance with Paragraph
5.20 of the CESMM. It is not
obligatory to make reference
to the drawing as here
shown, but it is considered
helpful to do so.

Item descriptions distinguish the different Commencing
Surfaces. Items for the
piles marked (a) in the diagram are billed in the specimen items at Items Code
P751.1 and P752.1. Piles
marked (b) in the diagram
are billed in the specimen
items at Items Code P751.2
and P752.2. Those marked (c)
in the diagram are given in
Items Code P751.3 and
P752.3.

Any treatments and coatings
required to be carried out
before delivery to the Site
would be described and
included in the items for
the piles. Any treatments
and coatings required to be
carried out on Site would be
measured under CESMM, Class
V.

Fig. P1.  Isolated steel piles for jetty part in tidal
          water.

Table 12.04   Interlocking Steel Piles

Generally - See Table 12.01

1st Division

| Interlocking steel piles | State section reference or mass per metre (Rule P/A10) |

| 2nd Division | State section modulus (Rule P/A10) |

3rd Division

The following separate items, each indicated by a bracketed letter below, are required for each group of piles

| (a) Length of special piles, if any          m | Give one or more items for total length of each type of special piles, if any (Rule P/M6). State type of special piles in the item descriptions (Rule P/A12). Measure length as that which is expressly required excluding extensions (Rule P/D6) |
| | Class corner, junction, closer and taper piles as special piles (Rule P/D7). Measure closure and taper piles only when expressly required (Rule P/M8) |
| (b) Driven area          m2 | Give item for total driven area of piles (Rule P/M6). Calculate area by multiplying the mean undeveloped horizontal lengths of the pile walls formed (including the lengths occupied by special piles) by the depths measured along the axes of the piles from the Commencing Surface to the bottom of the toes of the piles (Rule P/M7) |
| (c) Area of piles of length: | Give one or more items for total area of piles divided into length ranges given in 3rd Division (Rule P/M6) |
| not exceed-ing 14 m    m2 | Calculate area by multiplying the mean undeveloped horizontal lengths of the pile walls formed (including the lengths occupied by special piles) by the lengths of the piles expressly required to be supplied excluding extensions (Rule P/M7) |
| 14 - 24 m  m2 | Give lengths as those expressly required excluding extensions (Rule P/D6) |
| exceed-ing 24 m   m2 | State details of any treatments and coatings (Rule P/A11) |

COMMENTARY

Interlocking Steel Piles (Refer to Table 12.04)

The several separate items given for each group of interlocking piles and the information to be given in the item descriptions are noted in Table 12.04.

Items for driven area are measured as noted at (b) in Table 12.04.

The piles themselves are measured by area in m2. The area is calculated as noted against (c) in Table 12.04. The length used to calculate area and for the length classification is that which is expressly required to be supplied excluding the lengths of any extensions (another exception to the general rule that quantities are given nett). Items give the total area for each group of piles divided into items which distinguish the different Third Division length ranges.

COMMENTARY

## Interlocking Steel Piles (cont.

Special piles are measured as part of the area of the piles. Additionally they are made the subject of separate items which give the total length of each type in metres. See (a) in Table 12.04.

Where interlocking piles are used as the anchorage for anchored interlocking steel pile walls, they are given separately from the piles in the walls and are suitably identified.

Steel walings and tie rods for anchored pile walls are excluded from Classes P and Q of the CESMM. They are classified by features and are each given in items as provided in Class N. Any fishplates, spacers, back bolts and similar assembly fittings in connection with walings are identified and included in the items for the walings. The bolts, washers and any couplings used for the tie rods are similarly included in the items for the tie rods.

### PILING ANCILLARIES - CESMM CLASS Q

The pile shafts and work installing them by boring or driving are covered by Class P of the CESMM. Work outside that covered by Class P which is incidental to piling is classified "piling ancillaries" and is catered for by Class Q. Work in Class Q, other than backfilling empty bore of cast in place piles is restricted, by Rule Q/M1, to that which is expressly required.

## Table 12.05    Piling Ancillaries

| Generally | Measure work in this Class, other than backfilling empty bore of cast in place concrete piles, only where expressly required (Rule Q/M1). |
|---|---|

Deemed to include disposal of surplus materials unless otherwise stated (Rule Q/C1)

| 1st Division | 2nd Division | | 3rd Division |
|---|---|---|---|
| Cast in place concrete piles | Pre-boring | m | State diameter as 3rd Division features |
| | Backfilling empty bore with stated material        m | State material | |
| | Permanent casings each length:-<br><br>  not exceeding 13 m        m<br><br>  exceeding 13 m        m | State thickness and details of treatments and coatings (Rule Q/A2)<br><br>Measure lengths from Commencing Surface to bottoms of casings (Rule Q/M2)<br><br>Deemed to include driving heads and shoes (Rule Q/C2) | Use diameter of piles for 3rd Division classification (Rule Q/D1) |
| | Enlarged bases        nr | State diameter of enlarged bases for bored piles (Rule Q/A1) | |
| | Cutting off surplus lengths        m | State where lengths include permanent casings (Rule Q/A2) | |
| | Preparing heads        nr | | |

Table 12.05  Piling Ancillaries (cont.

| 1st Division | 2nd Division | | 3rd Division |
|---|---|---|---|
| Cast in place concrete piles | Reinforcement | t | State materials (Rule Q/A3) | Straight bars:- |
| | | | State details of any couplers expressly required for high tensile steel reinforcement (Rule Q/A4) | not exceeding 25 mm nominal size |
| | | | | exceeding 25 mm nominal size |
| | | | Calculate mass taking steel as 7.85 t/m3 and other material as stated in Contract (Rule Q/M4). Include the mass in laps in the mass measured (Rule Q/M3) | Helical bars of stated nominal size |
| | | | | Use cross-sectional size as defined in BS 4449 and BS 4461 for classification of nominal size (Rule Q/D2) |
| | | | Deemed to include supporting reinforcement (Rule Q/C3) | |
| Preformed concrete piles | Preboring | m | Deemed to include grouting voids between pile and bore (Rule Q/C4) | State cross-sectional area as 3rd Division features |
| Timber piles | Jetting | m | | |
| | Filling hollow piles with concrete | m | State specification of concrete (Rule Q/A5) | Use cross-sectional area of pile for 3rd Division classification (Rule Q/D3) |
| | | | Deemed to include removing material from within pile before concreting (Rule Q/C6) | |
| | Number of pile extensions | nr | For each group of pile extensions:- | |
| | Length of pile extensions:- | | (a) give separate item for number (Rule Q/M6 and Q/M9) | |
| | not exceeding 3 m | m | (b) give one or two items for lengths of pile extensions divided into 2nd Division length ranges (Rule Q/M6 and Q/M9) | |
| | exceeding 3 m | m | | |
| | | | Measure driving extended piles under Class P (Rule Q/M5) | |
| | | | Do not measure lengths formed with surplus cut off material (Rule Q/M7) | |
| | | | Include length of scarfed or other joints with length of timber pile extensions (Rule Q/M8) | |
| | | | Deemed to include work attaching extensions to pile (Rule Q/C5) | |

Table 12.05  Piling Ancillaries (cont.

| 1st Division | 2nd Division | | 3rd Division |
|---|---|---|---|
| Preformed concrete piles<br><br>Timber piles | Cutting off surplus lengths    m<br><br>Preparing heads    nr | | State cross-sectional area range as 3rd Division features<br><br>Use cross-sectional area of pile for 3rd Division classification (Rule Q/D3) |
| Isolated steel piles | Preboring        m )<br>Jetting         m )<br>Filling hollow piles with concrete      m )<br>Number of pile extensions       nr )<br>Length of pile extensions each length:- ) | The Rules referred to previously in this Table against these 2nd Division features, apply here | State mass range as 3rd Division features<br><br>Use mass of piles for 3rd Division classification (Rule Q/D4) |
| Interlocking steel piles | not exceeding 3 m        m )<br><br>exceeding 3 m    m )<br>Cutting off surplus lengths    m )<br>Preparing heads  nr ) | | State section modulus range as 3rd Division features<br><br>Use section modulus of piles for 3rd Division classification (Rule Q/D5) |
| Obstructions h | Measure only for breaking out of rock or artifical hard material encountered above founding stratum of bored piles (Rule Q/M11) | | |
| Pile tests    nr<br><br>Identify tests to preliminary piles (Rule Q/A6) | State type of loading or penetration tests as 2nd Division features<br><br>State when load is applied to raking piles (Rule Q/A7) | | State load and classify in accordance with 3rd Division features (Rule Q/A7) |
| | Non destructive integrity<br><br>Inclinometer installations | | |

COMMENTARY

Piling Ancillaries  (Refer to Table 12.05)

Item descriptions for piling ancillaries give the type and the 3rd Division cross-section range of the piles to which the work relates. Precise cross-sectional sizes of the piles are not given for items of piling ancillaries. Items are deemed to include removal of surplus material from the site, this includes excavated material, cut off lengths of piles and casings and materials left from tests.

COMMENTARY

## Piling Ancillaries (cont.

No provision is made in Class Q for items additional to those of the piles for the placing of concrete, in cast in place concrete piles, by special methods. Such as by tremie in waterlogged grounds. It is taken that this is deemed to be included in the items for piles where the Contractor may choose for himself the method of placing. Should it be expressly required that the concrete be placed by a particular method, a special measured item would be given either in Class Q or as a specified requirement item in Class A and the measurement convention adopted would be stated in the Preamble to the Bill of Quantities.

Descriptive features, units of measurement and references to the Rules applicable to the work as given in the CESMM, are noted or referred to in Table 12.05.

### *Backfilling Empty Bore*

The backfilling of empty bore for cast in place concrete piles is excepted from the Class Q general rule that work must be expressly required, because any empty bore may not be left but must be backfilled to comply with statutory safety regulations. The items are measured in linear metres and item descriptions state the backfilling material.

### *Permanent Casings*

Items for permanent casing are given in linear metres and distinguish between casings in lengths not exceeding 13 metres and those in lengths exceeding 13 metres. Item descriptions state materials, the casing thickness and give details of any treatments and coatings.

It is left for the contractor to provide any temporary casings unless they are expressly required and also expressly required to be removed. Where there are such express requirements the temporary casings should be identified in and included in the items for the concreted lengths of the piles in Class P.

### *Enlarged Bases*

Lengths occupied by enlarged bases, where required, are measured and included in the lengths given in Class P for both the concreted length of piles and the depth bored or driven. The numbered items given in Class Q for enlarged bases are intended to cover the work outside that of the normal cross-section of the pile shafts and that below the expressly required toe level which is necessary to form the enlarged base. Item descriptions give the diameter of the enlarged base in addition to the appropriate diameter range of the piles.

### *Pile Extensions*

An item for the number of pile extensions and a maximum of two other items for the length of pile extensions are given where extensions are formed with material other than that cut off from other piles. Items distinguish between extensions which do not exceed 3 metres long and those which exceed 3 metres long. Where the extensions are formed with material cut off from other piles, items for the number of pile extensions are given but no items for the lengths of extensions are given. The work of connecting the pile extensions to the piles is deemed to be included in the items given for the number of pile extensions.

COMMENTARY

## Piling Ancillaries (cont.

### *Cutting Off Surplus Lengths*

Items give the total length in linear metres of surplus lengths to be cut off. The specification will usually reserve for the Employer the ownership of cut off lengths for use in any lengthening of piles which may be required. Otherwise cut off lengths become the property of the Contractor and he is responsible for removing them from the Site.

### *Preparing Heads*

Numbered items are given to cover the work required to prepare the heads of piles to receive subsequent permanent work and this would include the breaking down of concrete and bending reinforcement as required. Preparing the ends of piles to receive extensions is not classified as preparing heads.

### *Reinforcement*

Reinforcement and prestressing steel is described and included in the items for preformed concrete piles measured under Class P. Reinforcement for cast in place concrete piles is given under Class Q. It is given by mass in tonnes in separate items from those for the piles. Helical reinforcement is given separately from straight bars and item descriptions state the actual nominal size of each size of bar. Items for straight bars group together those which do not exceed 25 mm nominal size in separate items from those which exceed 25 mm nominal size.

### *Obstructions*

Items are measured in operational hours for the time taken for breaking out rock or artificial hard material encountered above the founding stratum when constructing bored piles. The item is not measurable for normal boring to secure the toes of the piles in the founding stratum. Rule Q/M11 of the CESMM makes it clear that the item applies only to obstructions above the founding stratum. An item of obstruction is not measurable where the removal of an obstruction does not delay the boring operations. Preamble should make clear that the hourly rate is deemed to cover the whole piling team and equipment needed to remove the obstruction and also the costs of any delays caused to the boring operations.

### *Pile Tests*

It is usual to relate items for pile tests to specification clauses wherein the tests and other requirements are described. The Bill should make clear that the items for tests are deemed to include all requirements specified for the tests, including preparing piles for testing and the provision and removal of any temporary work installed for the purpose of the tests.

The actual test loads are stated in item descriptions for loading tests, the standard 3rd Division load range features being used for classification purposes. Item descriptions for pile tests identify those which are to preliminary piles. Item descriptions for loading tests state where the load is applied to raking piles.

EXAMPLE No. PE.1

Measured Example

A measured example of bored cast in place piles follows.

**200**

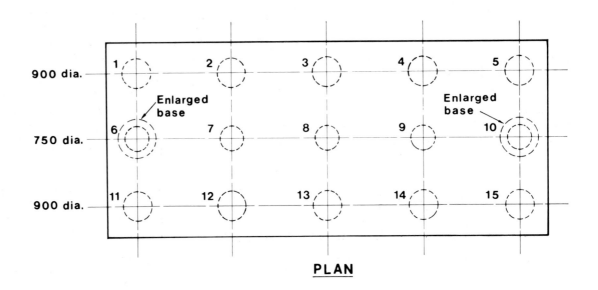

**PLAN**

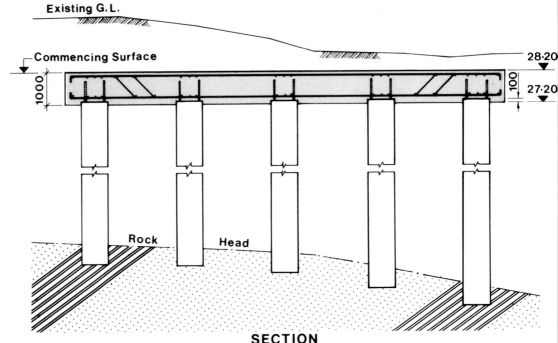

**SECTION**

| Pile No. | 1 | 6 | 11 | 2 | 7 | 12 | 3 | 8 | 13 | 4 | 9 | 14 | 5 | 10 | 15 |
|---|---|---|---|---|---|---|---|---|---|---|---|---|---|---|---|
| Rock Level | 19·60 | | | 19·50 | | | 19·30 | | | 18·80 | | | 18·30 | | |
| Base Level | 19·00 | | | 18·90 | | | 18·70 | | | 18·20 | | | 17·70 | | |

NOTES
1. Specified cut-off level 27·30
2. Concrete to be Grade 25, cement to B.S.4027

# PILE FDN. - DRG. No. P1D/1.

## EXAMPLE PE.1

|  |  | 1000 |
|--|--|------|
|  |  | 100 |
|  |  | 900 |

|  | | | | |
|------|------|------|------|------|
| 28.20 | 28.20 | 28.20 | 28.20 | 28.20 |
| 19.00 | 18.90 | 18.70 | 18.20 | 17.70 |
| *D.bored* 9.20 | 9.30 | 9.50 | 10.00 | 10.50 |
| 0.90 | 0.90 | 0.90 | 0.90 | 0.90 |
| *Conc.lgth* 8.30 | 8.40 | 8.60 | 9.10 | 9.60 |

(Piles

Piling to Bridge Support.

Comm Surf. top of pile cap.

Bored cast in place conc. piles, conc.grade C 25, ct to BS.4027

Diam 750 mm

5/  1   Number of piles (P141

8.30
8.40
8.60
9.10
9.60   } Concreted length (P142

9.20
9.30
9.50
10.00
10.50   } Depth bored, max. depth 10.50 m. (P143

Diam. 900 mm

5/  2   Number of piles (P151

(1)

## COMMENTARY

Rather than make waste calculations on the dimension sheets as here shown, it will be found convenient for the more extensive installation to prepare a separate schedule indicating for each pile the length, depth bored or driven, work required to heads, bases and the like, in a manner which will allow of like items being collected together for transfer to dimension sheets or for billing direct.

The precise diameters of the piles are stated in item descriptions. The 3rd Division ranges are overridden by Rule P/A4 of the CESMM.

The items assume that the site is to be reduced to the level of the top of the pile caps prior to piling commencing. This will form the working surface and it will also be the Commencing Surface for boring. The Commencing Surface must be identified in the item descriptions. See Table 12.01.

The concreted length is measured from the cut off levels expressly required to the toe levels expressly required. It includes the length occupied by enlarged bases but excludes any cut off tolerances. It is assumed that there is no specified requirement for the piles to be concreted to a level higher than the specified cut off levels for subsequent removal. Numbered items for each type of enlarged base are given notwithstanding that the length occupied by the bases is included in the pile length. These items are given subsequently. The length occupied by any cut off tolerance is neglected when measuring the lengths of piles.

The depth bored is measured along the axes of the piles from the Commencing Surface to the toe levels. The maximum depth is that which is not exceeded by any pile in the group. See Table 12.02.

PILE FDN - DRG. NO P1D/1

|  |  | Bored piles (cont. |
|---|---|---|
|  |  | Diam. 900 mm (cont |
| 2/ | 8.30 | } Concreted length (P152 |
| 2/ | 8.40 | |
| 2/ | 8.60 | |
| 2/ | 9.10 | |
| 2/ | 9.60 | |
| 2/ | 9.20 | } Depth bored max. |
| 2/ | 9.30 | } depth 10.50 m (P153 |
| 2/ | 9.50 | |
| 2/ | 10.00 | |
| 2/ | 10.50 | |

(Bases piles 6+10

Cast in place conc. piles.

| 2/ | 1 | Enlarged bases, diam. 1200 mm to 750 mm diam. shafts (Q154 |
|---|---|---|

(Rfcmt.

$1000 \div 150 = 6.666$

$750 - (2 \times 40) = 0.670$

$0.670 \times \pi = 2.106$

$2.106 \times 6.666 = 14.04$

$14.04^2 + 1.00^2 = 198.12$

$\sqrt{198.12} = 14.08$

Helical. lgth 1m 750 φ pile = **14.08**

$0.90 - (2 \times 40) = 0.82$

$0.82 \times \pi = 2.577$

$2.577 \times 6.666 = 17.178$

$17.18^2 + 1.00^2 = 296.15$

$\sqrt{296.15} = 17.24$

Helical. lgth 1m 900 φ pile = **17.21**

(2)

COMMENTARY

The convention, similar to that when preparing a Bill, of drawing lines across the description column is adopted here to denote the end of the items to which the sub-heading apply. See Fig.5. Page 22, Chapter 2.

Enlarged bases are requiired to piles Nos. 6 and 10. Items for enlarged bases state the diameter of the base and the diamter of the shaft from which they are enlarged.

The reinforcement details, (See next column) show the reinforcement cages to be of vertical bars and helical bindings. The wastes under the heading "Rfcmt" calculate the developed length of the helical spiral for one metre length of pile of each dia-meter. The workings in the wastes calculate a single circumference and then multiply it by the number there would be at the 150 mm pitch in a one metre length of pile. The total of the circumference so obtained represents the base of a triangle, the height (one metre) is taken as the perpendicular and the hypotenuse (found by the Theorem of Pythagoras) is the developed length of the spiral.

PILE FDN. - DRG. NO. P/D/1

Cast in place conc. piles (cont.

(mass helic Kg/m pile

| | | 750ø | 900ø |
|---|---|---|---|
| 14.08 × 0.616 = | | 8.673 | |
| 17.21 × 0.616 = | | | 10.601 |

Reinforcement M.S.
to BS.4449

(750ø

| 16/ | 8.30 | Stra. bars, nom. si. |
|---|---|---|
| 16/ | 8.40 | n.e. 25 mm    (Q211 |
| 16/ | 8.60 | |
| 16/ | 9.10 | |
| 16/ | 9.60 | |
| 16/5/ | 0.50 | |
| | | bars act. 25 mm ∴ |
| | | × 3.853 =        Kg |

| | 8.30 | Helical bars, nom. si. |
|---|---|---|
| | 8.40 | 10 mm.        (Q213 |
| | 8.60 | |
| | 9.10 | |
| | 9.60 | |
| 5/ | 0.50 | |
| | | × 8.673 =        Kg |

(900ø

| 2/16/ | 8.30 | Stra. bars, nom. si. |
|---|---|---|
| 2/16/ | 8.40 | e.25 mm    (Q212 |
| 2/16/ | 8.60 | |
| 2/16/ | 9.10 | |
| 2/16/ | 9.60 | |
| 2/16/5/ | 0.50 | bars act 32 mm ∴ |
| | | × 6.313 =        Kg |

| 2/ | 8.30 | Helical bars, nom. si. |
|---|---|---|
| 2/ | 8.40 | 10 mm.        (Q213 |
| 2/ | 8.60 | |
| 2/ | 9.10 | |
| 2/ | 9.60 | |
| 2/5/ | 0.50 | |
| | | × 10.601 =        Kg |

(3)

Details of the reinforcement cages taken in the Example are illustrated in the following diagram.

ELEVATION OF CAGES

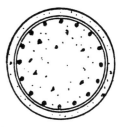

CROSS-SECTION OF PILES

The cages for the 750 mm diameter piles comprise 16 No. 25 mm diameter vertical bars with 10 mm diameter helical binding at 150 mm pitch. The cages for the 900 mm diameter piles are similar except that the vertical bars are 32 mm diameter.

The dimensions set down for the straight bar reinforcement are the lengths of the of bars in the piles timesed by the number of bars in the piles. Provision being made for the total lengths to be multiplied by the mass per metre of the appropriate size of bar. The dimensions set down for the helical reinforcement are the vertical heights of the spirals. provision being made for the totals to be multiplied by the mass (calculated from the developed length of bars) per metre of vertical height of spirals.

The mass of reinforcement would be reduced to tonnes for billing.

204

PILE FDN. - DRG. NO P/D/1

Cast in place conc. piles (cont.

Preparing heads

5/ 1       Diam. 750 mm
                              (Q184

2/5/ 1     Diam. 900 mm
                              (Q185

Pile tests.

1          Maintained loading
           with var reactions;
           test load 200 - 300 t,
           on working pile
                              (Q813

Note : If likely to be
encountered, obstructions
would be given as an
item. The quantities in
working hours being an
estimate of the time that
would be taken by any
piling team to remove
the obstructions. See
Item Code Q700 and Rule
M11 in Class Q of CESMM

(4)

Items for preparing heads are here measured on the assumption that the Specification calls for some work in connecting the heads to the pile cap. In cases where no work is expressly required to the pile heads the items would not be measured.

Work to the pile cap is not measured in the Example. Excavation for the cap would be classified "Excavation of foundations", stating it was around pile shafts (See Table 7.01 Chapter 7). A deduction from the volume of this excavation would be made for the volume of boring, between the top and base of the cap, measured with the piles.

Concrete in the pile cap and related ancillaries would be measured as provided in Classes F and G of the CESMM, respectively.

# 13 Roads and Pavings – CESMM Class: R

Briefly summmarised, the work covered by Class R includes sub-base, base and surfacing of roads, runways and other paved areas, together with kerbing, light duty pavements, footways, cycle tracks, traffic signs and surface markings. Earthworks to receive the work and any landscaping are measured in accordance with Class E. (See Chapter 7). Drainage for roads and the like is measured in accordance with Classes I, J, K and L (See Chapter 9). Fencing is measured in accordance with Class X (See Chapter 17). Supporting posts and foundations for traffic signs are included in the items for traffic signs in Class R. Gantries and other substantial structures to support traffic signs are measured in detail in accordance with the Classes appropriate to the particular work in them.

The classification table for Class R, includes descriptive features for bases, surfacing and concrete pavements. The features for heavy duty work of this description for roads, aircraft runways and such like, are those given in the First Division of the CESMM Class R, Codes 1 - 4 and their attached Second and Third Division features. Separate descriptive features applicable to work of this description for light duty pavements, footways, cycle tracks and the like, are given in the First Division of CESMM Class R, Code 7 and its attached Second and Third Division features.

For work included in Class R and for exclusions from the Class refer to the "Includes" and "Excludes" given at the head of the Class R classification table in the CESMM. References to work included in Class R are made in the "Excludes" for other Classes at the head of the classification tables in the Classes E, F, G, H, N and W of the CESMM.

Class R is not applicable to the maintenance of roads and pavings and this work is stated among the "Excludes" at the head of the Class R classification table.

---

Table 13.01   Class R

---

Generally   The expression "DTp Specified" means as specified in the "Specification for Road and Bridge Works" issued by the Department of Transport (Rule R/D1). See subsequent Commentary.

---

COMMENTARY

DTp Specified

The current edition, January 1988, of the Specification for Road and Bridge Works is the Fifth Edition, 1976 (7th impression 1987), as amended and extended by Supplement No. 1. 1978 (7th impression 1986 containing amendments Nos. 1 - 97) issued by the Department of Transport and obtainable from Her Majesty's Stationery Office. The edition and amendments appropriate to the Contract should be stated in the Preamble to the Bill of Quantities.

A new specification entitled "Specification for Highway Works" has been issued by the Department of Transport and is available from Her Majesty's Stationery Office together with "Notes for Guidance". Where this is used the meaning of "DTp Specified" can be related to the title of the new specification by an amendment to CESMM given in the Bill Preamble.

COMMENTARY

DTp Specified (cont.

    Unless otherwise stated, the statement "DTp Specified" in any item description has the effect of incorporating in the Contract those requirements prescribed in the "Specification for Road and Bridge Works" (issued by the Department of Transport) which relates to the material covered by the item.

Table 13.02 Sub-bases, Flexible Road Bases and Surfacing

| 1st Division | 2nd Division | | 3rd Division |
|---|---|---|---|
| Sub-bases, flexible road bases and surfacing | Classify in accordance with 2nd Division features   m2 | Identify materials for all courses and state spread rate of applied surface finishes (Rule R/A1)<br><br>Measure width of each course of material at the top surface of the course (Rule R/M1)<br><br>A manhole cover or other intrusion less than 1 m2 in area shall not be deducted (Rule R/M1)<br><br>State when applied to surfaces inclined at an angle exceeding 10 degrees to the horizontal (Rule R/A2)<br><br>Items involving in-situ concrete are deemed to include formwork and finishes (Rule R/C1) | State actual depth of each course (Rule R/A1) |
| | Geotextiles  m2 | State type and grade of materials (Rule R/A3) | |
| | Additional depth    m3 | State nature of material | |
| | Regulating course     t | State nature of material | |

COMMENTARY

Sub-bases, Flexible Road Bases and Surfacing (Refer to Table 13.02)

Each course of material is measured superficially and given in m2. The material in each course is identified and the actual depth or thickness of the course is stated in the item description. Stating the actual depth or thickness is a requirement of Rule R/A1 which overrides the Third Division features of Class R which give depth ranges. The Rule requires also that the spread rate of any surfaces finishes specified shall be stated. Layers, in courses of the same material specified to be spread and compacted in layers, are not classed as courses.

COMMENTARY

Sub-bases, Flexible Road Bases and Surfacing (cont.

Where different tolerances in surface levels or different consolidation requirements, etc., are prescribed for a course of the same material, items with additional description distinguish each difference.

Items for additional depth of stated material quantified by volume in m3 are given where additional depth is required in intermittent or isolated areas below the uniform depth of a course.

Items are given for regulating courses where they are required. Materials are stated in the item descriptions and quantities are given by mass in tonnes.

The areas of additional geotextiles in laps is included in the areas measured unless it is otherwise stated in amending Preamble. There is no Rule in Class R which say they are to be measured nett.

Concrete Pavements (Refer to Table 13.03)

The descriptive features given in the CESMM for concrete pavements generate separate items for concrete slabs, for any reinforcement in the slabs and for any waterproof membrane below the pavements. See Table 13.03 which notes or refers to the descriptive features, the units of measurement and the details which require to be given in item descriptions.

Quantities for the items for concrete slabs give the area in m2 for each depth of slab. The depth being the actual depth, as required by Rule R/A1. Where the specification calls for a concrete slab of monolithic construction to be spread and compacted in layers and/or for the slab to combine aerated and non-aerated concrete, whilst the make up of the slab must be identified, it is not necessary to separately itemise each layer. The depth given for a particular slab of this nature is the aggregate of the depths of its layers.

Necessary formwork and specified finishes to the top surface of the concrete are deemed to be included in the items for the carriageway slabs.

The materials and their thickness for waterproof membranes are identified in the item descriptions. Membranes are measured nett with no allowance for the additional material in laps. They are given in m2.

*Joints in Concrete Pavements*

Detail drawings are invariably provided for joints in concrete pavements. To comply with Rule R/A6 of the CESMM, which requires certain information to be given (See 3rd Division, Table 13.03), it is considered preferable for item descriptions to make reference to drawings from which the information can be obtained rather than to detail it in lengthy descriptions.

Measured items, quantified in linear metres, are given for all joints in concrete pavements, other than construction joints which are not expressly required. (See Rule R/M6 of the CESMM). The 2nd Division features use the same terms as the "Specification for Road and Bridge Works" to describe the joints. Formwork to joints is deemed to be included in the items (See "Generally", Table 13.03). Item descriptions are required to state the depth range of the joints as set out in the 3rd Division of the classification table. Actual depth is usually stated for joints of a depth exceeding 300 mm.

Table 13.03 Concrete Pavements and Joints in Concrete Pavements

Generally  Items deemed to include formwork and finishes to concrete
           (Rule R/C1)

| 1st Division | 2nd Division | | | 3rd Division |
|---|---|---|---|---|
| Concrete pavements | Carriageway slabs of DTp Specified paving quality concrete        m2 | | Measure width at top surface. No deduction for a manhole cover or other intrusion less than 1 m2 (Rule R/M1) | State actual depth of slab (Rule R/A1) |
| | Other carriageway slabs of stated strength        m2 | State strength of concrete | | State where inclined at an angle exceeding 10 degrees to the horizontal (Rule R/A2) |
| | Other in situ concrete slabs of stated strength    m2 | | | |
| | Steel fabric reinforcement to BS 4483        m2 | State type number or letter in accordance with BS 4483 (Rule R/A4)  Measure nett with no allowance for laps (Rule R/M2) | | Classify according to mass per m2 as 3rd Division features |
| | Other fabric reinforcement     m2 | State the material and size (Rule R/A4)  Measure nett with no allowance for laps (Rule R/M2) | | State nominal mass per m2 (Rule R/A4) |
| | Mild steel bar reinforcement to BS 4449        t  High yield steel bar reinforcement to BS 4449 or BS4461          t | Take mass as 7.85 t/m3 (Rule R/M3)  Include mass of steel supports to top reinforcement in mass measured (Rule R/M4)  Deemed to include supporting reinforcement other than steel supports to top reinforcement (Rule R/C2) | | State nominal size as 3rd Division features  Nominal size shall be cross-sectional size defined in BS 4449 and BS 4461 (Rule R/D2) |
| | Waterproof membrane below concrete pavements          m2 | State materials and thickness (Rule R/A5)  Measure nett with no allowance for laps (Rule R/M5) | | State where inclined as (Rule R/A2) |
| Joints in concrete pavements | Longitudinal joints   m  Expansion joints      m  Contraction joints    m  Warping joints        m  Butt joints           m | | | State depth range of joint as 3rd Division features  State the dimensions, spacing and nature of sealed grooves and rebates, waterstops, dowels and other components (Rule R/A6) |
| | Construction joints           m | Measure only where expressly required (Rule R/M6) | | |

COMMENTARY

Concrete Pavements (cont.

*Work Applied to Inclined Surfaces*

The rule stated in Rule R/A2 of the CESMM requires that item descriptions for work in Class R which is "applied to surfaces inclined at an angle exceeding 10 degrees to the horizontal" shall so state. The rule is considered not applicable to reinforcement in concrete slabs, joints in concrete pavements and traffic signs, because it is thought inappropriate to describe this work as "applied to surfaces".

*Intrusions*

The rule in the second sentence of Rule R/M1 of the CESMM provides that "The area of a manhole cover or other intrusion into a surface shall not be deducted where the area of the intrusion is less than 1 m2". The Rule does not extend to cover fabric reinforcement which infers that the area of the fabric is to be given nett after deducting the area of all openings.

Table 13.04   Kerbs, Channels and Edgings

| 1st Division | 2nd Division | 3rd Division | |
|---|---|---|---|
| Kerbs, channels and edgings | Classify as 2nd Division features | Straight or curved to radius exceeding 12 m | m |
| Deemed to include beds, backings, reinforcement, joints and cutting and formwork (Rules R/C3 and R/C1) | State materials and cross-sectional dimensions of components and their beds and backings (Rule R/A7) | Curved to radius not exceeding 12 m | m |
| | | Quadrants | nr |
| | State where inclined at an angle exceeding 10 degrees to the horizontal (Rule R/A2) | Drops | nr |
| | | Transitions | nr |
| | Measure excavation and filling under Class E (Rule R/M7), but see Note following | | |

NOTE:   Earthworks may be included in items for kerbs, channels and edging provided descriptions identify work and an appropriate statement is given in Preamble. See Note at foot of page 75 of CESMM.

COMMENTARY

Kerbs, Channels and Edgings (Refer to Table 13.04)

Item descriptions other than those which identify requirements by BS reference, state or otherwise identify material, cross-sectional dimensions and type of kerb, channel or edging. Item descriptions also state materials, cross-sectional dimensions and details of the required beds and backings.

Kerbs, channels and edgings are measured in linear metres. A single classification combines curved work of a radius exceeding 12 m with that which is straight. Work curved to a radius not exceeding 12 m is given separately. Items are deemed to include beds, backings, reinforcement, joints and cutting and formwork. Additional enumerated items are given for quadrants, drops (each dropper is measured) and for transitions. Related earthworks are excluded from the items but if considered more convenient minor earthworks, such as a trench, may be included by a statement to that effect in Preamble and identifying the work in the descriptions.

Table 13.05   Light Duty Pavements

| 1st Division | 2nd and 3rd Divisions |
|---|---|
| Light duty pavements      m2 | Refer to Class R, Code 7, 2nd and 3rd Division features.<br><br>Rules R/M1, R/D1, R/C1, R/A1 and R/A2 apply to light duty pavements. See Tables 13.01 and 13.02. |

Table 13.06   Traffic Signs and Surface Markings

| 1st Division | |
|---|---|
| Ancillaries | State materials, size and diagram number, taken from "Traffic signs and general directions" issued by the Department of Transport, in item descriptions for traffic signs and surface markings (Rule R/A8) |

| 2nd Division | 3rd Division | | |
|---|---|---|---|
| Traffic signs | Non-illuminated    nr<br><br>Illuminated         nr | Measure support gantries and other substantial structures associated with traffic signs in detail as provided in other appropriate Classes (Rule R/M9)<br><br>Items other than those measured in detail as Rule R/M9 are deemed to include foundations, supporting posts, excavation, preparation of surfaces, disposal of excavated material, removal of existing services, upholding sides of excavation, backfilling, concrete and finishes, reinforcement, joints and formwork (Rules R/C4 and R/C1) | |
| Surface markings | Non-reflecting road studs        nr | | State where applied to surfaces inclined at an angle exceeding 10 degrees to the horizontal (Rule R/A2) |
| | Reflecting road studs        nr | State shape and colour aspects (Rule R/A9) | |
| | Letters and shapes            nr<br><br>Continuous lines              m | | |
| | Intermittent lines              m | Exclude gaps from lengths measured (Rule R/M8) | |

COMMENTARY

Traffic Signs and Surface Markings (Refer to Table 13.06)

The descriptive features for traffic signs and surface markings and the units of measurement are set out in Table 13.06. The materials, size and diagram number (taken from "Traffic signs, regulations and general directions" issued by the Department of Transport) are added to the features in the item descriptions.

Items for traffic signs other than those measured in detail, as Rule R/M9, include supporting posts, foundations and associated work as set out in Rule R/C4. See Table 13.06. Item descriptions identify the posts and foundation. Signs with different posts and foundations are given in separate items which distinguish each difference. Item descriptions for traffic signs supported on gantries or structures which have been measured, in detail, separately from the signs, state that the gantries or structures are measured separately.

Where similar surface markings are applied to different base surfaces which involve differences in application and where different preparation is specified for the same base surface, item descriptions distinguish differences by stating or otherwise identifying the base surface or the preparation.

Road studs are classified "non-reflecting" or "reflecting". Item descriptions for reflecting road studs state the shape and the colour of aspects.

Surface marking with lines is given in linear metres. Item descriptions state the width of line. The length measured excludes the gaps in intermittent line markings.


EXAMPLE RE.1

Specimen Bill Items

The Example which follows gives specimen items from a Bill of Quantities for a motorway. Units of measurement are given against the items. The quantities have been omitted.

| Number | Item description | Unit | Quantity | Rate | Amount £ | p |
|--------|-----------------|------|----------|------|----------|---|
| | <u>ROADS AND PAVINGS</u>. | | | | | |
| | <u>Sub-bases, flexible road bases and surfacing, DTp Specified Sections 800 and 900</u>. | | | COMMENTARY | | |
| R118 | Granular material, DTp Specified, type 1, clause 803, depth 450 mm; sub-base. | m2 | | The specimen Bill items in the Example have been drafted on the assumption that the Particular Specification | | |
| R124 | Granular material, DTp Specified, type 2, clause 804, depth 150 mm; sub-base. | m2 | | provides that the Specification for the work shall be the "Specification for Road and Bridge Works" (See | | |
| R155 | Lean concrete, DTp Specified clause 807, depth 200 mm: roadbase to carriageways. | m2 | | earlier Commentary) and provides also for additional clauses for work not covered by the quoted Specification. | | |
| R225 | Dry bound macadam, DTp Specified clause 809, depth 200 mm; roadbase to hard-shoulders. | m2 | | Although not strictly necessary if the descriptions otherwise clearly identify | | |
| R232.1 | Dense bitumen macadam, DTp Specified clause 903, depth 60 mm; basecourse to carriageways. | m2 | | the work they represent, it is considered helpful, as shown in the Example, to make | | |
| R232.2 | Dense bitumen macadam, DTp Specified clause 903, depth 60 mm; basecourse to hardshoulders. | m2 | | reference to the appropriate Sections and clauses of the Specification. | | |
| R322.1 | Rolled asphalt, DTp Specified clause 907, depth 35 mm; wearing course to hardshoulders. | m2 | | Items are given for each course of base or surfacing They identify the materials and state the thickness in | | |
| R322.2 | Rolled asphalt, DTp Specified clause 907, depth 40 mm; wearing course to carriageways. | m2 | | accordance with Rule R/A1. To aid identification, added description has been given | | |
| R341.1 | Surface dressing with 20 mm nominal coated chippings, DTp Specified clause 907, depth 25 mm; on rolled asphalt surfaces of carriageways. | m2 | | locating the courses. | | |
| | <u>Concrete pavements, DTp Specified Section 1000</u>. | | | | | |
| R417 | Carriageway slabs of concrete, DTp Specified clause 1004, depth 280 mm, including surface finish DTp Specified clause 1021 and curing DTp Specified clause 1022. | m2 | | | | |
| | (1)     To Part 2.1 Summary     Page total | | | | | |

| Number | Item description | Unit | Quantity | Rate | Amount £ | p |
|--------|-----------------|------|----------|------|----------|---|
| | ROADS AND PAVINGS (cont. | | | | | |
| | Concrete pavements, DTp Specified Section 1000 (cont. | | | COMMENTARY | | |
| R443 | Steel fabric reinforcement to BS 4483, reference A193, nominal mass 3.02 kg/m2. | m2 | | Fabric reinforcement is measured nett with no allowance for laps. See Table 13.03. | | |
| R480 | Waterproof membranes below concrete pavements; 500 grade polythene film, as Specification clause 10.11. | m2 | | Item descriptions for joints in concrete pavements are required to state the depth range of the joints and the dimensions, spacing and nature of components. See Table 13.03. The specimen item descriptions in the Example use Specification and Drawing references from which information not stated in the description can be obtained. | | |
| | Joints in concrete pavements, including reinforcement, dowel bars, grooves and sealing shown on the Drawings or specified. | | | | | |
| R517 | Longitudinal joints, DTp Specified clause 1010, depth 280 mm; as Drawing No. S/10/22. | m | | | | |
| R527 | Expansion joints, DTp Specified clause 1009, depth 280 mm; as Drawing No. S/10/23. | m | | All joints are of one depth. The option afforded by Paragraph 5.14 of the CESMM of stating actual depth in place of depth range is here exercised. | | |
| R537 | Contraction joints, DTp Specified clause 1009, depth 280 mm; as Drawing No. S/10/24. | m | | | | |
| | Kerbs, channels and edgings, DTp Specified clause 1101, with concrete Class E foundations and haunching. | | | For the classification "Kerbs, channels and edging" the classification table for Class R in the CESMM provides 2nd Division descriptive features for precast concrete kerbs, edgings and channels, for in-situ concrete kerbs and edgings and for asphalt kerbs and channels. The specimen item descriptions state materials, cross-sectional dimensions and details of beds and backings as required by Rule R/A7 of the CESMM. See Table 13.04. | | |
| R651 | Precast concrete channels to BS 340, size 150 x 125 mm, straight or curved to radius exceeding 12 m; on 300 x 150 mm foundations and with 100 x 150 mm (extreme) haunching. | m | | | | |
| R652 | Precast concrete channels to BS 340, size 150 x 125 mm, curved to radius not exceeding 12 m; on 300 x 150 mm foundation and with 100 x 150 mm (extreme) haunching. | m | | | | |
| | (2) | | To Part 2.1 Summary | Page total | | |

| Number | Item description | Unit | Quantity | Rate | Amount | |
|--------|------------------|------|----------|------|--------|---|
| | | | | | £ | p |
| | ROADS AND PAVINGS (cont. | | | | | |
| | Ancillaries. | | | | | |
| | Traffic signs conforming to the diagrams or references stated in the item descriptions, which are taken from "The Traffic Signs, Regulations and General Directions" issued by the Department of Transport. | | | COMMENTARY | | |
| | | | | Materials for traffic signs and sizes need to be stated in item descriptions in addition to the diagram numbers from "The Traffic Signs, Regulations and General Directions" | | |
| | Non-illuminated, as BS 873: Part 2. | | | | | |
| R811.1 | Marker posts, exposed height 975 mm, with reflective markers both sides; as Detail "B", Drawing No. S/12/2. | nr | | | | |
| | Non-illuminated, manufactured from steel, vitreous enamel finish and with galvanised steel posts and fittings and mass concrete foundations all as BS 873: Part 1, DTp Specified Section 1200. | | | Descriptions as given in the Example may be shortened by reducing detail and giving Specification and Drawing reference, provided they clearly identify the work. Descriptions or Preamble should make clear the intended item coverage. | | |
| R811.2 | Reflectorised sign, size 2000 x 1125 mm, diagram 920; as Detail "C", Drawing No. S/12/2. | nr | | | | |
| R811.3 | Reflectorised sign, size 4500 x 1725 mm, diagram 917; as Detail "E", Drawing No. S/12/2. | nr | | | | |
| | Externally illuminated, manufactured from steel, vitreous enamel finish and with galvanised steel posts and fittings, external lighting lanterns and wiring from point of supply and mass concrete foundations all as BS 873: Part 1, DTp Specified Section 1200. | | | | | |
| R812 | Signs, size 1500 x 1500 mm, diagram 905; as Detail "F", Drawing No. S/12/3. | nr | | | | |

(3)              To Part 2.1 Summary        Page total

| Number | Item description | Unit | Quantity | Rate | Amount £ | p |
|--------|-----------------|------|----------|------|----------|---|
| | ROADS AND PAVINGS (cont. | | | | | |
| | Ancillaries (cont. | | | | | |
| | Surface markings conforming to the diagrams or references, stated in the item descriptions, which are taken from "The Traffic Signs, Regulations and General Directions" issued by the Department of Transport. | | | | | |
| | Reflecting road studs to BS 873: Part 4, as Specification clause 1204. | | | COMMENTARY | | |
| R822.1 | "Catseye" white aspect, size 265 mm long; to concrete surfaces. | nr | | The surface to which road studs and surface markings are applied has an effect on cost. The specimen item descriptions distinguish the different surfaces to which the work is applied. | | |
| R822.2 | "Catseye" red aspect, size 265 mm long; to asphalt surfaces. | nr | | | | |
| R822.3 | "Catseye" red aspect, size 265 mm long; to concrete surfaces. | nr | | | | |
| | Reflectorised thermoplastic material as BS 3262: Part 1, DTp Specified Section 1200. | | | | | |
| R823 | Letters, height 1.6 m, reference Part X of Schedule 7; on asphalt surfaces. | nr | | | | |
| R824.1 | Longitudinal continuous lines, width 200 mm diagram 1012.1; on concrete surfaces. | m | | | | |
| R824.2 | Longitudinal continuous lines, marginal strip, width 200 mm, diagram 1012.1; on rolled asphalt surfaces. | m | | | | |
| R824.3 | Transverse continuous lines, width 200 mm, as diagram 1001; on asphalt surfaces. | m | | | | |
| R825 | Longitudinal intermittent lines, width 100 mm, 1000 mm lines and 5000 mm gaps, as diagram 1005; on concrete surfaces. | m | | | | |

# 14 Rail Track – CESMM Class: S

Class S covers rail track foundations, rails, sleepers, fittings, switches and crossings. Excluded from the Class are overhead crane rails (included in Class M) and concrete track foundations (included in Classes F and G).

Earthworks in connection with railway track work are measured under Class E. Together with work in other Classes associated with rail track, it is usually grouped in the same part of the Bill of Quantities as the work measured under Class S (See Example SE.1 at the end of this Chapter). Items for the preparation of earthwork surfaces are measured, as provided in Class E, where track foundations measured under Class S or Class F are in direct contact with the earthwork formation surface. Preparation of excavated surfaces to receive filling, measured under Class E, is not measurable.

Table 14.01   Track Foundations

| 1st Division | 2nd Division | | | 3rd Division |
|---|---|---|---|---|
| Track foundations<br><br>State materials (Rule S/A1) | Bottom ballast | m3 | Applies to ballast placed before track is laid (Rule S/D1) | |
| | Top ballast | m3 | Applies to ballast placed after track is laid (Rule S/D2)<br><br>Include volume of sleepers in volume measured (Rule S/M1) | |
| | Blinding | m2 | | State thickness (Rule S/A2) |
| | Blankets | m2 | | |
| | Waterproof membranes | m2 | Do not measure area of laps (Rule S/M2) | |

COMMENTARY

Track Foundation (refer to Table 14.01)

*Ballast*

Items for ballast give the quantities in m3. Materials to be used for the ballast are stated in the item descriptions. Placing, compacting and grading requirements are also stated or identified in the descriptions. Separate items in accordance with the 2nd Division descriptive features, are given for bottom ballast (that placed before the track is laid) and top ballast (that placed after the track is laid). The volume occupied by the sleepers is included in the volume measured for the top ballast. The CESMM makes no provision for measuring and itemising the boxing in to the ends of the sleepers with ballast, or for forming the ballast to slopes at the sides or shoulders. It is taken that this work is intended to be included in the cube items given for the ballast. This is made clear in preamble.

*Concrete Track Foundation Slabs*

Concrete track foundation slabs are measured in accordance with Classes F and G of the CESMM. Where the concrete slabs are of continuous length and constant width this may be stated in the item descriptions for the placing.

COMMENTARY

Track Foundations (cont.

*Concrete Track Foundation Slabs (cont.*

Formwork, reinforcement, joints and inserts for fixings where required in the slabs are measured under Class G. The finishing to the top surface of the slabs carried out as part of the concrete placing process is included in the items for the concrete track foundation slabs by specific statement to that effect in the item descriptions for placing the concrete in the slabs and in the Preamble.

*Blinding, Blankets and Waterproof Membranes*

The separate items given for blinding the formation surface and for drainage blankets beneath the ballast are measured in m2. Item descriptions give the actual thickness and state or identify the materials, placing and consolidation requirements. Waterproof membranes are given in m2 and are measured net with no allowance for laps. The extent of the laps and any particular laying and jointing requirements should be given in the Specification. The materials to be used for the membranes and their grade or thickness are stated in the item descriptions.

Table 14.02   Taking up

| 1st Division | | | |
|---|---|---|---|
| Taking up | State amount of dismantling, details of disposal of the track and type of rail, sleeper and joint (Rule S/A3) | | |

| 2nd Division | | 3rd Division | |
|---|---|---|---|
| Bullhead rails<br><br>Flat bottom rails<br><br>Dock and crane rails | | Plain track   m | Measure along centre line of two rail track and exclude lengths occupied by switches and crossings (Rule S/M3) |
| | | Turnouts      nr<br><br>Diamond crossings   nr | Deemed to include taking up, check, guard and conductor rails (Rule S/C1) |
| Check and guard rails   m<br><br>Conductor rails   m | Measure along lengths of one rail; exclude lengths within crossings and switches (Rule S/M4) | | |
| Sundries   nr | | Buffer stops | State approximate weight and type of construction (Rule S/A4) |
| | | Retarders<br><br>Wheel stops<br><br>Lubricators<br><br>Switch heaters<br><br>Switch levers | |

COMMENTARY

Taking Up (refer to Table 14.02)

Taking up plain track includes for taking up rails, sleepers and all fittings. Quantities are given in linear metres of track, measured by taking a single measurement of length along the centre line of the two rail track excluding the lengths occupied by switches and crossings. Item descriptions state the amount of dismantling intended to be included in the items of taking up and give details of disposal of the track. They give details to identify the particular type of rail given at 2nd Division level in the CESMM and state also the type of joints in the rails and the type of sleepers. Distinction is not made between straight or curved track in the items of taking up.

Taking up turnouts and diamond crossings are enumerated and the items are deemed to include taking up all rails including check, guard and conductor rails and all sleepers and all fixings and fittings within the plan area of the turnouts and crossings.

Taking up check, guard and conductor rails, outside those in switches and crossings are measured in linear metres along the one rail. The items are intended to cover taking up rails and all fittings and fixings.

Enumerated items are given for taking up sundry accessories such as retarders, wheel stops etc., as listed in the last panel of Table 14.02. Item descriptions for buffer stops state their weight and type of construction.

Table 14.03   Lifting, Packing and Slewing

| 1st Division | | 2nd Division | 3rd Division |
|---|---|---|---|
| Lifting, packing and slewing        nr | Measure length along centre line of two rail track over roads, measure switch roads from toes of switches (Rule S/D3) | Bullhead rail track | |
| | | Bullhead rail track with turnout | |
| | State length of track, maximum distance of slew and maximum lift (Rule S/A5) | | |
| | | Flat bottom rail track | |
| | State where extra ballast is required (Rule S/A6) | | |
| | | Flat bottom rail track with turnout | |
| | Deemed to include opening out, packing and boxing in with ballast and insertion of closure rails (Rule S/C2) | | |
| | | Buffer stops | |

COMMENTARY

Lifting, Packing and Slewing (refer to Table 14.03)

Lifting, packing and slewing rail track is given as an enumerated item for a stated length of track. The length stated in the item description is the single length measured along the centre line of the two rail track over all roads. The switch roads are measured from the toes of the switches. (See Fig. S1.). Item descriptions state the maximum distance of slew, the maximum lift and also state if extra ballast is required. The standard classifications given in the CESMM calls for track of bullhead rails to be given in separate items from that of flat bottom rails and within each of these for track without turnout to be distinguished from that with turnout. No distinction is made in descriptions between straight and curved track.

COMMENTARY

Lifting, Packing and Slewing (cont.

| Number | Item description | Unit |
|---|---|---|
| S340 | RAIL TRACK.<br><br>Lifting, packing and slewing.<br><br>Flat bottom rail track with turn-out; length "X" m, maximum distance of slew 250 mm, maximum lift 150 mm including extra ballast. | nr |

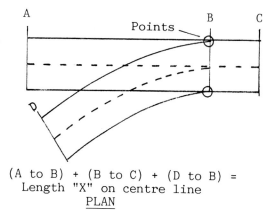

(A to B) + (B to C) + (D to B) = Length "X" on centre line

PLAN

Fig. S1. Lifting, packing and slewing rail track with turnout.

Table 14.04  Supplying

| 1st Division | 2nd Division | | | 3rd Division | |
|---|---|---|---|---|---|
| Supplying<br><br>Deemed to include delivery of components to Site (Rule S/C3) | Bullhead rails | t | State the section reference and mass per metre, or state cross-sectional dimensions and mass per metre (Rule S/A9) | Mass:-<br><br>not exceeding 20 kg/m<br><br>20 - 30 kg/m<br><br>30 - 40 kg/m<br><br>40 - 50 kg/m<br><br>exceeding 50 kg/m | |
| | Flat bottom rails | t | | | |
| | Dock and crane rails | t | | | |
| | Check and guard rails | t | | | |
| | Conductor rails | t | | | |
| | Twist rails | nr | Include mass of twist rails in mass of rails (Rule S/M5) | | |
| | Sleepers | nr | State type (Rule S/A7) | Timber<br>Concrete | State size and identify fittings attached by supplier (Rule S/A8)<br><br>Deemed to include fittings attached by supplier (Rule S/C4) |
| | Fittings | nr | State type (Rule S/A7)<br><br>Deemed to include fixings, keys, clips, bolts, nuts, screws, spikes, ferrules, track circuit insulators, pads and conductor rail unsulator packings (Rule S/C5) | Chairs<br><br>Baseplates<br><br>Pandrol rail fastenings | |
| | | | | Plain fishplates<br><br>Insulated fishplates | Measure by number of pairs (Rule S/M6) |
| | | | | Conductor rail insulators<br><br>Conductor rail side ramps | |

Table 14.04  Supplying (cont.

| 1st Division | 2nd Division | | 3rd Division |
|---|---|---|---|
| Supplying<br><br>Deemed to include delivery of components to Site (Rule S/C3) | Switches and crossings   nr | State type (Rule S/A10)<br><br>Deemed to include timbers, fittings and check rails (Rule S/C6) | Turnouts<br><br>Diamond crossings |
| | Sundries | State type (Rule S/A11) | Buffer stops nr   State approximate weight (Rule S/A12) |
| | | | Retarders   nr |
| | | | Wheel stops   nr |
| | | | Lubricators   nr |
| | | | Switch heaters   nr |
| | | | Switch levers   nr |
| | | | Conductor rail guard boards   m   Measure guard boards each side of rail (Rule S/M7)<br><br>Deemed to include fixings (Rule S/C7) |

COMMENTARY

Supplying (refer to Table 14.04)

*Rails*

Supplying rails and other components for rail track are given in separate items from those for laying the track. The items for supplying are deemed to include delivery of the rails and other components to the Site.

Items for the supply of rails distinguish the different types of rails and give the mass in tonnes for each type. Item descriptions state the section reference of the rails and the mass per metre, or alternatively the cross-sectional dimensions and the mass per metre as provided in Rule S/A9 of the CESMM. The 3rd Division mass ranges are overridden by this Rule and the ranges serve only as a means of coding. The mass measured for the rails includes the mass of twist rails. Additionally the twist rails are made the subject of enumerated items stating the rail type.

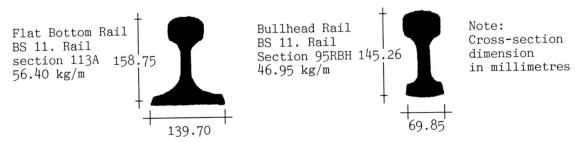

Flat Bottom Rail BS 11. Rail section 113A 56.40 kg/m   158.75   139.70

Bullhead Rail BS 11. Rail Section 95RBH 145.26 46.95 kg/m   69.85

Note: Cross-section dimension in millimetres

Fig. S2  Two standard rail sections BS 11.

COMMENTARY

Supplying (cont.

*Rails* (cont.

Where it is specifically required that rail track is to be supplied to the Site in prefabricated lengths, the supplying of the rails, sleepers and other components which make up the lengths should be grouped under a heading stating they are to be delivered to the Site in prefabricated lengths.

*Sleepers*

Items for supplying sleepers give the number of sleepers stating whether they are timber or concrete. Item descriptions state or identify the type (e.g. for concrete "prestressed, reference x") and size and state the fittings which are to be attached by the supplier. Fittings attached to the sleepers by the supplier are deemed to be included in the items for the sleepers. Fittings attached to the sleepers on the Site are enumerated and given as separate items.

The diagram (Fig. S3) shows a fully bonded, pretensioned, prestressed concrete sleeper, reference F27A as produced by Costain Concrete Co. Ltd., for British Rail. The fittings attached to the sleeper by the manufacturer are the 4 nr. pandrol inserts as shown. Fittings for each of these sleepers and which are enumerated sep-arately are 4 nr. pan-drol fasteners, 4 nr. insulators and 2 nr. rail pads. This type of sleeper is 2515 mm long and the cross-sectional dimensions are 264 x 204 mm, measured beneath the rail. Stating the BR. reference in the item descriptions is suffi-cient to satisfy the re-quirements of the CESMM, without stating the dimensions.

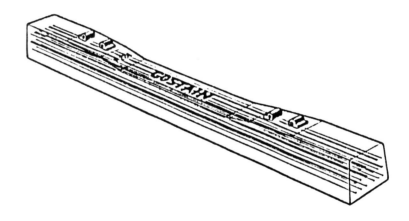

Fig. S3. Concrete sleeper, BR. reference F27A.

The dimensions of timber sleepers usually met with are 2600 x 250 x 130 mm for ordinary lengths of track and 2600 x 300 x 150 mm or 2600 x 300 x 170 mm for crossing timbers. Sleeper spacing usually met with is 26 nr. to the 18 m rail length or 28 nr. on curves.

*Fittings*

The supply of fittings listed in the classification table (See Table 14.04) are each enumerated stating the type. Fishplates are measured by the number of pairs. Items for fittings are deemed to include all accessories as noted in the 2nd Division panel against "Fittings" in Table 14.04.

*Switches and Crossings*

Numbered items are given for supplying switches and crossings stating the type. The stated type will usually be identified by reference to a detailed drawing.

Items are deemed to include all timbers, fittings and check rails within the plan area of the switches and crossings. Where required switch operating mechanism is given in separate items from those for the switches and crossings.

COMMENTARY

Supplying (cont.

*Sundries*

Sundry components incidental to rail track are listed for supplying against the 2nd Division feature in the CESMM. See the last panel in Table 14.04. Apart from conductor guard boards, it is provided that these components are enumerated. Conductor and guard rail boards are measured in linear metres on each side of the rail and are deemed to include fittings. Item descriptions state the type of the particular component. Additionally item descriptions for buffer stops state their approximate weight.

Laying (refer to Table 14.05)

Items for laying are deemed to include for work carried out after delivery of components to the Site. They are deemed to include laying sleepers, fittings, twist rails and short lengths of rails between switches and crossings.

Apart from the work which is classified as "Sundries" (See last panel in Table 14.05), laying is first classified according to the kind of rails used for the track. The classifications are given in the panel under 2nd Division in Table 14.05. Item descriptions state the type (usually the BR. or BS reference) of the rail section and its mass per metre. They also state the type of joints between the rails and the type of sleepers and identify any prefabricated lengths of track. Although not called for by the Rules of the CESMM, it is helpful to state the means of fixing the rails to the sleepers.

*Plain Track*

Laying plain track is measured by length and is given in linear metres. The length measured is a single length measured along the centre line of the two rail track including any lengths of curved track, but excluding the lengths occupied by switches and crossings. See Fig.S4.

Forming curves in plain track are measured the single length measured along the centre line of the two rail track and are given in linear metres. Items for those which exceed 300 m radius are given separately from those which do not exceed 300 m radius. No deduction is made from the lengths measured for laying plain track for the lengths given in the items for forming curves.

The adjoining diagram shows the section through rail track of BS 113A flat bottom rails and F27A concrete sleepers. The centre line of the gauge indicates the position at which the length is measured for laying plain track.

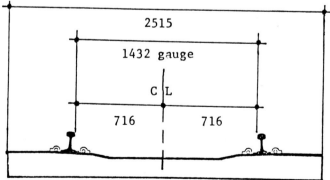

Fig. S4. Diagram showing centre line on which length is measured for laying plain rail track

Table 14.05 Laying

| 1st Division | | | |
|---|---|---|---|
| Laying | Deemed to include work carried out after delivery of components to the Site, or where track is not to be supplied by the Contractor, work carried out after delivery to the location stated in accordance with Rule S/A13. (Rule S/C8). | | |
| | Deemed to include laying sleepers, fittings, twist rails and short lengths between switches and crossings (Rule S/C9). | | |
| | Where track is not to be supplied by Contractor, state form in which it is to be laid and location (Rule S/A13). | | |

| 2nd Division | | 3rd Division | | |
|---|---|---|---|---|
| Bullhead rails<br><br>Flat bottom rails<br><br>Dock rails<br><br>Crane rails | State type and mass per metre of rail and type of joint and sleeper (Rule S/A15) | Plain track | m | Measure along centre line of two rail track and exclude lengths occupied by switches and crossings (Rule S/M8)<br><br>Identify prefabricated lengths (Rule S/A14) |
| | | Form curve in plain track radius:- | | |
| | | | | not exceeding 300 m    m |
| | | | | exceeding 300 m        m |
| | | Turnouts | nr | State type and length (Rule S/A16) |
| | | Diamond Crossings | nr | Deemed to include laying check rails (Rule S/C10) |
| | | Welded joints | nr | State rail section and type of weld (Rule S/A17) |
| | | Spot re-sleepering | nr | Applies to replacing sleepers in prefabricated track not supplied by Contractor (Rule S/D4) |
| Check rails<br><br>Guard rails<br><br>Conductor rails | Measure along lengths of one rail (Rule S/M9) | Rail | m | |
| | | Length ends | nr | |
| | | Side ramps | nr | |
| | | Welded joints | nr | State rail section and type of weld (Rule S/A17) |
| Sundries | | Buffer stops | nr | State approximate weight (Rule S/18) |
| | | Retarders | nr | |
| | | Wheel stops | nr | |
| | | Lubricators | nr | |
| | | Switch heaters | nr | |
| | | Switch levers | nr | |
| | | Conductor rail guard boards | m | Measure to each side of rail (Rule S/M7) |

COMMENTARY

Laying (cont.

*Switches and Crossings*

The laying of turnouts and diamond crossings are enumerated. Each are given in separate items. Making welded joints between the rails are enumerated. The type of weld is stated in the item descriptions. Item descriptions for laying turnouts and diamond crossings state the type and their length. The length stated in the item descriptions for turnouts and crossings is the aggregate of the single lengths measured along the centre line of the two rail track through all roads. (See Figs. S5. and S6.). The measurement for switched roads commence from the toe of the switch. Items for laying turnouts and crossings are deemed to include laying check rails.

The adjoining diagram shows the rail plan of a turnout. The length stated in item descriptions for laying turnouts is:-

   (A to B) + (A to C)   = Length measured
                               on centre line

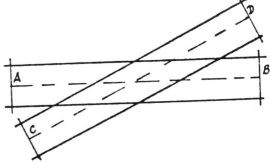

Fig. S5. Illustration of convention for measuring lengths given in item descriptions for laying turnouts.

The adjoining diagram shows the rail plan of a diamond crossing. The length stated in the item descriptions for laying diamond crossings is:-

   (A to B) + (C to D) = Length
measured on centre line

Fig. S6. Illustration of convention for measuring lengths given in item descriptions for laying diamond crossings.

*Sundries*

Items of work classified as "Sundries" in the CESMM (See last panel of Table 14.05), include buffer stops (approximate weight to be stated), wheel stops, lubricators, switch heaters and switch levers. These are enumerated and each given as separate items stating the type. Conductor rail guard boards are measured to each side of the rail and the quantity is given in linear metres.

     Where rail track is not supplied by the Contractor, the form in which it is supplied must be stated and the location at which the Contractor receives delivery and takes the materials over must also be stated. It will be usual to group under an appropriate heading in the Bill, the work to be done by the Contractor with materials supplied to him. The details to be stated in accordance with the foregoing should be given in such a heading. (See penultimate and last items on sheet (4) of subsequent Example SE.1). It is implied (See Rule S/C8 of the CESMM) that unloading and transporting and distributing the track materials or assemblies is included in the items. Any special or express requirements in respect of these must be stated.

EXAMPLE SE.1

Specimen Bill Items

The Example which follows gives specimen Bill items from a Bill of Quantities for permanent way work. Units of measurement are given against the items. The quantities have been omitted.

| Number | Item description | Unit | Quantity | Rate | Amount £ | p |
|--------|-----------------|------|----------|------|----------|---|
| | EARTHWORKS. | | | | | |
| | Excavation for. | | | | | |
| E210 | Cuttings, topsoil. | m3 | | COMMENTARY | | |
| E220 | Cuttings. | m3 | | Earthworks are measured under Class E. | | |
| E230 | Cuttings, rock. | m3 | | | | |
| | | | | Excavated material is deemed to be material other than topsoil, rock or artificial hard material, unless other- wise stated in the item descriptions. | | |
| | Excavation ancillaries. | | | | | |
| E522 | Preparation of excavated surfaces. | m2 | | | | |
| E523 | Preparation of excavated surfaces, rock. | m2 | | Items for the preparation of excavated and filled surfaces are measured where they are to receive Permanent Works, except surfaces which are to receive filling or land- scaping or surfaces for which formwork has been measured. | | |
| E531 | Disposal of excavated material, topsoil. | m3 | | | | |
| E532 | Disposal of excavated material. | m3 | | | | |
| E533 | Disposal of excavated material, rock. | m3 | | | | |
| | Filling. | | | | | |
| E624 | Embankments, selected excavated mat- erial other than topsoil or rock. | m3 | | Preparation and disposal are deemed to be carried out upon material other than topsoil, rock or artificial hard material unless otherwise stated in the item descriptions. | | |
| E641 | 150 mm Thickness, excavated topsoil; upon surfaces inclined at an angle 10 - 45 degrees to the horizontal. | m2 | | | | |
| | Filling ancillaries. | | | Item descriptions are required to state where grass seeding is upon surfaces inclined at an angle exceeding 10 degrees to the hori- zontal. | | | |
| E722 | Preparation of filled surfaces. | m2 | | | | |
| E723 | Preparation of filled surfaces, rock. | m2 | | | | |
| | Landscaping. | | | | | |
| E830 | Grass seeding; Specification clause 627, upon surfaces inclined at an angle exceeding 10 degrees to the horizontal. | m2 | | | | |

(1)          To Part 2 Summary          Page total

| Number | Item description | Unit | Quantity | Rate | Amount £ | p |
|--------|------------------|------|----------|------|----------|---|
| | **RAIL TRACK.** | | | | | |
| | <u>Track foundations</u>. | | | | | |
| S110 | Bottom ballast, granite; Specification clause 1400. | m3 | | | | |
| S120 | Top ballast, granite; Specification clause 1400. | m3 | | | | |
| S140 | Blankets, thickness 150 mm; imported natural sand. | m2 | | | | |
| S150 | Waterproof membranes, polythene sheeting, 1200 gauge; Specification clause 1423. | m2 | | | | |
| | <u>Supplying</u>. | | | | | |
| S414 | Bullhead rails, mass 46.95 kg/m; BS Rail Section No. 95RBH. | t | | | | |
| S425 | Flat bottom rails, mass 56.40 kg/m; BS Rail Section No. 113A. | t | | | | |
| S445 | Check and guard rails, mass 56.40 kg/m; BS Rail Section No. 113A. | t | | | | |
| S471 | Sleepers, timber; softwood impregnated, size 2600 x 250 x 130 mm. | nr | | | | |
| S472 | Sleepers, concrete; prestressed, BR. type F27, with pandrol inserts, Drawing No. S/3 and Specification clause 1521. | nr | | | | |
| S481 | Fittings, chairs; BR. type S1. | nr | | | | |
| S482 | Fittings, baseplates; pandrol, BR. type PAN 8, Drawing No. S/14 and Specification clause 1572. | nr | | | | |
| S483 | Fittings, pandrol rail fastenings and insulators; Specification clause 1523. | nr | | | | |
| S484 | Fittings, pairs of plain fishplates; Drawing No. S/5 and Specification clause 1506. | nr | | | | |

COMMENTARY

The description of material stated for ballast should include the required characteristics and the grading and compaction requirements in addition to the named type of stone. The descriptions in this Example make reference to the Specification where this information can be obtained.

Membranes are measured net, with no allowance for laps. In the absence of any CESMM requirement for descriptions to state the extent of the laps and jointing requirement, it is implied that the items for membranes include for laps and jointing requirements as set out in the Contract documents (in this case the quoted Specification clause).

In the Example, item descriptions for supplying rails state the section reference and mass per m. CESMM permits the cross-sectional dimensions and mass per m to be stated as an alternative.

In framing the descriptions in the Example for sleepers, fittings, switches and crossing and sundries, the option afforded by Paragraph 5.12 of CESMM of giving a Drawing or Specification reference has been adopted as more practical than providing elaborate written descriptions of the components.

| Number | Item description | Unit | Quantity | Rate | Amount £ | p |
|--------|-----------------|------|----------|------|----------|---|
| | RAIL TRACK (cont. | | | | | |
| | Supplying (cont. | | | COMMENTARY | | |
| S514 | Switches and crossings, turnouts; vertical design 113A flat bottom rails, BR. switch type CV, Drawing No. SC/4. | nr | | | | |
| S515 | Switches and crossings, diamond crossings; type DC3, 113A flat bottom rails, Drawing SC/6. | nr | | | | |
| S581 | Sundries, buffer stops; steel rail and timber sleeper construction, Drawing No. TA4, approximate weight 2.5 tonnes. | nr | | | | |
| S584 | Sundries, lubricators; "P & M Universal", Pammek design with 14 kg, grease container, Specification clause 1538. | nr | | | | |
| | Laying bullhead rails, mass 46.95 kg/m, BS Rail Section No. 95RBH. | | | | | |
| S611 | Plain track; fishplated joints, timber sleepers. | m | | | | |
| | Laying flat bottom rails, mass 56.40 kg/m, BS Rail Section No. 113A. | | | | | |
| S621.1 | Plain track; fishplated joints, timber sleepers. | m | | | | |
| S621.2 | Plain track; welded joints, concrete sleepers. | m | | | | |
| S623 | Form curve in plain track radius exceeding 300 m; welded joints, concrete sleepers. | m | | | | |
| S624 | Turnouts; vertical design, BR. switch type CV, Drawing No. SC/4, length 25.50 m, fishplated joints, timber sleepers. | nr | | | | |

COMMENTARY

Items for supplying switches and crossings are deemed to include timbers, fittings and check rails, in addition to the assembly of rails. The CESMM gives no "deemed to include" Rule for fixings and accessories for the items components classified as "Sundries". Item descriptions for items of sundries, or the Specification referred to in the items, should make clear the extent of the fittings and accessories intended to be included in the particular items of supply classified as "Sundries".

"Laying" includes work carried out after delivery of components to the Site.

In the Example, the type and mass per m of the rails is stated in the part of the description for laying which is given as a sub-heading to avoid having to repeat this information in each of the individual coded parts of the items.

The length given in the item description for the turnouts is measured on the centre line over all roads. (See Fig. S5. on last page in preceding Commentary).

| (3) | To Part 3 Summary | Page total | | |

| Number | Item description | Unit | Quantity | Rate | Amount £ | p |
|--------|------------------|------|----------|------|----------|---|
| | RAIL TRACK (cont. | | | | | |
| | <u>Laying flat bottom rails, mass 56.40 per kg/m, BS Rail Section No. 113A</u> (cont. | | | COMMENTARY | | |
| S625 | Diamond crossings; type DC3 Drawing No. SC/6, length 24.30 m, fishplated joints, timber sleepers. | nr | | The length given in the item description for diamond crossings is measured on the centre line over all the roads. See Fig. S6. on last page in preceding Commentary. | | |
| S627 | Welded joints between rails; by Quick Thermit process. | nr | | | | |
| | <u>Laying check rails, mass 56.40 per kg/m BS Rail Section No. 113A.</u> | | | | | |
| S651 | Rail; fishplated joints. | m | | | | |
| S652 | Length ends. | nr | | Items which are inset, see items codes S652 and S653 are described as "written short". The convention denotes they are parts of the preceding item from which they are inset and avoids having to repeat details from that Item. | | |
| S653 | Side ramps. | nr | | | | |
| | <u>Laying sundries.</u> | | | | | |
| S681 | Buffer stops; Drawing No. TA/4, mass 2.5 tonnes, approximate. | nr | | Where track components are not supplied by the Contractor, item descriptions for laying the track must state the form in which the track components are supplied and the location where he is to take delivery. See heading opposite in Example. | | |
| S684 | Lubricators; "P & M Universal" Pammek design, 14 kg container, Specification 1583. | nr | | | | |
| | <u>Laying flat bottom rails, mass 56.40 kg/m, BS Rail Section No. 113A, including taking delivery and unloading, from rail transport at No. 2 siding Ellis Street, and moving to position track components supplied by the Employer, Specification clause 1743.</u> | | | "Spot sleepering" is defined in CESMM as "replacing sleepers in prefabricated track not supplied by the Contractor". | | |
| S621.3 | Plain track; supplied in prefabricated sections length 18 m, fishplated joints, timber sleepers. | m | | | | |
| S628 | Spot re-sleepering; timber sleepers. | nr | | | | |

# 15 Tunnels – CESMM Class: T

The work covered by Class T of the CESMM, includes the lining and securing of tunnels, shafts and other subterranean cavities. Tunnels constructed by cut and cover are excluded from the Class. Headings are not specifically mentioned in Class T. The cross reference to them in the "Excludes" to Class E indicates that headings (small tunnels) other than those included in items for "pipe laying in headings" (See Items Code 21* and Rule C1. of Class L of CESMM) are to be measured as provided for tunnels. Pipe laying in headings, tunnels and shafts is specifically excluded from Class T and is included in Classes, I, J, K and L. Other specific exclusions from Class T are filling within tunnels (included in Class E) reinforcement in in situ linings (included in Class G) and geotechnical processes carried out from the ground surface (included in Class C).

---

Table 15.01   Tunnels, Shafts and other Subterranean Cavities

---

Generally -   Where work is expressly required to be executed under compressed air, state the gauge pressure in stages, the first stage shall be gauge pressure not exceeding one bar, with subsequent stages in increments of 0.4 bars. Class as specified requirements in Class A, the provision and operation of plant and services associated with the use of compressed air (Rule T/A1).

Tunnels constructed by cut and cover are excluded from this Class. The earthworks, in situ concrete and other components of tunnels so constructed shall be classed appropriately (Rule T/M1)

---

COMMENTARY

Tunnels, Shafts and other Subterranean Cavities (refer to Table 15.01)

Tunnelling and other subterranean work is usually divided so that it is grouped in the Bill of Quantities in parts under locational headings. In keeping with Paragraph 5.8 of the CESMM it is a matter of good practice that sub-division beyond that of location should be effected in the Bill to distinguish work having different characteristics, such as differences in ground conditions, working environment, methods of construction etc.

*Compressed Air*

Tunnelling work specified to be carried out under compressed air is given separately. It is itemised to distinguish work carried out within different stages of gauge pressures. (See Table 15.01). Item descriptions state, or are listed under headings that state, the gauge pressure applicable to the work to which they relate.

In addition to the items of work measured and given under Class T of the CESMM, items of "specified requirements" are given under Class A for the provision and operation of compressed air plant. The items distinguish between the establishment and removal of compressed air installations and facilities and their continuing operation and maintenance. (See CESMM, Code A278 and Rule A/A2). Where different gauge pressures are to operate, items for operation and maintenance need to be quantified. A suitable unit of measurement is linear metre of tunnel drive, giving separately the quantities for each of the appropriate stated stages of gauge pressures.

---

**Table 15.02    Excavation**

---

Generally - State whether tunnels and shafts are straight, curved or tapered. State the gradient of tunnels sloping at a gradient of 1 in 25 and steeper. State inclination to vertical of inclined shafts (Rule T/A3)

---

**1st Division**

---

Excavation    Deemed to include disposal of excavated material off Site and removal of existing services, unless otherwise stated (Rule T/C1).

State location of disposal area where excavated material disposed of on Site (Rule T/A4)

State where excavated material is to be used for filling (Rule T/A4)

---

| 2nd Division | | | 3rd Division |
|---|---|---|---|
| Tunnels in rock | m3 | Calculate the volume to the payment lines shown on the Drawings or, where no payment lines are shown, to the net dimensions of the volumes to be excavated (Rule T/M2) | State external diameter of the excavation cross-section of tunnels, shafts and other cavities |
| Tunnels in other stated material | m3 | | |
| Shafts in rock | m3 | | Where tunnels, shafts and other cavities are not of circular cross-section substitute maximum external dimension of cross-section for diameter and state their external cross-sectional dimensions (Rule T/A6) |
| Shafts in other stated material | m3 | Measure separately from soft material an isolated volume of rock only when it exceeds 0.25 m3 (Rule T/M3) | |
| Other cavities in rock | m3 | Calculate volume as described above for tunnels and shafts (Rule T/M2) | |
| Other cavities in other stated material | m3 | Class excavation, other than overbreak, outside the normal cross-section profile of tunnels and shafts as excavation of other cavities (Rule T/M2) | |
| Measure separately from soft material an isolated volume of rock only when it exceeds 0.25 m3 (Rule T/M3) | | Class transitions, breakaways and intersections which include work outside the normal profiles of tunnels and shafts as other cavities (Rule T/D1) | |
| | | Identify the cavity (Rule T/A2) | |
| Excavated surfaces in rock | m2 | Measure area of payment surfaces shown on the Drawings or, where no payment surfaces shown, the net area of the surfaces of the volumes to be excavated (Rule T/M4) | |
| Excavated surfaces in other stated material | m2 | | |
| | | State details of filling for voids caused by overbreak (Rule T/A5) | |

COMMENTARY

Excavation (refer to Table 15.02)

Excavation of tunnels, shafts and other cavities are each listed as separate classifications in Class T of the CESMM (See Table 15.02). Within each classification, excavation in rock and in any other material, stating the particular material, are each given separately. Material which will qualify to be classified as rock needs to be defined. An isolated volume of rock encountered in a volume of soft material, is measured separately when its volume exceeds 0.25 m3. Item descriptions for excavation state (a) whether tunnels and shafts are straight, curved or tapered (b) the gradient of tunnels sloping at a gradient of 1 in 25 and steeper, and (c) the inclination to the vertical of inclined shafts.

The volume of excavation is given in m3 and is calculated as provided in Rule T/M2 of the CESMM (See Table 15.02). Some examples of the payment lines for tunnels, established by the Rule T/M2 which obtains where no payment lines are shown on the Contract Drawings, are illustrated in the following diagrams (Fig.T1.).

Item descriptions for excavation circular in cross-section state the external diameter of the excavation cross-section of the tunnels, shafts and other cavities at Third Division level. They state the cross-sectional dimensions of the excavation where it is not circular in cross-section and the maximum dimension of cross-section is used for classification purposes at Third Division level.

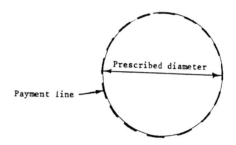

(a) Unlined, where no ground support required

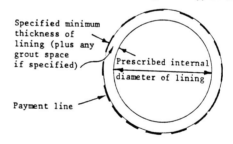

(b) Lined, where no ground support required

Disposing of the excavated material off the Site is deemed to be included in the items for excavation unless it is otherwise stated in the item descriptions. Where the excavated material is to be disposed of on the Site, the location of the disposal area is stated in the item descriptions for the excavation. Separate items with additional descriptions are given for otherwise similar excavation to distinguish different disposal requirements. Where the material excavated is to be used as filling material, this is stated in the item descriptions for the excavation from which the material results. Descriptions for filling items, for which the material is to be used should indicate it arises from identified tunnelling excavation.

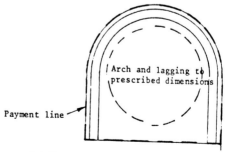

(c) Where ground support required

Fig. T1. Examples of payment lines established by Rule T/M2 of CESMM where none shown on the Drawings.

## Table 15.03  Linings

| Generally | State whether tunnels and shafts are straight, curved or tapered. State gradient of tunnels sloping at a gradient of 1 in 25 or steeper. State inclination to vertical of inclined shafts (Rule T/A7) |
|---|---|
| | Items for linings are deemed to include joints and finishes (Rule T/C2) |
| | Rules T/D1 and T/A2 (See Table 15.02) apply also to this Table |

### 1st Division

| In situ linings to tunnels | Measure thickness to payment lines as shown on the Drawings or, where no payment lines shown, to the net dimensions of the volumes to be lined. See Rule T/M2 (Rule T/M5) |
|---|---|
| In situ linings to shafts | Calculate volume as set out in Class F (Rule T/M6) |
| In situ linings to other cavities | State specification for concrete and whether it is reinforced and State when to head walls, shaft bottoms and other similar components (Rule T/A8) |

| 2nd Division | | | 3rd Division |
|---|---|---|---|
| Sprayed concrete primary | m2 | State minimum thickness (Rule T/A8) | State diameter |
| Sprayed concrete secondary | m2 | Reinforcing materials added to mix are not classed as reinforcement (Rule T/D3) | |
| Cast concrete primary | m3 | | |
| Cast concrete secondary | m3 | | |
| Formwork to stated finish | m2 | | |

Note on page 83 of CESMM: Concrete in lining work involving other than simple shapes may be classed as concrete (Class F) and concrete ancillaries (Class G)

| 1st Division | | 2nd Division | | 3rd Division |
|---|---|---|---|---|
| Preformed segmental lining to tunnels | Measure number of rings of segments | Precast concrete bolted | nr | State whether flanged or solid (Rule T/A11) | State diameter |
| | State or identify components which comprise each ring of segments. | Precast concrete expanded | nr | |
| Preformed segmental lining to shafts | State nominal ring width | Cast iron bolted | nr | State when with machined abutting surfaces (Rule T/A11) | |
| | State maximum piece weight (Rule T/A9) | Cast iron expanded | nr | | |
| Preformed segmental lining to other cavities | State when used in pilot tunnels and shafts. State where materials to remain property of Employer (Rule T/A10) | Nodular iron | nr | | |
| | | Fabricated steel | nr | | |
| | Deemed to include reinforcement and formwork (Rule T/C3) | | | |

Table 15.03 (cont.

| 1st Division | 2nd Division | 3rd Division | |
|---|---|---|---|
| Preformed segmental linings:- <br><br> to tunnels <br><br> to shafts <br><br> to other cavities | Lining ancillaries | Parallel circumferential packing <br><br> Tapered circumferential packing | For packings nr measure number of segments packed nr (Rule T/M7) |
| | | Stepped junctions nr | |
| | | Caulking of stated material m | |

COMMENTARY

Excavation (cont.

*Other Cavities*

Excavation, other than overbreak, which is outside the normal cross-sectional profile of tunnels and shafts, for transitions, breakaways, intersections of tunnels and shafts, or other such cavities, is classified "excavation other cavities". The item descriptions state the materials to be excavated and identify the cavities. The excavation is measured by volume and is given in m3.

*Excavated Surfaces*

Items for "excavated surfaces" are measured by area in m2 and are given in addition to those for the volumes of excavation. The areas measured are the net areas of the perimeter surfaces of the excavated voids, assuming the voids to be of the notional cross-section outlined either by the payment lines shown on the Drawings or established from the net dimensions of the volumes to be excavated, as appropriate. Item descriptions state the materials to which the excavated surfaces relate. The filling of voids caused by overbreak is intended to be included in the items. This intention is made clear and particulars of filling to voids is stated in the item descriptions.

Lining (Refer to Table 15.03)

Lining tunnels, shafts and other cavities are each given separately. Item descriptions for lining distinguish those to particular configurations of tunnels and shafts as noted against "Generally" in Table 15.03. Classification at Third Division level is by diameter. The diameter to be used for this classificiation is not defined in the CESMM and it is necessary to state in the item descriptions whether the diameter given is internal or external. No direction is given in the CESMM for the classification of linings which are not of circular cross-section. For these it is considered appropriate to adopt a similar rule to Rule T/A6 for their classification. See 3rd Division - Table 15.02.

Quantities for lining are computed net as provided in Paragraph 5.18 of the CESMM. Consequently, where intersections of tunnels with shafts entail breaking out the lining for the openings, the lining in the areas which are broken away for the openings is not measured, unless there is an express requirement for the opening to be broken out after the lining to the shaft has been constructed.

COMMENTARY

Lining (cont.

*In Situ Lining*

The thickness measured for in situ lining of designed cross-sectional profile is the net thickness measured from the internal face to the prescribed periphery. In the case of primary lining, the latter is that outlined by payment lines shown on the Drawings, or where no payment lines are shown, that established from the net dimensions of the volumes to be lined.

Item descriptions for in situ lining state the specification of the concrete and whether it is reinforced. They also state when linings are to head walls, shaft bottoms and other similar components. Cast concrete lining is measured by volume, calculated as set out in Class F and given in m3. Sprayed lining is given in m2 and descriptions state the minimum thickness. The classification table provides for formwork to cast in situ linings to be measured in m2 under Class T and requires that descriptions state the required finish. Where in situ linings are reinforced the reinforcement is measured separately under Class G. Reinforcing materials added to the mix of sprayed concrete linings are not classed as reinforcement.

*Preformed Segmental Lining*

Items for preformed segmental lining give the number of rings of segments of stated width. Item descriptions list or identify the components which comprise one ring of segments and state the maximum piece weight. They state whether precast concrete segments are solid or flanged and for iron and steel segments they state when the segments are required to have machine abutting surfaces. Item descriptions for preformed segmental lining state when they are used in pilot tunnels and shafts and are required to state when the materials used in pilot tunnels and shafts are to remain the property of the Employer.

Table 15.04  Support and Stabilization

1st Division

| Support and stabilization | Measure both temporary and permanent (Rule T/M8) |
|---|---|

| 2nd Division | 3rd Division | |
|---|---|---|
| Rock bolts        m | Mechanical | State size, type, shank detail and maximum length (Rule T/A12) |
| | Mechanical grouted | |
| | Pre-grouted impacted | |
| | Chemical end anchor | |
| | Chemical grouted | |
| | Chemically filled | |

Table 15.04  Support and Stabilization (cont.

| 2nd Division | 3rd Division | | | |
|---|---|---|---|---|
| Internal support | Steel arches: supply | t | Calculate mass as set out in Class M (Rule T/M9) | |
| | erection | t | | |
| | Timber supports: supply | m3 | Measure volume as set out in Class O (Rule T/M9) | |
| | erection | m3 | | |
| | Lagging | m2 | State materials used for lagging and for packing or grouting behind lagging (Rule T/A13) | |
| | Sprayed concrete<br><br>State specification of concrete, whether reinforced and minimum thickness (Rule T/A14) | m2 | Measure area at payment lines shown on Drawings or, where no payment lines shown, to net dimensions of support to be provided (Rule T/M9)<br><br>Reinforcing materials added to mix are not classed as reinforcement (Rule T/D3)<br><br>Class mesh or link reinforcement in sprayed concrete as mesh or link support (Rule T/D4) | |
| | Mesh or link | m2 | State size and mass of mesh or link fabric (Rule T/A14) | |
| Pressure grouting | Sets of drilling and grouting plant | nr | | |
| | Face packers | nr | Deemed to include collaring, securing and making good linings on completion (Rule T/C4) | For number of packers measure the number of injections (Rule T/M10) |
| | Deep packers of stated size | nr | State size | |
| | Drilling and flushing to stated diameter | m | State diameter | State lengths of holes in stages of 5 m (Rule T/A15) |
| | Re-drilling and flushing | m | | |
| | Injection of grout materials of stated composition | t | State composition | Exclude mass of water from mass measured (Rule T/M11) |
| Forward probing  m | State length of holes in stage of 5 m (Rule T/A15) | | | |

COMMENTARY

Support and Stabilization (refer to Table 15.04)

Items of work classed as "support and stabilization" are listed in Table 15.04. The Table notes the details to be given in the item descriptions of the work and indicates the units of measurement for the various items.

Rule T/M8 of the CESMM states that both temporary and permanent support and stabilization shall be measured. The Rule does not stipulate that the work measured shall be limited to that which is expressly required. This means that otherwise than where in accordance with the Contract the Contractor must conform to given requirements, the extent of the temporary support and stabilization admeasured and for which the Contractor is entitled to payment, is that he has actually provided, whether it is more or less than was envisaged in the Contract.

In keeping with the general policy of the CESMM for dealing with standing by and delays (See Commentary page 40, Chapter 3) items are not given for standing by tunnelling plant whilst support and stabilization is carried out.

*Temporary Support and Stabilization*

Where it is anticipated that temporary ground support will be required and it is to be given in the Bill of Quantities as measured items, the Engineer needs to provide drawings and details of his proposals to allow the quantities to be prepared. It is considered that by doing this it does not commit him to accept responsibility for the design of the temporary support work. The Specification should make clear the extent of the responsibility for the design of the temporary support and stabilization which the Contract places on the Contractor. Where the Contract affords the Contractor no discretion and he must conform to the Engineer's designed requirements, the Engineer is held responsible for the design and the temporary support and stabilization work is admeasured as designed. Where the Specification makes clear that the given drawing and detail are notional and that the Contractor is to be responsible for the design and the temporary support and stabilization, the work admeasured is that actually carried out by the Contractor. Where the latter condition is to obtain, it is sensible for the Contract to require the Contractor to intimate at the time of tender and obtain, prior to the acceptance of the tender, the Engineer's agreement to the use of any system of temporary support and stabilization which is not envisaged by the proposals in the tender documents. Fresh items and rates can then be agreed for any approved alternative systems.

*Permanent Support and Stabilization*

Support and stabilization which are part of the Engineer's design for the Permanent Works are measured from the Drawings, as provided in Paragraph 5.18 of the CESMM.

EXAMPLE TE.1

Measured Example

The measured example which follows includes the sewer tunnels between MH1 - 2 and MH2 - 3 as shown on Drawing No. T/D/1 and one shaft, MH3 as shown on Drawing No. T/D/2.

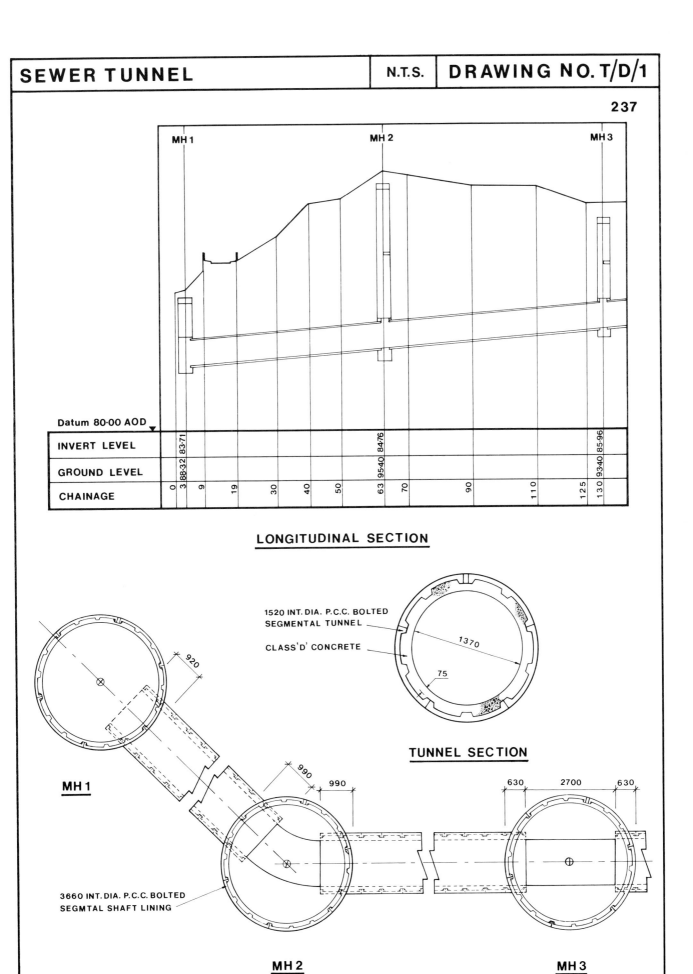

| | MH 1 | | | | | | MH 2 | | | | | MH 3 |

Datum 80·00 AOD ▼

| | | | | | | | | | | | | |
|---|---|---|---|---|---|---|---|---|---|---|---|---|
| **INVERT LEVEL** | 83·71 | | | | | | 84·76 | | | | | 85·96 |
| **GROUND LEVEL** | 88·32 | | | | | | 95·40 | | | | | 93·40 |
| **CHAINAGE** | 0  3 | 9 | 19 | 30 | 40 | 50 | 63 | 70 | 90 | 110 | 125 | 130 |

**LONGITUDINAL SECTION**

1520 INT. DIA. P.C.C. BOLTED
SEGMENTAL TUNNEL

CLASS 'D' CONCRETE

1370

75

**TUNNEL SECTION**

920

990

990

630   2700   630

**MH 1**

3660 INT. DIA. P.C.C. BOLTED
SEGMTAL SHAFT LINING

**MH 2**

**MH 3**

SEWER TUNNEL DRG No. T/D/1

EXAMPLE TE.1

|  | Tunnel | Shaft |
|--|--------|-------|
|  | 1370 | 3510 |
|  | 150 | 150 |
|  | 1520 | 3660 |
|  | 150 | 150 |
|  | 110 | 150 |
| Overall diams | 1780 | 3960 |

MH(1-2)+(2-3) 60.00 67.00 56.04

2/½/ 3.96 = 3.96 3.96 63.04

     56.04 63.04 119.04

$1.98^2 + 0.89^2 = 3.128$

$\sqrt{3.128} = 1.769$

$1.98 - 1.769 = \underline{0.211}$

<u>Tunnels M.H's 1-3</u>

<u>Note</u> Tunnels straight unless o/w stated.

Excavation

| $\frac{22}{7}$/ | 119.08 | ⎰ Tunnels in rock |
| | 0.89 | ⎱ diam 1.78 m |
| 4/$\frac{22}{7}$/½/ | 0.89 | (T111 |
| | 0.21 | |
| | 0.89 | |
| | 0.89 | |

| $\frac{22}{7}$/ | 119.08 | ⎰ Excavd. surfs. in |
| | 1.78 | rock voids filled |
| 4/½/ | 0.21 | with cement grout |
| | 1.78 | as Spec. clause 4.1 |
| | | (T170 |

$\dfrac{1.980}{1.769} = 1.1193 = \text{Sec } 26°40'$

$26.66 \times 2 = 53.33$

$\dfrac{53.33 \times 3.96 \times 22}{360 \times 7} = 1.844$

(1)

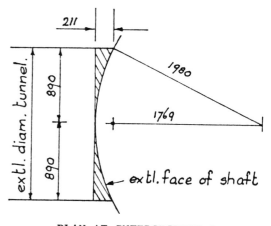

SEWER TUNNEL DRG. NO T/D/1

<u>Excavation ( cont.</u>

1780÷2=890        1844÷2=922

| 2/2/22 | 0.92 |
|---|---|
| 7 | 0.89 |
| | 0.11 |

*Other cavs. in p.c.c., extl.
c.s. dims. 1844 x 1780mm;
breakg out segments, inter-
sec. tunnel + shaft (T161*

890 + 922 = 1812

| 2/2/22 | 1.81 |
|---|---|
| 7 | 0.11 |

*Exc. surfs in p.c. conc.
voids filled w. cement
grout a.b.        (T180*

<u>Primary lining</u>

MH 1 2    MH 2 3
56.04      63.04
{ 0.99      0.99
  0.92      0.63
57.95      64.66

57.95 ÷ 0.61 = 95
64.66 ÷ 0.61 = 106
122.61        201

<u>Preformed segmental
linings to tunnels</u>

201

*Precast conc. boltd.
rings, flanged, intl.
diam. 1.52 m, ring
width 0.61 m, compris-
ing 5 segments and
Key piece, nom. max.
piece weight 0.120 t
with 20 bolts 40 wash
40 grummets longit-
udinal jointing strips
and circumferential
jointing rope ( T511*

( 2 )

COMMENTARY

Items for probing ahead and for temporary support for tunnels in rock should be measured in circumstances other than where there is good evidence they are unlikely to be required. The Example assumes the tunnel is in rock of a nature which will not require temporary support to the excavation. Items for these are not, therefore, measured. Preamble would provide that the rates for excavation are to include for temporarily supporting the excavation at all times.

The Example assumes there is an express requirement for the primary lining of the shaft to be constructed and for it to be broken away to form the openings for the intersections of the tunnels. The first two items in the adjoining column are measured for this work. If there was no such requirement, the primary lining would be measured net. i.e. each of the lower rings of segments would be of such number and type required for the lining area of the shaft excluding the openings (See CESMM, Paragraph 5.18).

The unit of measurement for segmental tunnel lining is the number of rings of segments. The number of rings is found by dividing the length of the linings by the ring width of 0.61 m.

Because the CESMM is silent on the matter, it is necessary to state whether the diameter of the lining given in the item descriptions is internal or external. The internal diameter stated in the item descriptions for the segmental lining is that to the inner face of the flanges. This would be made clear in Preamble. The other detail given in the item description for the lining is that which the CESMM requires shall be stated. See Table 15.03. The nominal maximum weight may be calculated from the largest piece in a ring of segments. In this case, the manufacturer's literature for the segments, proposed in the Example, gives the total weight for a standard ring of segments. This reduced by an allowance for the key has been divided by five to calculate the nominal maximum piece weight given.

SEWER TUNNEL DRG. NO T/D/1

Primary ling. (cont.

95
1
94    106
1
105

Preformed segmental
lining to tunnels (cont

| | | |
|---|---|---|
| 94/22/7 | 1.52 | |
| 94/6 | 0.61 | |
| 105/22/7 | 1.52 | |
| 105/6 | 0.61 | |

Lining ancillaries
caulking; wi. compound
as Spec. clause 2.90
(T574

Secondary lining

1780      1370
1370      1780
2) 410    2) 3150
205       1575

Conc. Class "D" as
Spec. clause 4.2

In situ linings to
tunnels

| | |
|---|---|
| 22/7 | 122.61 |
| | 0.21 |
| | 1.58 |

Cast conc. secondary
intl. diam. 1.37 m
(T241

| | |
|---|---|
| 201/ | 0.26 |
| | 1.00 |
| | 1.00 |

Ddt    { volume
       { of p.c.
       { segments

| | |
|---|---|
| 22/7 | 122.61 |
| | 1.37 |

Fmw. fair finish
diam 1.37 m.
(T251

(3)

COMMENTARY

The concrete tunnel segments envisaged in the Example are cast with caulking grooves on the internal circumferential and longitudinal sides. The lining ancillaries item is given for caulking these grooves.

The Drawing shows the tunnels to be lined with an in situ concrete secondary lining, this is measured in m3, as required by Class T of the CESMM. Item descriptions state the internal diameter of the lining. See Commentary to Column (2) of these dimensions.

The thickness inclusive of the segments and the mean diameter are calculated in waste in the adjoining column.

In the Example, no allowance is made for creep and the length of the lining is taken as that of the segments. See previous column of dimensions. The thickness (0.21 m) in the first set of dimensions for the concrete lining includes that of the precast segments. The second set deducts the volume of the segments as taken from the manufacturer's literature. The volume is given as 0.26 m3 per ring. This is entered with two dimensions each of 1.00 m to indicate it is a cubic dimension. The timesing is the number of rings.

The formwork to the internal surfaces of the lining is measured by area. The item descriptions state the diameter of the concrete surface supported.

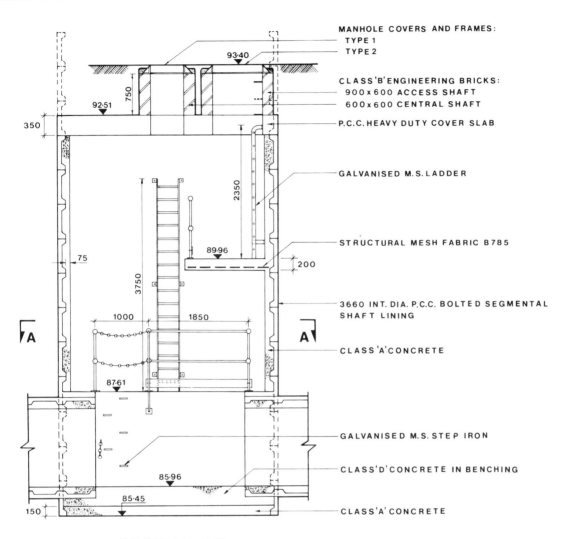

MANHOLE COVERS AND FRAMES:
- TYPE 1
- TYPE 2

CLASS 'B' ENGINEERING BRICKS:
- 900 x 600 ACCESS SHAFT
- 600 x 600 CENTRAL SHAFT

P.C.C. HEAVY DUTY COVER SLAB

GALVANISED M.S. LADDER

STRUCTURAL MESH FABRIC B 785

3660 INT. DIA. P.C.C. BOLTED SEGMENTAL SHAFT LINING

CLASS 'A' CONCRETE

GALVANISED M.S. STEP IRON

CLASS 'D' CONCRETE IN BENCHING

CLASS 'A' CONCRETE

## SECTION B-B

SCALE 0 — 1 — 2 m

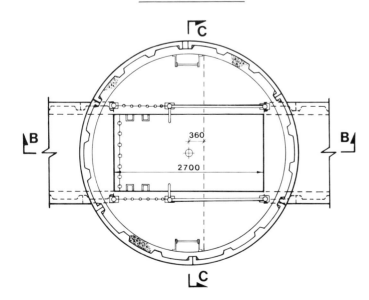

## SECTIONAL PLAN A-A

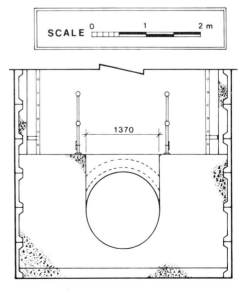

## SECTION C-C

242

MANHOLE No 3 DRG.No.T/D/2

Extl.diam.3.96 ∴ rad=1.98m

|  | 93.40 |
|--|-------|
|  | 93.10 |

Shaft      0.30

Note: All shafts straight unless o/w stated.

Excavation

| 22/7 | 1.98 | Shafts in topsoil, |
|------|------|--------------------|
|      | 1.98 | diam. 3.96 m       |
|      | 0.30 | (T143.1            |

93.10
91.27
1.83

| 22/7 | 1.98 | Shafts in made      |
|------|------|---------------------|
|      | 1.98 | ground, diam 3.96 m |
|      | 1.83 | (T143.2             |

91.27
85.45
5.82

| 22/7 | 1.98 | Shafts in rock, |
|------|------|-----------------|
|      | 1.98 | diam 3.96 m;    |
|      | 5.82 | (T133           |

| 22/7 | 3.96 | Excavd. surfs. in |
|------|------|-------------------|
|      | 0.30 | topsoil    (T180.1 |

| 92 51 | 93.10 |
|-------|-------|
| 0.35  | 92.16 |
| 92.16 | 0.94  |

| 22/7 | 3.96 | Excavd. surfs. in       |
|------|------|-------------------------|
|      | 0.94 | made ground (T180.2     |

(4)

COMMENTARY

The dimensions taken are for one shaft only (Manhole No. 3) as shown on Drawing No. T/D/2.

The calculation of the external diameter of the shaft is given in waste in Column (1) of the dimensions for this Example.

Item descriptions for excavation state the material to be excavated, the diameter of the shaft and also whether the shaft is straight, curved or tapered. They also state the inclination to the vertical where shafts are inclined. It is assumed the borehole logs would indicate the materials in made ground.

No payment lines are shown on the Drawings and the excavation measured is the nett volumes to be excavated. Depths are taken from reduced levels as follows:-

| Ground level | 93·40 | |
|--------------|-------|--|
| TOPSOIL | 93·10 | |
| MADE GROUND | | |
| | 91·27 | |
| SANDSTONE | | |
| Bottom of shaft | (85·45) | |

The items for excavated surfaces in contact with the temporary rings of segments at the top of the shaft are given in separate items from those in contact with the permanent rings because no grouting is required behind the temporary rings.

MANHOLE NO.3 DRG. NO T/D/2

|  |  |  |  |  |
|---|---|---|---|---|
|  |  |  |  | 1.83 |
|  |  |  |  | 0.94 |
|  |  |  |  | 0.89 |

Excavation (cont.

| $\frac{22}{7}$ | 3.96 | | | Excavd. surfs. in made ground, voids filled with cement grout as Spec. clause 4.1   (T180.3 |
| | 0.89 | | | |

| $\frac{22}{7}$ | 3.96 | | | Excavd. surfs. in rock, voids filled with cement grout a.b.   (T170.1 |
| | 5.82 | | | |

| $\frac{22}{7}$ | 1.98 | | | Excavd. surfs. in rock; shaft bottoms   (T170.2 |
| | 1.98 | | | |

$$92.16$$
$$85.45$$
$$6.71 \div 0.61 = 11$$

Primary lining
Preformed segmental lining to shafts.

| | 11 | | | Precast conc. boltd. rings, flanged, intl. diam. 3.66 m, ring width 0.61 m, comprising 6 segments and key piece, nom. max. piece weight 0.31 t, with 36 bolts, 72 washs. 72 grummets, 7 longitudinal jointing strips and circumferential jointing rope.   (T613 |

(5)

244

MANHOLE No 3 DRG. NO. T/D/2

Primary lining (cont.

| 10/22/7 | 3.66 | |
| 11/7 | 0.61 | |

{ Lining ancillaries,
{ caulking ab.ff 574.2

General items
Specified reqmts.
Temp. Works

Safety measures to
top of Shafts

sum — Establishment and
removal of three
temporary rings
of precast conc.
segments, intl diam.
3.66 m, ring width
0.61m to top of
MH.3. as shown on
Drawing No T/D/2
and in accordance
with Spec. clause 3.
(excav. measd sep)(A279.1

sum — Maintenance of
temporary rings
of segments to
top of MH.3.
until cover slab
fixed and in
position (A279.2

(6)

COMMENTARY

The lining ancillaries item is measured for caulking the grooves in the shaft segments.

The Example assumes an express requirement for three temporary rings of shaft segments to be erected for safety reasons at the top of the shaft. These are shown on Drawing No. T/D/2. In accordance with Rule A/D1 of the CESMM, these Temporary Works are given as Specified Requirements. Items which separate establishment and removal from operation or maintenance are given as required by Rule A/A2.

The item description for establishment makes clear that the excavation for the temporary rings is measured separetely.

## MANHOLE No 3 DRG No. T/D/2

Secondary linings

| | |
|---|---|
| U/s cov. slab. | 92.16 |
| Top of benchg. | 87.61 |
| | 4.55 |

|  |  |
|---|---|
| 3960 | 3510 |
| 3510 | 3960 |
| 2)450 | 2)7470 |
| 225 | 3735 |

In situ lining to shafts.

$\frac{22}{7}$ / 3.74
0.23
4.55

Cast conc. secondary. diam. 3.51 m; conc. Class "A" as Spec. clause 4.2 (T343

0.61)4.55
7.46

$7\frac{1}{2}$ / 0.75
1.00
1.00

Ddt ditto { volume { of p.c. { segments

$\frac{22}{7}$ / 3.51
4.55

Fmw. fair finish intl diam. 3.51m
(T353

3.66
3.81
2)7.47
3.74 ÷ 2 = 1.87

$\frac{22}{7}$ / 1.87
1.87
0.15

Cast conc. primary to form shaft bottom. conc. Class "A" a.b.
(T330

Benching

| | 87.61 |
|---|---|
| 2.16 | 85.45 |
| 0.15 | 2.16 |
| 2.01 | |

2)3.96
1.98

(7)

### COMMENTARY

To simplify measurement, the thickness of the in-situ concrete lining, entered in the first set of dimensions in the adjoining column, includes that of the precast concrete segments. The next set of dimensions deducts the volume of the segments (0.75 m3 per ring) as taken from the manufacturer's literature. The timesing factor is the number of rings. The height of the in situ lining is measured from the top of the benching to the underside of the precast concrete cover slab. This is equal in height to 7.46 rings of segments.

The in situ lining to the bottom of the shaft is a primary lining and the description in the Example classifies it accordingly. As required by Rule T/A8 of the CESMM the item description states it is to shaft bottoms. The 3rd Division classification by diameter is not applicable to flat shaft bottom and 0 is used as the last digit in the code number. See Paragraph 4.6 CESMM and Paragraph of same reference in Chapter 2.

246

## MANHOLE NO 3 DRG. No. T/D/2

Benching (cont.

| | | |
|---|---|---|
| 22/7 | 1.98 | **Provn. of conc.** |
| | 1.98 | **Class "D" as Spec.** |
| | 2.01 | clause 4.2    (F253 |

&

**Placg. of conc.,
mass benchings to
m.h. bottom 3.81 m
diam x 2.01 m (extreme)**
(F480

| | | |
|---|---|---|
| | 2.70 | {Ddt. Both last items |
| | 1.37 | |
| | 0.97 | (main channel |
| ½/22/7 | 2.70 | 630 – 211 · 419 |
| | 0.69 | 630 |
| | 0.69 | (ditto.    " 419 |
| 2/22/7 | 0.89 | 3)1468 |
| | 0.89 | 489 |
| | 0.49 | (projecting ends of |
| 3½/ | 0.75 | {tunnels |
| | 1.00 | (volume of p.c. |
| | 1.00 | (segments. |

| | | |
|---|---|---|
| 2/22/7 | 0.92 | {Add. Both last items |
| | 0.89 | (segments over |
| | 0.11 | (deducted previously |
| 22/7 | 3.74 | 1.65 |
| | 0.15 | fall. 0.02 |
| | 0.15 | 1.67 |
| | | **Fmw. fair finish to intl. surfs. of in situ conc. "U" shaped channel, length 2.70m, max. dimensions of cross-section 1.37 x 1.67 m, inc. fmw. to ends**    (G290 |
| | 1 | |

(8)

COMMENTARY

The excavation and lining of the shaft has been classified in accordance with Class T. Internal work in the shaft is given in accordance with other Classes.

The in situ concrete benching is measured by volume as provided in Class F. Measurement of the benching is simplified in the Example, by first including the precast segments in the volume measured and afterwards deducting their volume on the basis of that given in the manufacturer's literature.

The "Add" item which follows the "Ddt" in the adjoining column of dimensions adds the two items of concrete over deducted by (i) the tunnel projecting into the shaft, and (ii) the flange of the shaft segments extending into the bottom lining.

Because the section of the channel changes due to the fall in the invert it is inappropriate to measure the formwork as of constant cross-section. It is given in the Example as a special numbered item in preference to measuring it by area.

MANHOLE No 3  DRG No T/D/2

Benching (cont.

| | | |
|---|---|---|
| $\frac{22}{7}$/ | 1.76<br>1.76 | Conc. accessories fin of top surfs., steel trow. fin. (G812 |
| | 2.70<br>1.37 | Ddt ditto (channel |

$$2)\overline{1\cdot370}\qquad\begin{array}{r}1\cdot650\\0\cdot685\\\hline0\cdot965\end{array}$$
$$\phantom{2)}0\cdot685$$

| | | |
|---|---|---|
| 2/ | 2.70<br>0.97 | Conc. accessories fin. of formed surfs of "U" shaped channel as Spec. clause (G823 |
| $\frac{1}{2}$/$\frac{22}{7}$/ | 2.70<br>1.37 | |
| 2/$\frac{1}{2}$/$\frac{22}{7}$/ | 0.69<br>0.69 | (ends |
| 2/ | 1.37<br>0.97 | (ends |
| 2/$\frac{22}{7}$/ | 0.69<br>0.69 | Ddt Last item (tunnel (openings |

Intermediate slab

| | | |
|---|---|---|
| $\frac{1}{2}$/$\frac{22}{7}$/ | 1.76<br>1.76<br>0.20 | Provn. of conc. Class "A" as Spec. clause 4.2  (F243 |

&

Placg. of conc., rfcd. susp. slabs, thickn 150 – 300 mm (act 200); inter slab.  (F532

$$2\sqrt{1755^2-360^2}=\begin{array}{r}3510\\3435\\\hline2)\overline{6945}\\\hline3473\end{array}$$

| | | |
|---|---|---|
| | 3.47<br>0.36<br>0.20 | Ddt. Both last items |

(9)

COMMENTARY

Items for finishing surfaces are given where a separate finiishing treatment to the surface of the concrete is required. The Example assumes a specified treatment to the formed surface of the channel after the removal of the formwork.

The intermediate concrete landing is measured as provided in Class F of the CESMM. The plan shape of the landing is segmental. In the Example the dimensions set down for it are those for a semi-circle followed by the deduct of the want to reduce the semi-circle to the required segment. See diagram below.

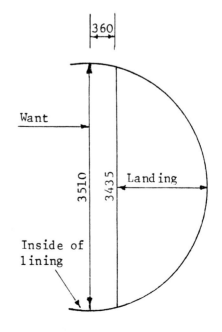

MANHOLE NO 3 DRG NO. T/D/2

Inter. slab (cont.

$$\frac{\pi \, 3.51^2}{8} = 4.840$$

Less 3.47 × 0.36 = 1.249

3.435 ) 3.591

av width landing = 1.045

½/22/ 1.76
7   1.76

Fmw. fair finish plane horiz. width 1.05m (average); soffit of intermed. landing slab, curved cut ag. shaft lining   (G214

&

Rfcmt h.y. steel fabric to BS.4483 ref.B785 nom mass 8.14 Kg/m2; in inter landg slab curvd cut ag. shaft (measd. nett)   (G568

&

Conc. accessories, fin of top surfs., steel trow. fin (G812

3.47
0.36

Ddt. Last three items

Exposed edge

3.44

Fmw. fair finish, plane vert, width 0.1 - 0.2.

(G242

(10)

COMMENTARY

The formwork to the soffit of the intermediate landing slab is measured by area and is classified plane horizontal stating and average width. Because of its shape it is thought reasonable to provide additional description which includes location. This applies also to the item description for the reinforcement.

The Example assumes that the soffit and edge surface of the concrete landing are to be left fair from the formwork and that no separate finishing treatment to the surface of the concrete is required.

The measurement convention of first measuring a semi-circle and deducting a want to reduce it to a segment is adopted for the measurement of the formwork and the reinforcement.

The average width for the classification of the formwork to the soffit of the landing is found by dividing the area by the length on the front edge. See waste at the top of the adjoining column.

The formwork to the edge of the landing being of a width not exceeding 200 mm is measured in linear metres.

MANHOLE NO. 3 DRG. NO. T/D/2

<u>Cover</u>

Precast conc. (cov. slabs.

| 1 | Heavy duty cover slab to shaft, diam 3.96 m (overall), thickn. 350 mm in four pieces as Drawing No. 5/3 (H530 |

2/2/600=2400  2/900=1800
4/215 = 860   2/600·1200
        3260          3000
        93.40   4/215  860
        92.51         3860
        0.89    0.89
Less cover    0.14
              0.75

<u>BKw. (access shafts.</u>

| 3.86 | |
| 0.75 | Engin. bkw. as Spec. |
| 3.26 | clause 6.12, thickness |
| 0.75 | 225 mm, vert stra. walls; access shafts. (U321 |

| 3.00 | |
| 0.75 | Engin. bkw. Surf |
| 2.40 | features fair facg. |
| 0.75 | (U378 |

<u>Misc. Metalwk</u>

| 1 | Cast iron coated M.H. cover and fra, type 1 as Spec. clause 2.39 and Drg No 4/21 (N299.1 |

| 1 | Cast iron coatd MH cov + fra, type 2 as Spec. clause 2.39 and Drg No 4/22 (N299.2 |

(11)

COMMENTARY

Precast concrete cover slabs, either standard or manufactured to drawn and specified requirements, are available from the manufacturers of precast segments. The cover slab here measured is assumed to be Contractor designed to suit stated dimensions and loading requirements. It is classified under Class H. The mass per unit will depend on the Contractor's design and is not stated in the item description. The zero in the Code number signifies that the Third Division descriptive features in Class H are not appropriate to the item.

The engineering brickwork enclosing the access shafts is classified vertical walls under Class U. It is assumed that bricks, mortar and jointing and pointing are described in the Specification clause given in the description. Inner faces of the work are taken in the Example to be finished to a fair face. Step irons in the brickwork are measured later with the items of miscellaneous metalwork.

Miscellaneous metalwork is measured under Class N of the CESMM. Code N2 is used in the Example as the First Division code for miscellaneous metalwork components in coated cast iron.

MANHOLE No 3. DRG. No. T/D/2

Incl. components

Conc. access.

2/ 5    Inserts galv. m. steel step irons as Spec. clause 2.40, type 2 and casting in to project from one surf. of conc. (G832

Misc. metalwork Galv. m. steel handrails as Spec. clause 2.56 and Drg. No. 23 inc. mortices in conc. for fixings

1    Handrails of solid steel sections, as detail "J" length 3.35m x 1.10m high; inter landing. (N199.3

2    Handrails of solid steel sections & with safety chain, as detail "K", length 2.85m over-all x 1.00m high; side of channel. (N199.4

Misc. metalwork Galv m. steel safety chain as Spec. clause 2.55, length 1.45m inc morts in conc. for fixings (N199.5

(12)

COMMENTARY

Items for inserts include the supply of the inserts unless otherwise stated. Item descriptions identify the position of the insert in relation to the surface of the concrete. See Rules C7 and A/15 CESMM Class G.

The First Division code number N1 is used in the Example to represent "Galvanised mild steel". Classification at Second Division level uses the appropriate standard features or the digit 9 where the standard features are not appropriate to the component measured.

Because they are not straightforward runs of handrailing, it is thought preferable to give the handrails with their associated safety chains as enumerated items and to give them special codes.

MANHOLE NO 3 DRG. NO. T/D/2

Intl. components

Misc. metalwork
Galv. m. steel ladders
as Spec. clause 2.57
and Drg. No. 26
inc. mortices in conc.
for fixings

| | | | |
|---|---|---|---|
| 2/ | 2.35 | | Ladders wi. retd. |
| | 3.75 | | strings (In No. 3) |
| 3/2/ | 0.20 | | (retns. (N 130 |

| | | | |
|---|---|---|---|
| 3/ | 1 | | Misc. metalwork |

Galv. m. steel step
irons as Spec. clause
2.40, type 1 and
buildg'. in to engin.
bkw. (N 199.2

Backfill at top

| 93.40 | 0.89 |
|---|---|
| 92.51 | 0.15 |
| 0.89 | 0.74 |

| | | | |
|---|---|---|---|
| 22/ | 1.98 | | Earthworks |
| 7/ | 1.98 | | Fillg. to structures |
| | 0.74 | | imported fillg. matl. |

type "C" as Spec.
clause 1.17 (E 615

| | 600 | 900 |
|---|---|---|
| 2/215 | 430 | 430 |
| | 1030 | 1330 |

| | | | |
|---|---|---|---|
| | 1.03 | | Ddt. Last item |
| | 1.03 | | |
| | 0.74 | | access shaft |
| | 1.33 | | |
| | 1.03 | | ( " " |
| | 0.74 | | |

(13)

---

Ladders are here measured in linear metres as required by Class N of the CESMM. It is considered of help to give the number of ladders in the item description.

Whilst the building in to brickwork of such items as pipes and ducts are required by Class U of the CESMM to be given as separate items, it is thought reasonable to include the building in with the item for the step irons.

The Example assumes that the Specification requires that unless otherwise specified, excavated material is for disposal. The Example assumes that the excavated material is unsuitable for filling. Filling material is taken as imported. Had it been required that excavated material be used for filling a volume of excavation of shaft or tunnel equal to that required for filling would have been re-classified stating the excavated material was to be used for filling. See Rule T/A4 of CESMM.

252

MANHOLE No 3. DRG No T/D/2

Reinstate at top.

| | | |
|---|---|---|
| 22/7 | 1.98<br>1.98 | Earthworks<br>Filling, thickn.,<br>150 mm, imported top-<br>soil; making out<br>grassland over shafts.<br>(E642 |
| | | + |
| | | Landscapg. grass<br>seedg. Spec. clause<br>3.9; making out<br>over shafts (E830 |
| | 1.03<br>1.03<br>1.33<br>1.03 | Ddt. Both last items<br>(access shaft<br>( " " |

(14)

COMMENTARY

The Example assumes that there is no express requirement for the preservation of topsoil. The adjoining item for reinstatement provides for topsoil to be imported. Had there been an express requirement to preserve the topsoil, the item description for "Excavation, shafts in topsoil" (Column 6 of the Example) would have stated an Excavate Surface of "underside of topsoil". Also the remaining items for the excavation of shafts would have stated a Commencing Surface of "underside of topsoil". Additionally, items for excavation of shafts in topsoil would have distinguished where the topsoil was for disposal from that where it was for re-use as filling.

# 16 Brickwork, Blockwork and Masonry – CESMM Class: U

Brickwork in manholes and brickwork incidental to pipework are excluded from Class U and are included in Class K of the CESMM. Brickwork in sewer renovation is also excluded and is included in Class Y. Otherwise it is appropriate to measure and classify all other brickwork and all blockwork and masonry in accordance with Class U. The classification table for this Class provides descriptive features for each of the materials. The rules of measurement and the descriptive features are the same for each material, with minor exceptions.

---

Table 16.01   Brickwork, Blockwork and Masonry

---

Generally – Include the volumes and areas of joints in the volumes and areas measured, but exclude the volumes and areas of copings and sills (Rule U/M2)

No deduction from or addition to the volumes and areas measured for intruding or projecting surface features. No deduction for holes and openings not exceeding 0.25 m2 cross-sectional area (Rule U/M2)

---

1st Division

| | | |
|---|---|---|
| Common brickwork | | State materials dimensions and types of brick, block and stone or give equivalent reference to applicable BS (Rule U/A1) |
| Facing brickwork | | |
| Engineering brickwork | | |
| Lightweight blockwork | | |
| Dense concrete blockwork | | |
| Artificial stone blockwork | | State bonding pattern, type of mortar and type of jointing and pointing (Rule U/A3) |
| Ashlar masonry | State surface finish (Rule U/A2) | |
| Rubble masonry | Deemed to include fair facing (Rule U/C1) | |

---

2nd Division

| Thickness:- | | |
|---|---|---|
| not exceeding 150 mm | m2 | State actual nominal thickness (Rule U/A5) |
| 150 - 250 mm | m2 | State mean thickness of battered walls (Rule U/D4) |
| 250 - 500 mm | m2 | Ignore presence of surface feature to determine thickness of walls, facings and casing (Rule U/D3) |
| 500 mm - 1 m | m2 | |
| exceeding 1 m | m3 | Use mean dimensions to calculate areas and volumes (Rule U/M3) |
| Columns and piers of stated cross-sectional dimensions | m | Classify as piers, isolated walls having a length on plan not exceeding four times their thickness (Rule U/D2) |
| | | State cross-sectional dimensions |
| | | Use mean dimensions to calculate heights (Rule U/M3) |

Table 16.01  Brickwork, Blockwork and Masonry (cont.

| 3rd Division | | |
| --- | --- | --- |
| Vertical straight walls<br><br>Vertical curved walls | | State if in cavity or composite construction and measure each skin separately (Rule U/M1 and Rule U/A4) |
| Battered straight walls<br><br>Battered curved walls | Classify walls or facings battered on one or both sides as battered walls or facings (Rule U/D1) | |
| Vertical facing to concrete<br><br>Battered facing to concrete<br><br>Casing to metal sections | | |

COMMENTARY

Brickwork, Blockwork and Masonry (refer to Table 16.01)

Class U of the CESMM provides for brickwork, blockwork and masonry to be classified according to type, thickness and the work to which they apply. Fair facing is deemed to be included in the items for masonry, otherwise surface features in the work and ancillaries are classified and given in separate items from those for the brickwork, blockwork and masonry.

When used in item descriptions, the standard classification types given at 1st Division level need to be amplified by stating the materials, dimensions and type, or alternatively, references to applicable British Standards for the bricks, blocks or stone. The bonding patterns, type of mortar and jointing and pointing to be used must also be stated in the item descriptions. Item descriptions for masonry must state the surface finish.

All walls exceeding one metre in thickness are given in m3; those not exceeding one metre in thickness are given in m2. In each case the actual thickness is stated in the item descriptions; the thickness ranges given in the classification table of the CESMM serve only as a means of coding.

Isolated walls having a length on plan not exceeding four times their thickness are classified as piers (See Fig. U1). The classification will not apply to those parts of walls of a plan length of not exceeding four times their thickness which result because of openings in walls. Columns and piers are given by height in linear metres stating the cross-sectional dimensions.

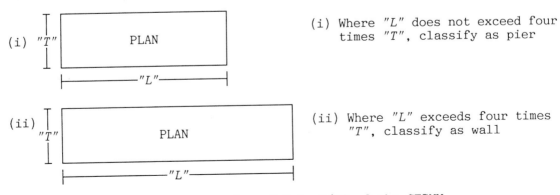

(i) Where "L" does not exceed four times "T", classify as pier

(ii) Where "L" exceeds four times "T", classify as wall

Fig. U1.  Diagramatic illustration of Rule U/D2 of the CESMM.

COMMENTARY

Brickwork, Blockwork and Masonry (cont.

Rule U/D5 of the CESMM provides that columns and piers attached to walls of the same material shall be classed as pilasters. See later Commentary on "Surface Features".

The volumes and areas measured for brickwork, blockwork and masonry include the volumes and areas of the mortar joints. Copings and sills are excluded from the volumes and areas measured. No addition to or deduction from the volumes and areas measured are made for the volumes and areas of projecting or recessed surface features. No deductions are made for holes and openings not exceeding 0.25 m2 cross-sectional area.

The thickness of walls, facings and casings are taken as that of the wall, the facing or the casing ignoring recessed and projecting features. See Fig. U2(i) and (ii). The recessed, projecting and other features are measured as separate items described as surface features. Different thicknesses of work in the same wall (not brought about by surface features) are each measured separately. See Fig. U2(iii). The thickness of battered walls is taken as the mean thickness. See Fig. U2(iv). Battered walls whose thickness extends into more than one standard thickness range are divided into separate thicknesses items for each thickness range.

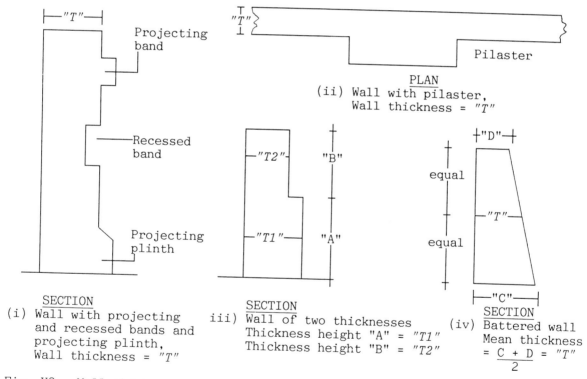

Fig. U2. Wall thicknesses as defined in Rules U/D3 and U/D4 of the CESMM.

Mean dimensions are used to calculate the areas and volumes of the walls, facings and casings. This entails measuring plan lengths or girths and also heights, or average heights, on a line at the middle of the thickness, where work is of uniform thickness, and at the middle of the average thickness where work of an irregular thickness, is given as an average thickness.

COMMENTARY

Brickwork, Blockwork and Masonry (cont.

   Each skin of cavity construction and each skin or layer of composite construction is measured separately. Any fixings and ties required to tie the skins together are given as separate items measured under "Ancillaries". See later Commentary. In composite construction where a skin or layer is of varying thickness, it may be convenient to measure each thickness separately. Where it is not, item descriptions state the proportion of the various thicknesses or an average thickness; they may state both where it is considered it would be helpful to do so. See Specimen Item Descriptions Fig. U3. The diagram in Fig. U3, shows Class A brickwork in an outer facing skin to English bond and a Class B inner skin to English bond. Both skins are similar except for the materials used. The average thickness is, therefore, the same for each skin and is calculated as follows:- (50% x 220 mm thickness) + (50% x 108 mm thickness) = 164 mm average thickness. The plan dimensions and heights to calculate the areas of the skins would be taken on a line at the middle of the average thickness, e.g. 82 mm in from the outer face for the Class A brickwork and 82 mm in from the inner face for the Class B brickwork.

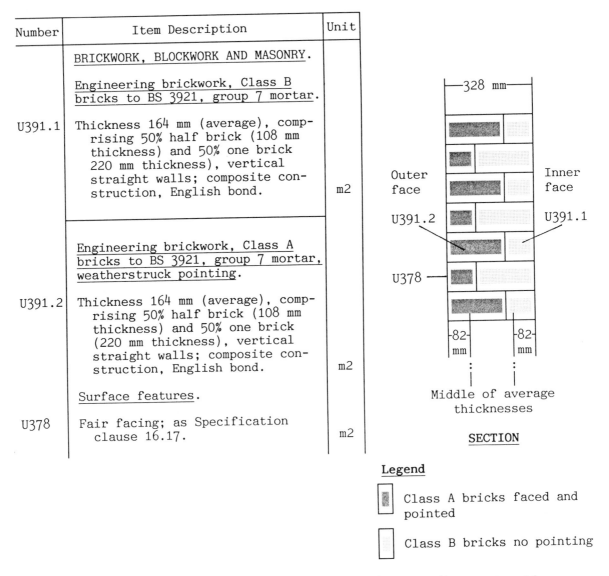

| Number | Item Description | Unit |
|--------|------------------|------|
| | BRICKWORK, BLOCKWORK AND MASONRY. | |
| | Engineering brickwork, Class B bricks to BS 3921, group 7 mortar. | |
| U391.1 | Thickness 164 mm (average), comprising 50% half brick (108 mm thickness) and 50% one brick 220 mm thickness), vertical straight walls; composite construction, English bond. | m2 |
| U391.2 | Engineering brickwork, Class A bricks to BS 3921, group 7 mortar, weatherstruck pointing. | |
| | Thickness 164 mm (average), comprising 50% half brick (108 mm thickness) and 50% one brick (220 mm thickness), vertical straight walls; composite construction, English bond. | m2 |
| | Surface features. | |
| U378 | Fair facing; as Specification clause 16.17. | m2 |

Fig. U3.  Specimen item descriptions for brickwork composite construction.

Table 16.02 Surface Features and Ancillaries

| 1st Division |
|---|
| The 1st Division descriptive features and the precis of Rules given in the 1st Division panel of Table 16.01 are applicable for this Table |

| 2nd Division | 3rd Division | | | |
|---|---|---|---|---|
| Surface features | Copings and sills, materials stated | m | | Include sufficient detail to identify special masonary and special cut bricks and blocks (Rule U/A6) |
| | Rebates and chases | m | | |
| | Cornices | m | | |
| | Band courses | m | | State cross-sec-tional dimensions where cross-sectional area exceeds 0.05 m2 (Rule U/A7) |
| | Corbels | m | | |
| | Pilasters | m | Class as pilasters columns and piers attached to walls (Rule U/D5) | |
| | | | | Measure mean lengths (Rule U/M4) |
| | Plinths | m | | |
| | Fair facing | m2 | Measure at the face of areas expressly required to be fair faced (Rule U/M4) | State spacing of intermittent surface features (Rule U/A6) |
| Ancillaries | Joint reinforcement | m | State materials and dimensions (Rule U/A8) | |
| | Damp-proof courses | m | Measure nett with no allowance for laps (Rule A/M5) | |
| | Movement joints | m | State dimensions and nature of com-ponents including face or internal details (Rule U/A9) | |
| | Bonds to existing work | m2 | | |
| | Infills of stated thickness | m2 | State materials (Rule U/A8) | |
| | Fixings and ties | m2 | State type and spacing (Rule U/A8) | |
| | | | Measure area of brickwork, blockwork and masonry fixed or tied. Measure one area where two areas of brickwork, blockwork or masonry are fixed together (Rule U/M6) | |
| | Built in pipes and ducts, cross-sect-ional area:- | | Deemed to include supply of pipes and ducts, unless otherwise stated (Rule U/C2) | |
| | | | State lengths where exceeding 1 m (Rule U/A10) | |
| | not exceeding 0.05 m2 | nr | | |
| | stated exceeding 0.05 m2 | nr | | |

COMMENTARY

Surface Features and Ancillaries (refer to Table 16.02)

*Surface Features*

In addition to giving items for the volumes and areas of the brickwork, blockwork or masonry, items are given for any surface features in the work. Standard descriptive features are listed in the Class U classification table of the CESMM. (See Table 16.02). Walls, facings, etc., are measured at their classified thickness over surface features. The items for the surface features (other than copings and sills - See previous and later Commentary) covers the extra labour and material forming the feature that would not be inherent in the straightforward wall, facing etc.

Surface feature items identify the brickwork, blockwork or masonry in which they occur. Item descriptions must include sufficient detail to identify any special masonry or cut or special bricks or blocks forming part of the features. The spacing of intermittent surface features must be stated in item descriptions.

Projecting and sunk surface features are described in accordance with appropriate descriptive features and are further classified according to cross-sectional area of the projection or sinking. Surface feature items for copings and sills include the whole of the work in the copings and sills. Item descriptions describe the types of copings and sills and state the materials of which they are formed and further classify them according to their cross-sectional area. Columns and piers attached to walls or facings of the same material are given as surface feature items classed as pilasters and further classified according to cross-sectional area. In all the foregoing items the cross-sectional classification separates those of a cross-sectional area exceeding 0.05 m2 from those not exceeding that area. It is necessary to state the cross-sectional dimensions in the item descriptions for surface features, where the cross-sectional area exceeds 0.05 m2. Items for flush surface features, other than fair facing, state the height of horizontal flush features or the width of vertical flush features and in each case the depth of the feature into the wall where it would otherwise not be apparent. Items for projecting, sunk and flush surface features and for copings and sills are measurable in unfaced and fair faced work. Their surface area is included in the area given for fair facing where they are expressly required to be fair faced.

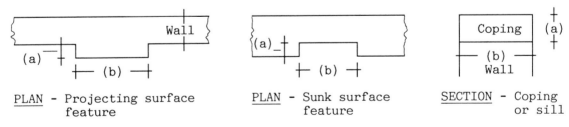

PLAN - Projecting surface        PLAN - Sunk surface        SECTION - Coping
       feature                          feature                      or sill

Fig. U4. Cross-sectional areas of surface features. Where the product of (a) x (b) exceeds 0.05 m2 the cross-sectional dimensions must be stated in the item description of the surface feature.

Fair facing is measured in m2. Other surface features are measured their mean length in linear metres. The areas of fair facing are measured at the face of the work expressly required to be fair faced. The facing of ashlar and rubble masonry walls, facings and casings is deemed to be included in the items referred to in Table 16.01 and "fair facing" as an additional surface feature item is not measured for this work. Otherwise fair facing, where expressly required, is measured whether the material required to be fair faced is faced brickwork, common brickwork or blockwork. The descriptive features referred to in the 1st Division of Table 16.01 refer to the materials. The surface feature item of "fair facing" covers the extra labour finishing the work to a fair face.

COMMENTARY

Surface Features and Ancillaries (cont.

*Surface features (cont.*

| Number | Item description | Unit |
|--------|------------------|------|
| | <u>BRICKWORK, BLOCKWORK AND MASONRY.</u><br><br><u>Ashlar masonry, Yorkshire stone, squared and coursed, sawn finish, group 8 mortar, weather struck pointing.</u> | |
| U725 | Thickness 200 mm, vertical facing to concrete. | m2 |
| | <u>Surface features.</u> | |
| U771 | Copings; 600 x 175 mm cross-sectional dimensions, weathered and twice throated, as Drawing No. U/1. | m |
| U777 | Plinths; finished with 175 mm high chamfered plinth course, as Drawing No. U/1. | m |
| | <u>Ancillaries.</u> | |
| U782 | Damp proof courses, pitch polymer, 250 mm wide. | m |
| | <u>Rubble masonry, Yorkshire stone, coursed, clean cut finish, group 8 mortar, weather struck and cut pointing.</u> | |
| U895 | Thickness 200 mm nominal, with bond stones, thickness 325 mm, to 15 per cent of face area, vertical facing to concrete | m2 |

DRAWING NO. U/1

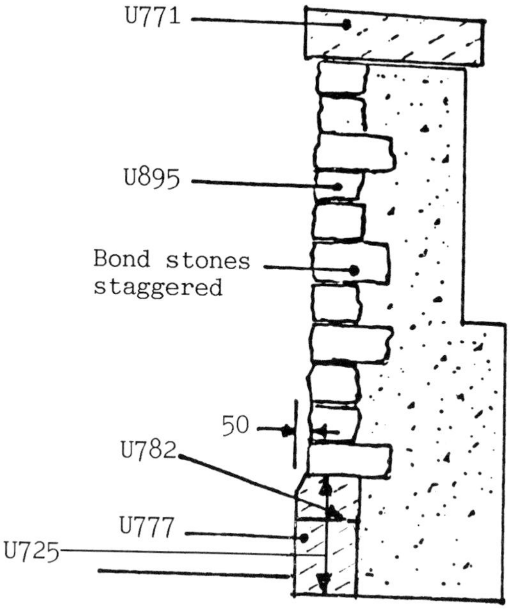

SECTION

Fig. U5. Specimen item descriptions for rubble faced concrete wall with ashlar surface features.

In the specimen item descriptions given previously in Fig. U3 it was considered appropriate to give the average thickness of the irregular facing skins. In the case of the irregular rubble masonry facings, Item U895 in Fig. U5, it is considered a clearer description of the work results from stating the general thickness and giving details of the area of the additional thickness of the bond stones. The general thickness of the work and the bond stone thickness fall into different standard thickness ranges which would be impractical to separate. When coding the item, the digit 9 is used at 2nd Division level to indicate that the thickness of the work does not fall within a standard thickness range.

The specimen item descriptions in Fig. U5. do not include those for the concrete wall. The concrete would be measured in accordance with Class F. The item for placing the concrete would indicate it was placed behind single skin masonry construction. Formwork to the back of the wall would be measured as provided in Class G.

COMMENTARY
<u>
</u>

Surface Features and Ancillaries (cont.
<u>
</u>

*Ancillaries*

Joint reinforcement and damp proof courses are given in linear metres. They are measured net with no allowance for laps. Item descriptions state the materials and their dimensions.

Movement joints are measured in linear metres. Item descriptions state the dimensions and nature of the components in the joints including face and internal details.

Bonds to existing work, infills of stated thickness and fixings and ties are each given as separate items quantified in m2. Item descriptions for infills state the materials of the infills and its actual thickness. Item descriptions state the type and spacing of the fixing and ties. The areas measured for the fixings and ties is the area of the brickwork, blockwork or masonry tied to other materials. Where two areas of brickwork, blockwork or masonry abut and are fixed or tied to each other only one area is measured, this is measured at the interface of the tied materials or as the area of the cavity where there is a cavity between the two skins of materials.

The building in of pipes and ducts are enumerated, they are classified as not exceeding 0.05 m2 cross-sectional area and of stated cross-sectional area where the cross-sectional area exceeds 0.05 m2. The items are deemed to include the supply of the pipes and ducts unless otherwise stated. The lengths of built in pipes and ducts is stated in the item descriptions where they exceed 1 m.

| Number | Item description | Unit |
|--------|------------------|------|
| | BRICKWORK, BLOCKWORK AND MASONRY. <br><br> <u>Facing brickwork, Specification clause 28.9.</u> <br><br> <u>Ancillaries.</u> | |
| U283 | Movement joints; vertical, in 103 mm thick wall, 10 x 93 mm filler, 10 x 10 mm polysulphide face pointing. | m |
| U286 | Fixings and ties; zinc coated vertcal twist type, to BS 1243, 203 mm long, between brickwork, 900 mm horizontal and 450 mm vertical spacings, staggered. | m2 |

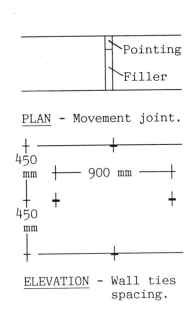

PLAN - Movement joint.

ELEVATION - Wall ties spacing.

Fig. U6. Specimen item descriptions for movement joints and fixings and ties.

EXAMPLE UE 1
<u>
</u>

Measured Example
<u>
</u>

A measured example for a brickwork wall with surface features follows.

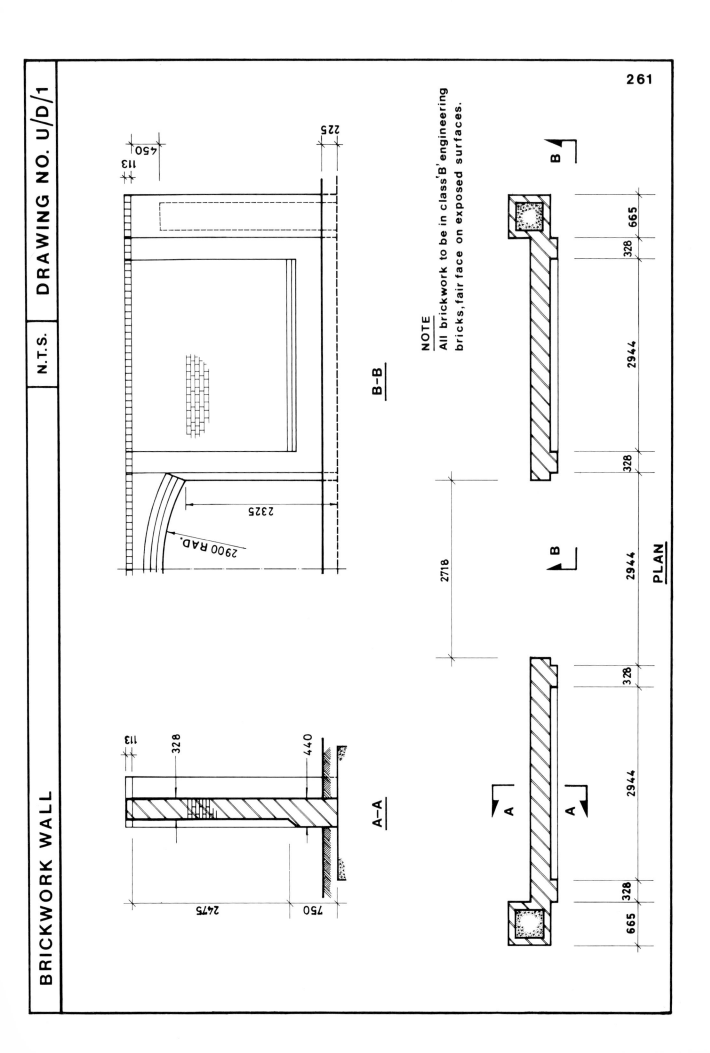

# BRICKWORK WALL

N.T.S. | DRAWING NO. U/D/1

113
328
440

A-A

113
450
225

2900 RAD.
2325

B-B

750
2475

NOTE
All brickwork to be in class 'B' engineering
bricks, fair face on exposed surfaces.

665 328 2944 328

665 328 2944 2718

B

A A B

2944

PLAN

BRICKWORK WALL DRG. No. U/D/1

EXAMPLE UE.1

Engin. bkw. Class B bks. to BS 3291, group 7 mortar, weath. struck pointg. unless o/w stated

<u>Wall</u>

| 750 | 3/2944 = 8832 |
| 2475 | 4/ 328 = 1312 |
| 3225 | 10144 |

| 10.14 |
| 3.23 |

Thickn. 328 mm, vert. stra. walls; English bond. (U331.1

<u>Piers</u>

| 3225 | 4/665 = 2660 |
| 450 | 4/103 = 412 |
| 2775 | 2248 |

| 2/ 2.25 |
| 2.78 |

Thickn. 103 mm, vert. facg. to conc. stretcher bond. (U315

&

Ancills. Fixgs. and ties wi metal anchors as Spec. clause 3.19, to slots (m/s) (U386

| 2/ 0.45 |

Piers 665 x 665 mm c.s. dims; English bond. (U360

<u>Surf. features, Class B engin. bkw.</u>

| 3/ 2.94 |
| 4/ 0.33 |

Copings; bk. on edge (U371.1

| 2/ 0.67 |

Copings; bk. on edge 665 x 113 mm c.s. dims (U371.2

(1)

COMMENTARY

The first item in the adjoining column is that of the brickwork in the wall. Its length is measured between the end piers over the opening. The whole of the wall is first measured as 328 mm thick. The opening is dealt with as an adjustment later. Copings, arch, plinth and pilasters are measured later as surface features. The brickwork in the wall does not exceed one metre in thickness and is measured by area stating the thickness of the work.

The drawing indicates that the brickwork to the lower part of the end piers is facing to concrete columns. Above the columns the piers are in solid brickwork. It is assumed that the concrete is not infill but concrete columns cast using formwork prior to the commencement of the brickwork and that the brick facing is tied with brick anchors to dovetailed slots cast in the concrete. The concrete, formwork, dovetailed slots and other work in the concrete columns are not measured in the Example. Dovetailed slots cast in to concrete are classed as inserts and are measured under Class G of the CESMM.

Items for copings need not distinguish cross-sectional sizes, where the copings do not exceed 0.05 m2 cross-sectional area. The copings to the 328 mm and that to the 440 mm wall thickness can, therefore, be added together in one item. The coping to the piers exceeds 0.05 m2 cross-sectional area and the cross-sectional dimensions are stated in the item description.

BRICKWORK WALL DRG. No. U/D/1

| | | | |
|---|---|---|---|
| | | Engin. bkw. a.b. | |
| | | Surf. features a.b. | |
| 2/ | 2.94 | Plinths, 113 × 750 mm c.s. dims. ui 2 cos. s. pattern splyd. plinth bricks | (U377 |
| 2/ | 2.48 | Pilasters | (U376 |

```
3338    3338    2660
 150     750     328
3188    2588    2332
```

| | | | |
|---|---|---|---|
| 2/ | 10.14 | { Fair facg. as Spec. | |
| | 3.19 | { clause 3.14 | (U378 |
| 2/2/ | 0.11 | | |
| | 3.19 | (pilaster returns | |
| 2/2/ | 0.11 | ( " " | |
| | 2.59 | | |
| 2/ | 2.94 | (plinth splay | |
| | 0.04 | | |
| 3/ | 2.94 | ( top of coping | |
| | 0.33 | | |
| 4/ | 0.33 | ( " " " | |
| | 0.44 | | |
| 2/ | 2.33 | (faces of piers | |
| | 3.19 | | |
| 2/ | 0.67 | ( top of piers | |
| | 0.67 | | |

Ancills.
Pitch polymer damp
proof courses

| | | | |
|---|---|---|---|
| 2/ | 2.25 | Width 103 mm | (U382.1 |
| | 2.94 | Width 328 mm | (U382.2 |
| 2/ | 3.60 | Width 440 mm | (U382.3 |

(2)

The item description for the plinth includes "sufficient detail to identify special or cut bricks". The cross-sectional area exceeds 0.05 m2 and cross-sectional dimensions are, therefore, stated in the item description.

The cross-section of both pilasters are similar and each do not exceed 0.05 m2 cross-sectional area. It is, therefore, not necessary to state the cross-sectional dimensions in the item descriptions.

The surface feature item "Fair facing" is measured to the exposed surface of the brickwork, including the surfaces of other surface features. The work is measured overall leaving the opening to be adjusted later in the Example.

The CESMM calls for details of the pointing to be included in the item descriptions for walls, facings, etc. The area of pointing cannot be determined from the area of these items, it is reflected in the areas of fair facing. Consequently, it is essential that in the Bill of Quantities, the items for fair facing should be given under the heading of brickwork or blockwork to which they relate.

The item descriptions for damp proof courses state the materials and their dimensions. They are measured net with no allowance for laps. It is assumed the extent of the laps is given in the specification. The damp proof course is measured across the opening and is adjusted later in the Example.

BRICKWORK WALL DRG.No. U/D/1

Arch and opg.

½/2718 = 1359

$\frac{1359}{2900}$ = 0.4686 = Sin 28°

2900
(Cos 28°) 0.88295 × 2900 = 2561
rise of arch   339

2900
28° × 2 = 56°   ½/328 = 164
3064

arch soffit = 56 × 2.90 × 0.017453 = 2.83
arch = 56 × 3.06 × 0.017453 = 2.99

Engin. bKw. a.b.
Surf. features a.b.

2.99 | Arches, segmental 328 × 328 mm c.s. dims. in h. bk. rings (U379
2325
150
2175

2/ 0.33 | Fair facg. a.b. (U378
2.18 | (jambs
2.83 |
0.33 | (soffit

Engin. bKw. a.b.

2.72 | Ddt. Thickn. 328 mm
2.33 | vert. stra. walls a.b. (U331.1
2/3 | 2.72 |
0.34 | (segmental part opg

Surf. features. a.b.

2/ 2.72 | Ddt. Fair facg. a.b.
2.18 | (U378
2/2/3/ 2.72 |
0.34 |

Ancills
2.72 | Ddt. Pitch pol. d.pc. a.b. width 328mm (U382.2

(3)

COMMENTARY

The wall in which the arch and opening occurs is measured as a blank wall previously. Items under the heading "Arch & Opg" adjust that previously measured by deducting the work in the opening and adding the items for the arch and returns.

Waste calculations take half the span of the arch as the height of a triangle and the arch radius as the hypotenuse and using trigonometry tables or a suitable calculator find the angle of the sector. The cosine of this angle is used with the radius to calculate the height to the springing of the arch. This deducted from the radius gives the rise of the arch (for use later). The arch is 328 mm high on face. Half this height added to the radius gives the mean radius of the arch.

Length of arc = number of degrees x radius x .017453. This formula is used to calculate the mean girth on face of the arch and also to calculate the length of the intrados.

No provision is made in the CESMM for arches. In the Example the arch has been treated in the same way as a flush band and classed as a surface feature. No adjustment has been made to the area of the wall for the area of the arch. This convention would need to be made clear in the preamble to the Bill of Quantities.

Brickwork in vertical straight walls is deducted for the opening. The dimensions for the segmental part of the opening are expressed in terms of the approximate formula - chord x two thirds height of segment.

Fair facing and damp proof courses having previously been measured over the opening are deducted in the penultimate and last items, respectively.

# 17 Painting, Waterproofing and Miscellaneous Work – CESMM Classes: V, W and X

The rules of measurement for painting (Class V) and waterproofing (Class W) are to a great extent similar. The scope of miscellaneous work (Class X) is limited and does not merit a separate chapter. The three Classes are here dealt with in a single chapter.

*PAINTING - CESMM CLASS V*

Class V of the CESMM is applicable to in situ painting which is carried out after the delivery of the components to the Site. Painting carried out prior to delivery of components will be included with the components. For "Includes" and "Excludes" refer to the head of the Class V classification table in the CESMM.

## In situ Painting (refer to Table 17.01)

Item descriptions for painting state the materials to be used and either the number of coats or the film thickness. They also describe the surfaces to be painted in accordance with tabulated Second Division features. Additionally, some items are further classified by appropriate Third Division features. (See Table 17.01, which gives also the units of measurement).

The First Division classifies paint types. Separate descriptive features are provided for primer paints. Items for painting systems which require surfaces to be primed in situ before the application of further painting treatment will give the priming separately when it is of a different type of paint from that used for the further painting treatment.

The preparation of surfaces for painting is deemed to be included in the items for painting. It is necessary for the painting items to identify the preparation where more than one type of preparation is specified for the same surface.

### Painting Surfaces Other than Metal Sections and Pipework

Plate VW.1 illustrates angles of inclination for painting surfaces exceeding one metre in width, other than surfaces of metal sections and pipework.

Painting surfaces not exceeding one metre in width (other than those of metal sections and pipework) are measured linearly stating tabulated width ranges. The Third Division descriptive features use the word "width" (not girth) which on strict interpretation means each surface width is classified as a surface of appropriate width. For example, the classification of each of the four faces of a component of small square cross-section as a surface of appropriate width. It is found more practical to classify the surfaces of such members according to their developed width, i.e. the aggregate of the four connected widths and to note in Preamble that this convention has been adopted.

The margin between the lower and upper limits of the standard width classifications, for painting measured linearly, is fairly large. There will be cases where it will be of benefit to classify some surface widths with greater precision, or to indicate location.

---

Table 17.01   In situ Painting

---

Generally - No deduction for holes and opening each less than 0.5 m2 (Rule V/M1)

---

1st Division

| | |
|---|---|
| Lead, iron or zinc based primer paint | State materials to be used and either the number of coats or the film thickness (Rule V/A1) |
| Etch primer paint | |
| Oil paint | Items deemed to include preparation of surfaces before painting (Rule V/C1) |
| Alkyd gloss paint | |
| Emulsion paint | |
| Cement paint | |
| Epoxy or polyurethene paint | |
| Bituminous or coal tar paint | |

| 2nd Division | 3rd Division |
|---|---|
| Metal, other than metal sections and pipework | Classify in accordance with the tabulated 3rd Division ranges:- |
| Timber | (i)  surfaces exceeding 1 m wide, by angle of inclination (Plate VW.1.)                          m2 |
| Smooth concrete | |
| Rough concrete | (ii) surfaces not exceeding 1 m wide, by width, not distinguished by inclination (Rule V/M2)  m |
| Masonry | Use the classification "isolated groups of surfaces" where more convenient than measuring in detail.  See Note at foot of page 87 of CESMM.  The classification is applicable only where the total surface area of a group does not exceed 6 m2 (Rule V/D1).  When this classification is used, descriptions must identify the work to be painted and state its location (Rule V/A3).  Give separate items for groups of different shape and dimension (Rule V/M3).                          nr |
| Brickwork and blockwork | |
| Identify preparation of surfaces where more than one type of preparation is specified for same surface (Rule V/A2) | |

| | | | 3rd Division |
|---|---|---|---|
| Metal sections | m2 | Ignore additional area of connecting plates, brackets, rivets, bolts, nuts and similar projections (Rule V/M4).  Items deemed to include painting these (Rule V/C2). | |
| Pipework | m2 | Measure length over valves and fittings, and multiply by girth of pipe or lagged pipe with no deduction or addition for flanges, valve or projecting fittings and hangers (Rule V/M5).  Items deemed to include painting projecting valves, fittings and hangers (Rule V/C3). | |

COMMENTARY

In situ Painting (cont.

*Painting Metal Sections*

The area measured for painting metal sections is the overall length multiplied by the girth of the members, ignoring any additional area of the projections of connecting plates, brackets, rivets, bolts and the like.

The dimensions which would be taken for the painting of the steel column shown in Fig. V1 (assuming the size of section to be 305 x 305 mm) are given to the right of the diagram.

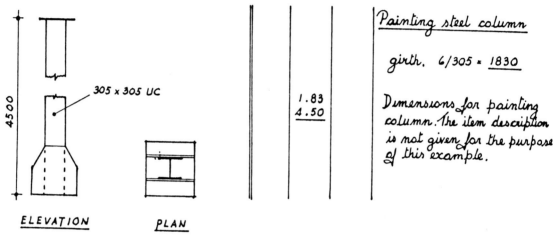

Fig. V1. Painting Steel Column

*Painting Pipework*

The area measured for painting pipework is the length, measured over valves and fittings, multiplied by the barrel girth of the pipework. The additional area of flanges, valves and other projecting fittings is not measured. The barrel girth for un-lagged pipework will be that of the pipe. The barrel girth of lagged pipework will be that of the lagging. Painting pipework with flanges, painting pipework without flanges and painting lagged pipework, are each given separately.

An example of the dimensions which would be taken for painting the pipework shown in Fig. V2, are given below to the right of the diagram.

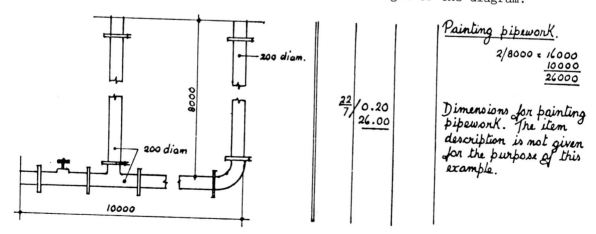

Fig. V2. Painting Pipework.

COMMENTARY

Specimen Item Descriptions for Painting

| Number | Item description | Unit |
|--------|------------------|------|
| | PAINTING.<br><br>Calcium plumbate primer paint to BS 3698, Type A, on metal other than metal sections and pipework. | |
| V111 | Galvanised steel upper surfaces inclined at an angle not exceeding 30 degrees to the horizontal; in one coat. | m2 |
| | Red lead primer paint to BS 2523, Type B. | |
| V170.1 | Surfaces of previously primed steel sections; in one coat. | m2 |
| V170.2 | Surfaces of steel sections; in two coats. | m2 |
| | Oil paint as Specification clause VS 17.3, in three coats (two undercoats, one coat gloss finish) on previously primed metal other than metal sections and pipework. | |
| V311 | Steel upper surfaces inclined at an angle not exceeding 30 degrees to the horizontal. | m2 |
| V317 | Steel surfaces of width 300 - 1 m. | m |
| V318 | Steel isolated groups of surfaces; screen, outlet chamber. | nr |
| | P.V.A. based emulsion paint as Specification clause VS 17.7, in three coats, satin finish. | |
| V563 | Brickwork; surfaces inclined at an angle exceeding 60 degrees to the horizontal. | m2 |
| | Pitch coating, as Specification clause 17.23, minimum dry film thickness 100 microns, on shop primed steel. | |
| V880 | Pipework: flanged. | m2 |

COMMENTARY

Rule V/A1 of the CESMM makes it necessary to amplify the standard descriptive features. The First Division features in the specimen items are amplified by reference to specification clauses where the type of paint would be fully described. The further requirement of Rule V/A1 is met by stating the number of coats in the item descriptions.

It is necessary for the item descriptions for painting to identify the surface to which the paint is to be applied, so that its preparation may be allowed for in the painting items. Different cost characteristics arise between the preparation of ferrous surfaces and non-ferrous surfaces and also between treated, primed and unprimed surfaces. The specimen item descriptions, therefore, distinguish each particular type of surface.

In the specimen item descriptions, the repetetive descriptive features form the subject of sub-headings and the variable features are listed under the appropriate sub-headings. This format may be adapted by putting less description in the sub-heading and more in the items which follow, or vice versa, according to personal preference or the requirements of a particular Bill.

| PAINTING<br>CESMM, CLASS:V | ZONES<br>of inclination relative to<br>features in 3rd Division | WATERPROOFING<br>CESMM, CLASS:W |
|---|---|---|
| 3rd Division<br><br>Upper surfaces inclined at an angle not exceeding 30 degrees to the horizontal | | 3rd Division<br><br>Upper surfaces inclined at an angle not exceeding 30 degrees to the horizontal |
| Upper surfaces inclined at 30 - 60 degrees to the horizontal | | Upper surfaces inclined at 30 - 60 degrees to the horizontal |
| Surfaces inclined at and angle exceeding 60 degrees to the horizontal | | Surfaces inclined at an angle exceeding 60 degrees to the horizontal |
| Soffit surfaces and lower surfaces inclined at an angle not exceeding 60 degrees to the horizontal | | Not applicable to Waterproofing |

PLATE VW.1

Specific "Includes" in Class W of the CESMM are damp-proofing, tanking and roofing. Waterproofed joints and damp-proof courses are excluded from the Class, as noted in the "Excludes" at the head of the classification table in the CESMM.

---

Table 17.02  Waterproofing

Generally - State the materials to be used and the number and the thickness of coatings or layers (Rule W/A1)

Measure area as that of the surface covered. No deduction for holes and openings each less than 0.5 m3 (Rule W/M1)

Items deemed to include for preparing surfaces, for forming joints, overlaps, mitres, angles, fillets and built-up edges and for laying to falls or cambers (Rule W/C1)

| 1st Division | 2nd Division | 3rd Division | |
|---|---|---|---|
| Damp-proofing<br><br>Tanking<br><br>Roofing | Asphalt<br><br>Sheet metal<br><br><br>Waterproof sheeting<br><br>Waterproof coatings<br><br>Rendering in ordinary cement mortar<br><br>Rendering in waterproof cement mortar | Upper surfaces not exceeding 30 degrees to the horizontal (See Plate VW.1.) | m2 |
| | | Upper surfaces 30 - 60 degrees to the horizontal (See Plate VW.1.) | m2 |
| | | Surfaces exceeding 60 degrees to the horizontal (See Plate VW.1.) | m2 |
| | | Curved surfaces (applies only to curved surfaces less than 10 m radius. Not to be distinguished by inclination Rules W/D1 and W/M3) | m2 |
| | | Domed surfaces (applies only to domed surfaces less than 10 m radius. Not to be distinguished by inclination Rules W/D1 and W/M3) | m2 |
| Protective layers | Sand asphalt<br><br>Flexible sheeting<br><br>Sand<br><br>Sand and cement screed<br><br>Tiles | Surfaces of a width not exceeding 300 mm (not to be distinguished by inclination or curvature Rule W/M2) | m |
| | | Surfaces of width 300 mm - 1 m (not to be distinguished by inclination or curvature (Rule W/M2) | m |
| | | Use classification "isolated groups of surfaces" where more convenient than measuring in detail. See Note at foot of page 89 of CESMM. The classification is only applicable where the total surface area of a group does not exceed 6 m2 (Rule W/D2). When the classification is used, descriptions must identify the work and state its location (Rule W/A2). Give separate items for groups of different shape and dimension (Rule W/M4) | nr |
| Sprayed or brushed waterproofing    m2 | | | |

COMMENTARY

Waterproofing (refer to Table 17.02)

For the purpose of measurement, waterproofing, other than sprayed or brushed waterproofing, is divided into items for the types of waterproofing and items for any protective layers required. The measurement conventions are the same for each. Features together with a summary of CESMM Rules and units of measurement for waterproofing are set out in Table 17.02. A comparison of this Table with Table 17.01 indicates that the classification "soffit surfaces" is provided for painting but not for waterproofing. The classification "curved surfaces" and "domed surfaces" are provided for waterproofing but not for painting. Apart from these differences the rules for measuring waterproofing are similar to those for measuring painting.

Item descriptions describe the work in accordance with the descriptive features listed in Table 17.02. Second division features are amplified to state the materials and the number of coatings or layers. At 3rd Division level, features provide for work to surfaces one metre wide and greater, other than that to surfaces curved or domed to less than 10 m radius, to be described according to listed angles of inclination (See Plate VW1). The descriptive features "curved surfaces" and "domed surfaces" are applicable to work applied to such surfaces which are less than 10 m radius and one metre in width or greater. The inclination of these surfaces is not distinguished. Standard features for work to surfaces of a width not exceeding one metre provide for width to be described as either "width not exceeding 300 mm" or "width 300 mm - 1 m" as appropriate. Item descriptions for surfaces of a width not exceeding one metre do not distinguish inclination or curvature. Work to surfaces not exceeding one metre in width is given in linear metres. That to surfaces one metre wide and greater is given in m2. See subsequent Commentary for work described as to "isolated groups of surfaces".

*Isolated Groups of Surfaces*

Waterproofing to a group of surfaces of a total surface area not exceeding 6 m2, such as that to a sump, an isolated plinth or the like, may be given as a numbered item rather than as a series of items measured as previously described. Item descriptions for the numbered items identify the work to be waterproofed and state location (See notes against the 3rd Division feature on Table 17.02).

*Items Deemed to Include*

Requirements will be specified for the work which is deemed to be included in the waterproofing items. (See notes in first panel of Table 17.02). Tenderers need to ascertain the extent of the work from the drawings and allow for it in the items for the measured work or elsewhere in their tender. In respect of preparation, it is necessary, where the same waterproofing is applied to more than one base material and where there is more than one preparation requirement for the same base material, for the item description for the waterproofing to distinguish different preparation requirements.

Layers of subsidiary materials forming part of a waterproofing system are usually included with the main material in an item for the system. For example, isolating membranes and insulating board layers associated with asphalt would be described and included in items with the asphalt coatings. Non-structural screeds beneath waterproofing may also be included in such items, but where because of thickness differences their inclusion would unduly increase the extent of itemisation for the waterproofing, the screeds would be billed as separate items.

COMMENTARY

Waterproofing (cont.

*Specimen Item Descriptions*

Specimen item descriptions for the asphalt tanking to the floor and walls of
the basement shown in Figure W1 which gives a part of the cross-section, are
given at the side of the diagram.

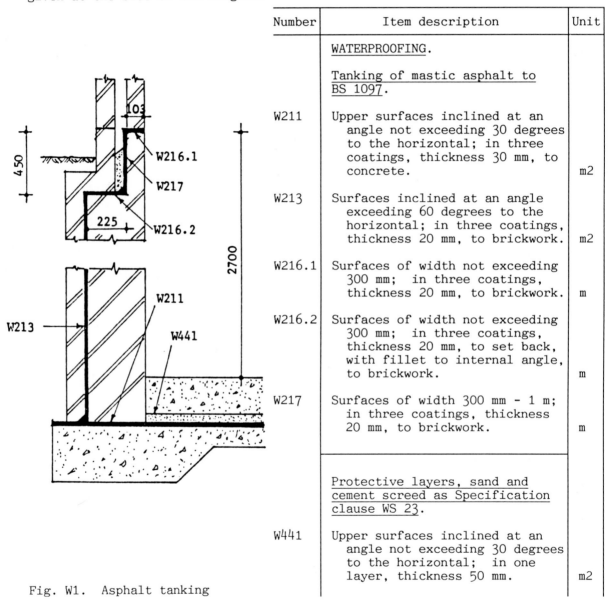

| Number | Item description | Unit |
|---|---|---|
| | WATERPROOFING. | |
| | Tanking of mastic asphalt to BS 1097. | |
| W211 | Upper surfaces inclined at an angle not exceeding 30 degrees to the horizontal; in three coatings, thickness 30 mm, to concrete. | m2 |
| W213 | Surfaces inclined at an angle exceeding 60 degrees to the horizontal; in three coatings, thickness 20 mm, to brickwork. | m2 |
| W216.1 | Surfaces of width not exceeding 300 mm; in three coatings, thickness 20 mm, to brickwork. | m |
| W216.2 | Surfaces of width not exceeding 300 mm; in three coatings, thickness 20 mm, to set back, with fillet to internal angle, to brickwork. | m |
| W217 | Surfaces of width 300 mm - 1 m; in three coatings, thickness 20 mm, to brickwork. | m |
| | Protective layers, sand and cement screed as Specification clause WS 23. | |
| W441 | Upper surfaces inclined at an angle not exceeding 30 degrees to the horizontal; in one layer, thickness 50 mm. | m2 |

Fig. W1.  Asphalt tanking

Where it is considered it will simplify pricing, or aid identification,
waterproofing work not exceeding one metre in width may be given in items
which state actual width in preference to grouping several widths in an item
which uses the standard width range given in the Class W classification
table of the CESMM.

Table 17.03  Fences, Gates and Stiles and Drainage to Structures above ground

| 1st Division | | 2nd Division | 3rd Division |
|---|---|---|---|
| Fences      m<br><br>Deemed to include end posts, straining posts and gate posts (Rule X/C2) | State types and principal dimensions of both fences and foundations (Rule X/A2)<br><br>Exclude length occupied by gates and stiles from length measured (Rule X/M1)<br><br>State when erected on a curve of radius not exceeding 100 m or on a surface inclined at an angle exceeding 10 degrees (Rule X/A1)<br><br>Deemed to include excavation, preparation of surfaces, disposal of excavated material, upholding sides of excavation, backfilling, removal of existing services, concrete, formwork and reinforcement (Rule X/C1) | State type as 2nd Division features | State height range as 3rd Division features<br><br>Measure height from Commencing surface (Rule X/D1) |
| Gates and Stiles     nr | State type and principal dimensions (Rule X/A3) | State type as 2nd Division features | Give width, measure between inside faces of posts (Rule X/D2) |
| Drainage to Structures above ground | State types, principal dimensions and materials of components (Rule X/A4) | State material as 2nd Division features | Gutters       m<br>Fitting to gutters       nr<br>Downpipes       m<br>Fittings to downpipes       nr<br><br>Identify fittings in accordance with Rule X/D3 |

COMMENTARY

Fences, Gates and Stiles (refer to Table 17.03)

The "Includes" and "Excludes" listed in Class X and Class E, respectively, of the CESMM, indicate that excavation and foundations are included in the Class X items for fences. The extent of the work included in the items is set out in Rule X/C1 and X/C2. See Table 17.03.

Class X provides for fencing to be given as an all inclusive linear item. When billing safety fences it is often more convenient to enumerate end anchorages, additional intermediate posts and such like, rather than separately itemising various lengths to distinguish differences. Where this is done amending Preamble is necessary indicating that notwithstanding that the CESMM makes no provision for their separate itemisation, the stated items have been given separately in the Bill of Quantities.

COMMENTARY

Specimen Item Descriptions for Miscellaneous Work

| Number | Item description | Unit |
|--------|------------------|------|
| | MISCELLANEOUS WORK. | |
| | Fences, as Specification clause 4.3, refer also to Preamble clause 17.1. | |
| X112 | Timber post and rail, four railed stockproofed fences, height 1.20 m above finished surface of verges; driven posts, as Drawing No. 4D/4. | m |
| | Safety fences, as Specification clause 4.8. | |
| X191 | Safety rail fences, single sided tensioned , height 750 mm above surface of hard shoulder, as Drawing No. 4D/6. | m |
| | Gates, as Specification clause 4.5, refer also to Preamble clause 17.2. | |
| X216 | Oak single field gates, width 4.25 m height 1.30 m, with painted mild steel hangings and fastenings, 200 x 200 mm oak posts and 450 x 450 x 600 mm grade C20 concrete foundations. | nr |
| | Drainage to structures above ground. | |
| | Cast iron gutters, as Specification clause 27.2. | |
| X321 | Gutters; box width 200 mm, depth 150 mm, on brackets to brickwork. | m |
| X322.1 | Fittings to gutters; stop ends on 200 x 150 mm gutters. | nr |
| X322.2 | Fittings to gutters; outlets for 150 mm diameter pipes on 200 x 150 mm gutters. | nr |
| | Cast iron pipes, as Specification clause 27.3. | |
| X323 | Downpipes; diameter 150 mm, with holderbats to brickwork. | m |
| X324 | Fittings to down pipes; anti-splash shoes on 150 mm diameter downpipes. | nr |

COMMENTARY

The Commencing Surface for fencing may be difficult to determine. It seems practical to measure the height from a stated finished surface of the Works. If this is done amending Preamble is required. In this Example it is given the hypothetical clause number 17.1. Wording in the Bill of Quantities would be on the following lines:-

Preamble clause 17.1

Heights of fences are herein measured from the surfaces stated in the item descriptions, notwithstanding that Rule X/D1 of the CESMM states they shall be measured from the Commencing Surface.

Rule X/C2 of the CESMM states that gate posts are deemed to be included in the items for fencing, the gate posts and foundations here are somewhat different from those for the fence posts. Rather than complicate the description for the fences it is thought more practical to give them with the gates. Amending Preamble given the hypothetical clause number 17.2, would be given in the Bill as follows:-

Preamble clause 17.2

Nothwithstanding Rule X/C2 of the CESMM, gate posts and their foundations are herein included in the items for the gates.

Although billed here with fencing and gates, it is likely that the gutters and downpipes would be given in the Part of the Bill for the structure or building to which they relate.

COMMENTARY

Drainage to Structures above ground (refer to Table 17.03)

In the absence of any guidance in Class X of the CESMM, pipes and gutters are measured along their centre lines inclusive of the lengths occupied by fittings. Additional enumerated items, which identify the types of fittings, are given for any fittings. This would be made clear in Preamble.

Where substantial or unusual brackets or supports are used for gutters or downpipes, they are usually given separately from the linear items. Otherwise, the linear items for gutters are usually given to include the fixing brackets or holderbats.

Table 17.04   Rock Filled Gablons

| 1st Division | | 2nd Division | | | 3rd Division |
|---|---|---|---|---|---|
| Rock filled gablons | State type and grading of filling, size of mesh, diameter of mesh wire and details of protective coatings (Rule X/A5)<br><br>Filling deemed to be imported unless stated otherwise (Rule X/D4) | Box | nr | Applies when exceeding 300 mm thick (Rule X/D4) | State size |
| | | Mattress | m2 | Applies when not exceeding 300 mm thick thick (Rule X/D4) | |

COMMENTARY

Rock Filled Gablons (refer to Table 17.04)

Items for rock filled gablons cover their provision and installation, including fabricated wire mesh cages, with protective coating if stated, filled with imported rock filling, sited in the required positions. Where any system of anchorage is required it should be specified and the Bill items should make clear by additional description whether the items for gablons are to include the anchorages or whether anchorages have been measured separately. Excavation and incidental work for the seating of the gablons would be measured separately under the appropriate Classes of the CESMM.

Gablons are classified "box", those over 300 mm thick and "mattress", those not exceeding 300 mm thick. Box gablons are given by number stating the size. Mattress gablons are measured superficially and are given in m2. The details stated in item descriptions are given in Rule X/A5 (See Table 17.04).

# 18 Sewer Renovation – CESMM Class: Y

The work included in Class Y as listed in the "Includes" at the head of the classification table covers the preparation and renovation of existing sewers, new manholes within the length of existing sewers and work to existing manholes. Specific "Excludes" are: grouting carried out from outside the sewer (included in Class C) and extras to excavation and backfilling for new manhole and other chambers (included in Class L).

Temporary Works and the provision and maintenance of equipment and services for sewer renovations might include such work as pumping and diversion work, temporary access work, lighting for work in confined spaces, closed circuit television surveys, proving the dimensions of existing sewers, testing, safety systems and other associated work which is not part of the Permanent Works. Because of the special circumstances which obtain in sewer renovation, the specification may specifically require that the Contractor carries out some or all of the items of temporary work, such as the foregoing, in accordance with express requirements. Temporary work which is so specified is given in items of Specified Requirements under Class A. Where it is not specifically required that the Contractor shall carry out an item of temporary work in accordance with an express requirement, Bill items are not given for it and it is considered to be a general obligation of the Contractor under the Fifth Edition of the I.C.E. Contract.

---

Table 18.01 Sewer Renovation and Ancillary Works

---

Generally – In each item or group of items, state location of work so that it may be identified by reference to the Drawings (Rule Y/A1)

State principal dimensions and profiles of existing sewers (Rule Y/A2)

State materials forming existing sewers (Rule Y/A5).

Measure lengths of sewers along their centre lines, between in-side surfaces of manholes but excluding backdrops (Rule Y/M1)

State where work is expressly required to be carried out manually or by remote control methods (Rule Y/A3)

State where work is expressly required to be carried out by excavation and, except for manholes, state maximum depth of excavation in stages of 1 m measured to invert (Rule Y/A4)

For work expressly required to be carried out by excavation, measure crossings, reinstatement and other pipework ancillaries in Class K and extras to excavation and backfilling in Class L (Rule Y/M2)

Items for work expressly required to be carried out by excavation are deemed to include preparation of surfaces, disposal of excavated material, upholding sides of excavation, backfilling and removal of existing services (Rule Y/C1)

COMMENTARY

Sewer Renovation and Ancillary Work - generally (refer to Table 18.01)

To comply with Rule Y/A1 of the CESMM, work is usually given under locational headings so that it can be identified by reference to the Drawings.

Item descriptions state the principal dimensions and profiles of the existing sewers and the materials of which they are formed. Lengths of sewers are measured along their centre lines from inside surface to inside surface of manholes. They exclude the lengths of pipes and fittings in any backdrops to manholes.

Where an express requirement restricts the Contractor's choice of method of renovation, item descriptions state whether the work is to be carried out by manual means from within the sewer, or by remote control methods, or by excavation, as the case may be. Rules applicable to work expressly required to be carried out by excavation are given in Table 18.01.

---

Table 18.02 Preparation of Existing Sewers

| 1st Division | Preparation of existing sewers | Refer to Table 18.01 for the general Rules and details to be given in descriptions |
|---|---|---|
| 2nd Division | | 3rd Division |
| Cleaning  m | Measure lengths as stated in Rule Y/M1, Table 18.01<br><br>Deemed to include making good resultant damage (Rule Y/C2) | |
| Removing intrusions nr<br><br>Deemed to include making good (Rule Y/C3) | State materials forming intrusions (Rule Y/A6)<br><br>Use this classification where artificial intrusions into bores of existing sewers are to be removed before renovation (Rule Y/D1) | Laterals, bore not exceeding 150 mm<br><br>Laterals, stated profile and size exceeding 150 mm in one or more dimension<br><br>Other stated artifical intrusions |
| Plugging laterals    nr | State materials for plugging | Bore not exceeding 300 mm<br><br>Stated profile and size exceeding 300 mm in one or more dimension |
| Filling laterals and other pipes    m3 | State materials for filling | |
| Local internal repairs    nr | Deemed to include cutting out and re-pointing (Rule Y/C4) | Area: not exceeding 0.1 m2    The area here stated shall be the finished surface area (Rule Y/D2)<br>0.1 - 0.25 m2<br>stated exceeding 0.25 m2 |

COMMENTARY

Preparation of Existing Sewers (refer to Table 18.02)

The classifications for preparation given in the CESMM cover work in preparing the existing sewers for renovation.

Reference should be made to Table 18.01 and the Commentary on that Table for general Rules and requirements which may be applicable to "preparation of existing sewers" but are not necessarily mentioned in the Commentary on the following individual classifications.

*Cleaning*

Item descriptions give the size, the cross-sectional profile and the materials of which the existing sewer is formed in addition to identifying the cleaning requirement. The different kinds of sewers and different cleaning requirements are separately itemised and details are given to enable the location of each particular kind of sewer and each particular cleaning requirement to be identified by reference to the Drawings. Items are deemed to include making good any damage caused by the cleaning, but not damage revealed by the cleaning.

Quantities are given in linear metres of sewer cleaned. Lengths are measured as noted in Table 18.01.

*Removing Intrusions*

Intrusions are isolated projections which protrude beyond the internal surfaces of the true profile of the existing sewer. Removing intrusions prior to the renovation of sewers are given as enumerated items, which are deemed to include making good. Pipe intrusions of a bore not exceeding 150 mm are grouped together. For those exceeding 150 mm in one or more dimension the size and profile is stated. Other artificial intrusions are described. The materials of which intrusions are formed are stated in the items descriptions for removing intrusions.

*Laterals*

Any drains or sewers connected to the main sewer which is being renovated are termed laterals. "Live" laterals may call for cleaning, in which case the cleaning is measured in the same way as the main sewer. Laterals which are to be abandoned may be specified to have their ends plugged or it may be specified that their length is filled. Numbered items are given for plugging. Filling items give the quantities of filling materials in m3. In both cases the materials forming the laterals and the materials for plugging or filling are stated in the item descriptions. Items distinguish between laterals of a bore not exceeding 300 mm and those which exceed 300 mm in one or more dimension. Items for the latter state the profile and the size of the laterals.

*Local Internal Repairs*

The classification "local internal repairs" applies to isolated areas of repairs to the existing sewer structure carried out from within the sewer. The finished surface area of the individual areas of repair are classified within 3rd Division area ranges, or of stated area where they exceed 0.25 m2, and are given as numbered items. Items for internal repairs are deemed to include for cutting out and repointing.

Table 18.03  Stabilization of Existing Sewers

| 1st Division | Stabilization of existing sewers | Refer to Table 18.01 for the general Rules and details to be given in descriptions | |
|---|---|---|---|
| 2nd Division | | | 3rd Division |
| Pointing  m2 | State materials for pointing<br><br>Make no deduction from area for opening or voids not exceeding 0.5 m2 (Rule Y/M3) | Deemed to include preparation of joints (Rule Y/C5) | |
| Pipe joint sealing  nr | State materials for pipe joint sealing | | |
| External grouting | Use this classification for grouting voids outside and from within existing sewer other than voids grouted in the course of annulus grouting (Rule Y/D3)<br><br>Measure only where expressly required to be carried out as a separate operation from annulus grouting (Y360) (Rule Y/M4) | | Number of holes  nr  State where carried out through pipe joints (Rule Y/A7)<br><br>Injection of grout  m3  State materials for injection |

COMMENTARY

Stabilization of Existing Sewers (refer to Table 18.03)

Stabilization of existing sewers is envisaged by the CESMM to be carried out by pointing or pipe joint sealing or external grouting. Classifications are provided for each of these operations at 2nd Division level. The general Rules and requirements regarding the inclusion in item descriptions of location, dimensions and profile and the materials forming the existing sewer (See Table 18.01) are applicable to the items for stabilization, in addition to those noted against the classifications which follow.

*Pointing*

The classification "pointing" is applicable to hand pointing and pressure pointing. Separate items distinguish different types of pointing and their location identified as provided in Rule Y/A1 of the CESMM. Pointing is measured in m2. The area measured is that of the surface pointed with no deduction for voids or openings not exceeding 0.5 m2. Areas of any extent which have been measured as "local internal repairs" (See Table 18.02) are deducted from the areas of pointing in which they occur. Descriptions state the materials used for the pointing. Items are deemed to include preparing the joints to receive the pointing.

*Pipe Joint Sealing*

Enumerated items using the classification "pipe joint sealing" are given for the work of both joint sealing and repairs to cracked joints whether they are longitudinal or circumferential. Item descriptions state the extent of the sealing, where it is not a complete pipe joint. The materials used for pipe joint sealing are stated in the item descriptions.

COMMENTARY

Stabilization of Existing Sewers (cont.

*External Grouting*

The classification "external grouting" is used for grouting work described in Rule Y/D3 of the CESMM. (See Table 18.03), where it is expressly required to be carried out as a separate operation from annulus grouting. The items measured for external grouting are an item for the number of injection holes, stating if through pipe joints, and a second item classified as "injection of grout" stating the grout materials and giving volume in m3 of the voids to be grouted in each location identified in accordance with Rule Y/A1 of the CESMM. The voids to be filled in external grouting are inaccessible for taking dimensions to calculate volume. Volume for the injection of grout items is calculated using a factor which converts mass of grout materials to volume of voids filled. This conversion factor can be obtained from the manufacturer of the grout materials or by sample testing. Preamble is included in the Bill of Quantities, stating conversion factors and stating they will be used to calculate volume where the voids to be filled are inaccessible for the taking of dimensions to calculate the volume.

Table 18.04   Renovation of Existing Sewers

| 1st Division | Renovation of existing sewers | Refer to Table 18.01 for general Rules and details to be given in descriptions | |
|---|---|---|---|
| 2nd Division | 3rd Division | | |
| Sliplining m | Polyethylene<br><br>Polypropylene | | State type of lining, its minimum finished size and its thickness or grade (Rule Y/A8)<br><br>Measure lengths as Rule Y/M1 (See Table 18.01) |
| In situ jointed pipe linings m | Polyethylene<br><br>Polypropylene<br><br>Glass reinforced plastic | State offset where lining is curved to an offset which exceeds 35 mm per metre (Rule Y/A9) | |
| Segmental linings m | Glass reinforced plastic<br><br>Glass reinforced concrete<br><br>Cast gunite<br><br>Resin concrete | | |
| Stated proprietary linings m | | | |
| Gunite coating m | State thickness | Measure lengths as Rule Y/M1 | |
| Annulus grouting m3<br><br>Do not include volume measured for external grouting (Y232) in this volume (Rule Y/M5) | | State materials for grouting<br><br>Use this classification for annulus grouting of voids between new linings and existing sewers and for other voids grouted when grouting annular voids (Rule Y/D4) | |

COMMENTARY

## Renovation of Existing Sewers (refer to Table 18.04)

In the CESMM, the 1st Division classification "Renovation of existing sewers" is applicable to work which involves internal lining or internal gunnite coating. The lining techniques listed at 2nd Division level are:-

(i) *Sliplining* - this is lining with continuous pipes, i.e. pipes jointed before placing in their permanent positions;

(ii) *In Situ Jointed Pipe Lining* - this is lining with lengths of pipes jointed at their permanent positions;

(iii) *Segmental Lining* - this is lining with segments of circular or non circular cross-section. They are usually made up of lower and upper segments with longitudinal as well as circumferential joints; and

(iv) *Stated Proprietary Lining* - these are lining systems of any proprietary type.

Linings and coatings are measured as provided in Rule Y/M1 and are billed in linear metres. Item descriptions for linings state the materials from which they are manufactured, their type, their minimum finished size and their grade or thickness. Additionally, item descriptions for in situ jointed pipe linings and for segmental linings state where linings are curved to an offset which exceeds 35 mm per metre of length. Item descriptions for gunnite coating state the materials and thickness.

The void between the new lining and the existing sewer invariably has to be filled with grout. The applicable CESMM classification for this is "annulus grouting". It is measured in m3. The volume measured includes the volume of other voids which are grouted when grouting the annular voids, but excludes the volume of any external grouting. If it is possible to take the dimensions, volume is calculated from the dimensions. If it is not possible to take such dimensions, or if the volume measured would be unrealistic because of leakage into voids outside the measurable volume, the volume is determined from the mass of grout using the conversion factor previously described in the Commentary on "External grouting".

The general Rules and requirements outlined in Table 18.01 are applicable to the items for renovation of existing sewers.

---

Table 18.05  Laterals to Renovated Sewers

| 1st Division | | | |
|---|---|---|---|
| Laterals to renovated sewers | | Deemed to include the work involved in connecting to lining within 1 m from the inside face of the lined sewer (Rule Y/C6) | |

| 2nd Division | | | 3rd Division |
|---|---|---|---|
| Jointing | nr | State type of lining to which the laterals are to be connected and identify those laterals which are to be re-graded (Rule Y/A10) | Bore:  not exceeding 150 mm<br><br>150 - 300 mm<br><br>Stated profile and size exceeding 300 mm in one or more dimension |
| Flap valves | nr | State size | Remove existing<br><br>Replace existing<br><br>New flap valve of stated size |

COMMENTARY

Laterals to Renovated Sewers (refer to Table 18.05)

The classification "laterals to renovated sewers" is applicable to the connection of laterals to relined sewers. The reconnected laterals are given as numbered items giving the bore range or the size and profile, as appropriate, in accordance with the 3rd Division features (See Table 18.05). The items also state the type of lining to which the laterals are to be reconnected and distinguish laterals which are to be regraded. Work included in the items is confined to regrading or any other work in making the connection which is within a length of 1 m from the face of the lined sewer. Work beyond the length of 1 m is measured in detail in accordance with the appropriate classifications.

The removal, replacement or renewal of flap valves to laterals are identified and are each given separately and enumerated, stating the size.

---

Table 18.06   New Manholes and Existing Manholes

| Generally | Items for manholes are deemed to include metalwork, different arrangements of inlets and outlets, and access shafts of different heights and connection of pipes to manholes. Items for manholes with backdrops are deemed to include the pipes and fittings comprising the back drops. (Rule Y/C8). |
| --- | --- |
| | Items for new manholes are deemed to include excavation, preparation of surfaces, disposal of excavated material, upholding sides of excavation, backfilling, concrete, reinforcement, formwork, joints, finishes and reinstatement. (Rule Y/C7). |

| 1st Division | | 2nd Division | 3rd Division | |
| --- | --- | --- | --- | --- |
| New manholes in new locations   nr | State types and loading duties of covers (Rule Y/A12) | Brick<br><br>Brick with backdrop | Depth:<br><br>not exceeding 1.5 m | Measure from tops of covers |
| New manholes replacing existing manholes   nr | State type or mark number, identify different configurations of manholes (Rule Y/A11) | In-situ concrete<br><br>In situ concrete with backdrop | 1.5 - 2 m<br><br>2 - 2.5 m<br><br>2.5 - 3 m | to channel inverts or tops of base slabs which- |
| Deemed to include breaking out and disposal of existing (Rule Y/C9) | | Precast concrete<br><br>Precast concrete with backdrop | 3 - 3.5 m<br><br>3.5 - 4 m<br><br>stated exceeding 4 m | ever is the lower (Rule Y/D5) |
| Existing manholes   nr | State details of work required (Rule Y/A13) | Abandonment | | |
| | State type or mark number, identify different configurations of manholes (Rule Y/A11) | Alterations | | |

COMMENTARY

## New Manholes and Existing Manholes (refer to Table 18.06)

### *New Manholes*

New manholes in sewer renovations are given as numbered items. The standard classifications distinguish those in new locations from those which replace existing manholes. Item descriptions state the type of construction and the depth range in accordance with 2nd and 3rd Division features, respectively. Item descriptions also identify the manholes to which they relate by stating type or mark number. Each type or mark number and each different configuration of manhole are given as a separate item. Rule Y/C8 of the CESMM (See Table 18.06) makes it unnecessary to make distinction between manholes having different arrangements of inlets and outlets and access shafts. For work deemed to be included in the items for new manholes, see "Generally" Table 18.06. Items for new manholes which replace existing are deemed to include breaking out and disposal of the manhole replaced.

### *Existing Manholes*

Separate numbered items are given for the work of altering or abandoning existing manholes. Item descriptions describe or identify the work intended to be included in the items. The type or mark number of the manholes is stated and their configuration identified.

## Table 18.07 Interruptions

| 1st Division | | 2nd Division | 3rd Division |
|---|---|---|---|
| Interruptions h | Measure only where minimum pumping capacity is expressly required and for periods during normal working hours when flow in sewer exceeds installed pumping capacity and work is interrupted (Rule Y/M6) | Preparation of existing sewers<br><br>Stabilization of existing sewers | |
| | | Renovation of existing sewers | Sliplining<br><br>In-situ jointed pipe lining<br><br>Segmental lining<br><br>Stated proprietory lining<br><br>Gunite coating<br><br>Annulus grouting |
| | | Work on laterals to renovated sewers<br><br>Work on Manholes | |

COMMENTARY

Interruptions (refer to Table 18.07)

To assist tenderers with, among other things, an assessment of the temporary work of overpumping, contract documents will usually give flow information of the sewer to be renovated. This will usually include estimates of peak dry weather flow and peak storm flow for a given return period. The latter will be taken as the likely minimum overpumping requirements.

Items need not be given in the Bill of Quantities for overpumping and it can be considered a general obligation under the ICE Conditions of Contract. However, the cost of this temporary work can be substantial and it appears undesirable for the Contractors to be placed in a position where he must speculate as to the extent of overpumping he will need to provide. It is considered more satisfactory for minimum overpumping or diversion requirements to be given in the Specification and for Specified Requirement items to be given under Class A for providing pumping capabilities to meet the peak flow requirements. Where this is done, items for interruptions (See Table 18.07) giving estimated quantities in normal working hours, are given in the Bill. The periods when flow in the sewers exceeds the expressly required pumping capacity and work is interrupted is admeasured, in units of normal working hours, against the items of interruptions.

EXAMPLE No. YE.1

Specimen Bill of Quantities

The Example which follows is a specimen Bill of Quantities for a Sewer Renovation contract. It includes some typical Class A - General items in addition to the work items. Units of measurement are given against the items. The quantities have been omitted. A location drawing on the lines illustrated below would accompany the Bill (along with the other drawings and Specification) when it was put to tender.

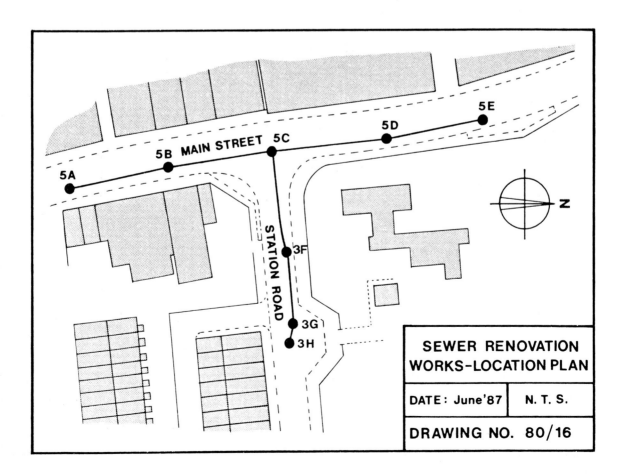

| Number | Item description | Unit | Quantity | Rate | Amount £ | p |
|--------|------------------|------|----------|------|----------|---|
| | GENERAL ITEMS. | | | | | |
| | See adjoining Commentary | | | COMMENTARY | | |
| | Specified requirements. | | | Class A items, other than a selection of items of particular application which may be used (if expressly required) in the General Items Part of a Bill of Quantities for Sewer Renovation, are not included in the Example. | | |
| | Equipment for use by the Engineer's staff. | | | | | |
| | Grout testing equipment as Specification clause "X". | | | | | |
| A232.1 | Establishment and removal. | sum | | | | |
| A232.2 | Maintenance. | sum | | The setting out of the items billed in the Example is different from that in Example AE.1, Chapter 3, to illustrate an alternative item layout for the General Items Part of a Bill of Quantities. | | |
| | Sewer safety equipment. | | | | | |
| | Safety harnesses as Specification clause "X". | | | | | |
| A239.1 | Establishment and removal, * nr. sets. | sum | | | | |
| A239.2 | Maintenance, * nr. sets. | sum | | | | |
| | Temporary Works. | | | | | |
| | Traffic regulations; as Specification clause "X". | | | | | |
| A272.1 | Establishment and removal of work and facilities at North end of Main St. | sum | | | | |
| A272.2 | Maintenance of work and facilities at North end of Main St. | sum | | | | |
| A272.3 | Establishment and removal of work and facilities at junction of Main St. and Station Rd. | sum | | | | |
| A272.4 | Maintenance of work and facilities at junction of Main St. and Station Rd. | sum | | | | |
| | Stanks and overpumping equipment as Specification clause "X". | | | See Table 18.07 and the Commentary following the Table in regard to Items Code A276.1 and .2. | | |
| A276.1 | Establishment and removal; from Manhole 5A - 5E. | sum | | | | |
| A276.2 | Maintenance; from Manhole 5A - 5E. | sum | | | | |

| Number | Item description | Unit | Quantity | Rate | Amount £ | p |
|--------|-----------------|------|----------|------|----------|---|
| | GENERAL ITEMS. | | | | | |
| | Specified requirements (cont. | | | | | |
| | Temporary Works (cont. | | | | | |
| | Stanks and overpumping equipment as Specification clause "X". | | | | | |
| A276.3 | Establishment and removal; from Manhole 5C - 3H. | sum | | | | |
| A276.4 | Maintenance; from Manhole 5C - 3H. | sum | | | | |
| | Surveys | | | | | |
| | Pre-lining and dimension proving surveys as Specification clause "X". | | | | | |
| A279.1 | Establishment and removal of equipment. | sum | | | | |
| A279.2 | Maintenance of equipment. | sum | | | | |
| A279.3 | Preparation of report. | sum | | | | |
| | Closed circuit television surveys as Specification clause "X". | | | | | |
| | At commencement. | | | | | |
| A279.4 | Establishment and removal of equipment. | sum | | | | |
| A279.5 | Maintenance of equipment. | sum | | | | |
| A279.6 | Video tape recording and preparation of report. | sum | | | | |
| | On completion | | | | | |
| A279.7 | Establishment and removal of equipment. | sum | | | | |
| A279.8 | Maintenance of equipment. | sum | | | | |
| A279.9 | Video tape recording and preparation of report. | sum | | | | |
| | Sewer safety equipment. | | | | | |
| | Safety harnesses as Specification clause "X". | | | | | |
| A299.1 | Establishment and removal. | sum | | | | |
| A299.2 | Maintenance. | sum | | | | |

COMMENTARY

In practice, where it is considered desireable, separate items may be given for surveys in each of several locations identified by reference to a drawing.

Closed circuit television surveys are necessary for "non-man-entry" sewers.

(2)            To Part 1 Summary          Page total

| Number | Item description | Unit | Quantity | Rate | Amount £ | p |
|---|---|---|---|---|---|---|
| | GENERAL ITEMS. | | | | | |
| | Specified requirements (cont. | | | | | |
| | Sewer safety equipment (cont. | | | | | |
| | Atmosphere testing equipment as Specification clause "X". | | | | | |
| A299.3 | Establishment and removal. | sum | | | | |
| A299.4 | Maintenance. | sum | | | | |
| | | | | COMMENTARY | | |
| | Means of communication as Specification clause "X". | | | In practice where it is considered desirable, separate items may be given for safety | | |
| A299.5 | Establishment. | sum | | equipment in each of several | | |
| A299.6 | Maintenance. | sum | | locations identified by reference to a drawing. | | |
| A299.7 | Removal. | sum | | | | |
| | Escape breathing apparatus as Specification clause "X". | | | | | |
| A299.8 | Establishment. | sum | | | | |
| A299.9 | Maintenance. | sum | | | | |
| A299.10 | Removal. | sum | | | | |
| | Lighting as Specification clause "X". | | | | | |
| A299.11 | Establishment. | sum | | | | |
| A299.12 | Maintenance. | sum | | | | |
| A299.13 | Removal. | sum | | | | |
| | Note: In practice a Part Summary would be given at the end of the Part 1, General Items section of the Bill of Quantities. See Page 28, Chapter 2. | | | | | |
| | (3)       To Part 1 Summary       Page total | | | | | |

| Number | Item description | Unit | Quantity | Rate | Amount | |
|---|---|---|---|---|---|---|
| | | | | | £ | p |
| | SEWER RENOVATION AND ANCILLARY WORK. | | | | | |
| | SEWER IN MAIN STREET - MANHOLES 5A - 5E, LOCATION DRAWING NO. 80/16 | | | COMMENTARY | | |
| | EXISTING BRICK SEWER NOMINAL INTERNAL SIZE 1200 mm WIDE x 1800 mm HIGH, OVAL. | | | The work is given under a locational heading so that it can be identified | | |
| | Preparation of existing sewers. | | | by reference to the Drawing. See Table 18.01 and | | |
| Y110.1 | Cleaning; as Specification clause 19.3 | m | | Commentary. | | |
| | Removing intrusions. | | | Height is often given as the first dimension of the set of two cross-sectional dimensions for | | |
| Y121 | Laterals, bore not exceeding 150 mm; cast iron. | nr | | a sewer, whereas, in Bill preparation it is custom-ary to give it as the | | |
| Y123 | Displaced protruding single bricks. | nr | | second. The heading for the existing brick sewer makes clear width and height. | | |
| | Plugging laterals with concrete Class C30/20. | | | "Preparation of existing sewers" is discussed in the Commentary on Page | | |
| Y131.1 | Bore not exceeding 300 mm. | nr | | 278. Notes on the Rules are given in Table 18.02. | | |
| Y132.1 | Rectangular, internal cross-sectional dimensions 450 x 350 mm. | nr | | | | |
| Y132.2 | Oval, internal cross-sectional dimensions 600 x 900 mm. | nr | | | | |
| | Filling laterals with grout Class G4. | | | | | |
| Y141 | Bore not exceeding 300 mm. | m3 | | | | |
| Y142 | Circular, bore 450 mm. | m3 | | | | |
| | Local internal repairs. | | | | | |
| Y152 | Area 0.1 - 0.25 m2. | nr | | Table 18.03 and the Commentary which follows | | |
| Y153 | Area 0.5 m2; curved vaulting with arch bricks. | nr | | the Table, refer to "Stabilization of exist-ing sewers". | | |
| | Stabilization of existing sewers. | | | | | |
| Y210.1 | Pointing brickwork; by hand in cement mortar Class M3. | m2 | | | | |
| Y210.2 | Pointing brickwork; pressure injected epoxy mortar. | m2 | | | | |

| Number | Item description | Unit | Quantity | Rate | Amount £ | p |
|--------|-----------------|------|----------|------|----------|---|
| | SEWER RENOVATION AND ANCILLARY WORK. | | | | | |
| | SEWER IN MAIN STREET - MANHOLES 5A - 5E LOCATION DRAWING NO. 80/16 (cont. | | | COMMENTARY | | |
| | EXISTING BRICK SEWER NOMINAL INTERNAL SIZE 1200 mm WIDE x 1800 mm HIGH, OVAL (cont. | | | The Example assumes that a conversion factor for grout and the circumstances where its use is applicable is given in the Preamble clause referred to in the sub-heading "External grouting". See Table 18.03 and Commentary. | | |
| | Stabilization of existing sewers (cont. | | | | | |
| | External grouting, refer to Preamble clause 14 | | | | | |
| Y231 | Number of holes. | nr | | For Notes on the Rules and Commentary on Items under the sub-heading "Renovation of existing sewers", see Pages 280 and 281. | | |
| Y232 | Injection of grout; Class G7. | m3 | | | | |
| | Renovation of existing sewers. | | | | | |
| | Lining with Stanton plc., reinforced plastic matrix sewer liners as Specification clause 19.7. | | | | | |
| Y340 | Oval, minimum internal cross-sectional dimensions 1000 mm wide x 1600 mm high, thickness 10 mm. | m | | | | |
| Y360.1 | Annulus grouting; Class G7 grout as Specification clause 19.9. | m3 | | In compliance with Rules Y/A11 and Y/A12 of the CESMM, (See Table 18.06 and Commentary). The loading duty of manhole covers are stated. The type or mark number of the manholes are stated. Different configurations of manholes are identified, i.e. manholes of difference plan and vertical section shapes (other than those produced by the items deemed to be included by Rule Y/C8, see "Generally", Table 18.06) are distinguished by separate itemisation. | | |
| | Laterals to renovated sewers. | | | | | |
| Y411.1 | Jointing, bore not exceeding 150 mm; to reinforced plastic matrix liner. | nr | | | | |
| Y412.1 | Jointing, bore 150 - 300 mm; to reinforced plastic matrix liner. | nr | | | | |
| | New manholes in new locations. | | | | | |
| | Precast concrete as Drawing No. 81/17, with Grade A cast iron coated heavy duty covers. | | | | | |
| Y554 | Depth 2.5 - 3 m; Design Group 1, chamber 1800 mm internal diameter (location reference No. MH 5A). | nr | | For further Commentary on manholes, see next page. | | |
| Y556 | Depth 3.5 - 4 m; Design Group 2, chamber 1800 mm internal diameter with taper (location reference No. MH 5E). | nr | | | | |

| Number | Item description | Unit | Quantity | Rate | Amount £ | p |
|--------|-----------------|------|----------|------|----------|---|
| | SEWER RENOVATION AND ANCILLARY WORK. | | | | | |
| | SEWER IN MAIN STREET - MANHOLES 5A - 5E LOCATION DRAWING NO. 80/16 (cont. | | | COMMENTARY | | |
| | EXISTING BRICK SEWER NOMINAL INTERNAL SIZE 1200 mm WIDE x 1800 mm HIGH, OVAL (cont. | | | | | |
| | New manholes replacing existing. | | | | | |
| | Precast concrete as Drawing 81/17, with Grade A cast iron coated heavy duty covers. | | | | | |
| Y655 | Depth 3 - 3.5 m; Design Group 2, chamber 1800 mm internal diameter with taper (location reference No. MH 5C). | nr | | | | |
| | Existing manholes; rectangular brick, internal plan dimensions 1250 x 1690 mm | | | | | |
| Y720 | Alterations; reforming benching, plugging and flushing up ends of annulus at entry both sides, pointing internal surfaces of brickwork (...m2) as Drawing No. 81/20. (location reference Nos. MH 5B and MH 5D). | nr | | | | |
| | Interruptions as Specification clause 17.4. | | | | | |
| Y810.1 | Preparation of existing sewers. | h | | | | |
| Y820.1 | Stabilization of existing sewers. | h | | | | |
| Y834 | Renovation of existing sewers, Stanton plc., reinforced plastic matrix lining. | h | | | | |
| Y836.1 | Renovation of existing sewers, annulus grouting. | h | | | | |
| Y840 | Work on laterals to renovated sewers. | h | | | | |
| Y850.1 | Work on manholes. | h | | | | |

COMMENTARY

The Example assumes that the Drawing stated in the descriptions for new manholes illusrates typical construction details for given design groups with varying dimensions. The items give plan dimensions as well as depths to allow for identification.

For alterations to existing manholes the CESMM does not call for depth to be stated in the item descriptions. It is helpful to state the depth if it is thought relevant to the alteration work. The Example assumes that the Drawings stated in the items for alterations to manholes shows typical details with dimensions which may vary. Plan dimensions are given to identify the requirements for particular manholes. The Example assumes that the area of pointing required would be calculated and be given in m2 within the brackets in the description.

See preceding page for further Commentary on manholes.

The circumstances under which and when interruptions are measureable are given in the Rules referred to in Table 18.07 and are discussed in the Commentary following the Table.

| Number | Item description | Unit | Quantity | Rate | Amount £ | p |
|--------|-----------------|------|----------|------|----------|---|
| | SEWER RENOVATION AND ANCILLARY WORK | | | | | |
| | SEWER IN STATION ROAD - MANHOLES 5C - 3H, LOCATION DRAWING NO. 80/16. | | | COMMENTARY | | |
| | EXISTING CAST IRON SEWER NOMINAL INTERNAL DIAMETER 1200 mm. | | The sewer renovation work in Station Road is given under a locational heading which distinguishes it from that in Main Street.  This ensures the different locations and characteristics of the work are more readily identified. | | | |
| | Preparation of existing sewers. | | | | | |
| Y110.2 | Cleaning; as Specification clause 19.4. | m | | | | |
| | Plugging laterals with concrete Class C30/20. | | | | | |
| Y132.3 | Circular, bore 450 mm. | nr | | | | |
| | Stabilisation of existing sewers. | | | | | |
| Y220 | Pipe joint sealing; circumferential joints 1200 mm diameter, preformed bituminous strip and joint sealant as Specification clause 19.5. | nr | | | | |
| | Renovation of existing sewers. | | | | | |
| | In situ jointed pipe lining, glass reinforced plastic as Specification clause 19.6. | | | Table 18.04 and the Commentary which follows the Table deal with lining work. | | |
| Y323.1 | Minimum internal diameter 900 mm, thickness 10 mm. | m | | | | |
| Y323.2 | Minimum internal diameter 900 mm, thickness 10 mm, curved to an offset of 40 mm per metre. | m | | | | |
| Y360.2 | Annulus grouting; Class G7 grout as Specification clause 19.9. | m3 | | | | |
| | New Manholes replacing existing. | | | | | |
| | In situ concrete as Drawing No. 82/18 with Grade A cast iron coated heavy duty covers. | | | Refer to pages (5) and (6) of this Example for Commentary on manholes. | | |
| Y635 | Depth 3 - 3.5 m; design group 3, rectangular chamber, internal plan dimensions 1250 x 1650 mm (location reference Nos. MH3F and MH3G). | nr | | | | |

(7)          To Part 2 Summary        Page total

| Number | Item description | Unit | Quantity | Rate | Amount £ | p |
|---|---|---|---|---|---|---|
| | SEWER RENOVATION AND ANCILLARY WORK. | | | | | |
| | SEWER IN STATION ROAD - MANHOLES 5C - 3H, LOCATION DRAWING NO. 80/16 (cont. | | | | | |
| | EXISTING CAST IRON SEWER NOMINAL INTERNAL DIAMETER 1200 mm. (cont. | | | | | |
| | Existing manholes. | | | | | |
| | Brick rectangular, internal plan dimensions 1250 x 1650 mm. | | | | | |
| Y710 | Abandonment; depth 3 - 3.5 m, filling and capping as Specification clause 19.12. (location reference MH3H). | nr | | | | |
| | Interruptions as Specification clause 17.4. | | | | | |
| Y810.2 | Preparation of existing sewers. | h | | | | |
| Y820.2 | Stabilization of existing sewers. | h | | | | |
| Y832 | Renovation of existing sewers, in situ jointed pipe lining. | h | | | | |
| Y836.2 | Renovation of existing sewers, annulus grouting. | h | | | | |
| Y850.2 | Work on manholes. | h | | | | |

COMMENTARY

The CESMM does not call for the size to be given in item descriptions for the abandonment of manhole. In the adjoining item it is considered necessary to give this information because there is no drawn information other than that on the location plan.

Note: In practice a Part Summary would be given at the end of Part 2 of the Bill of Quantities. See Paragraph 5.23 in Chapter 2.

# Index